D0982834

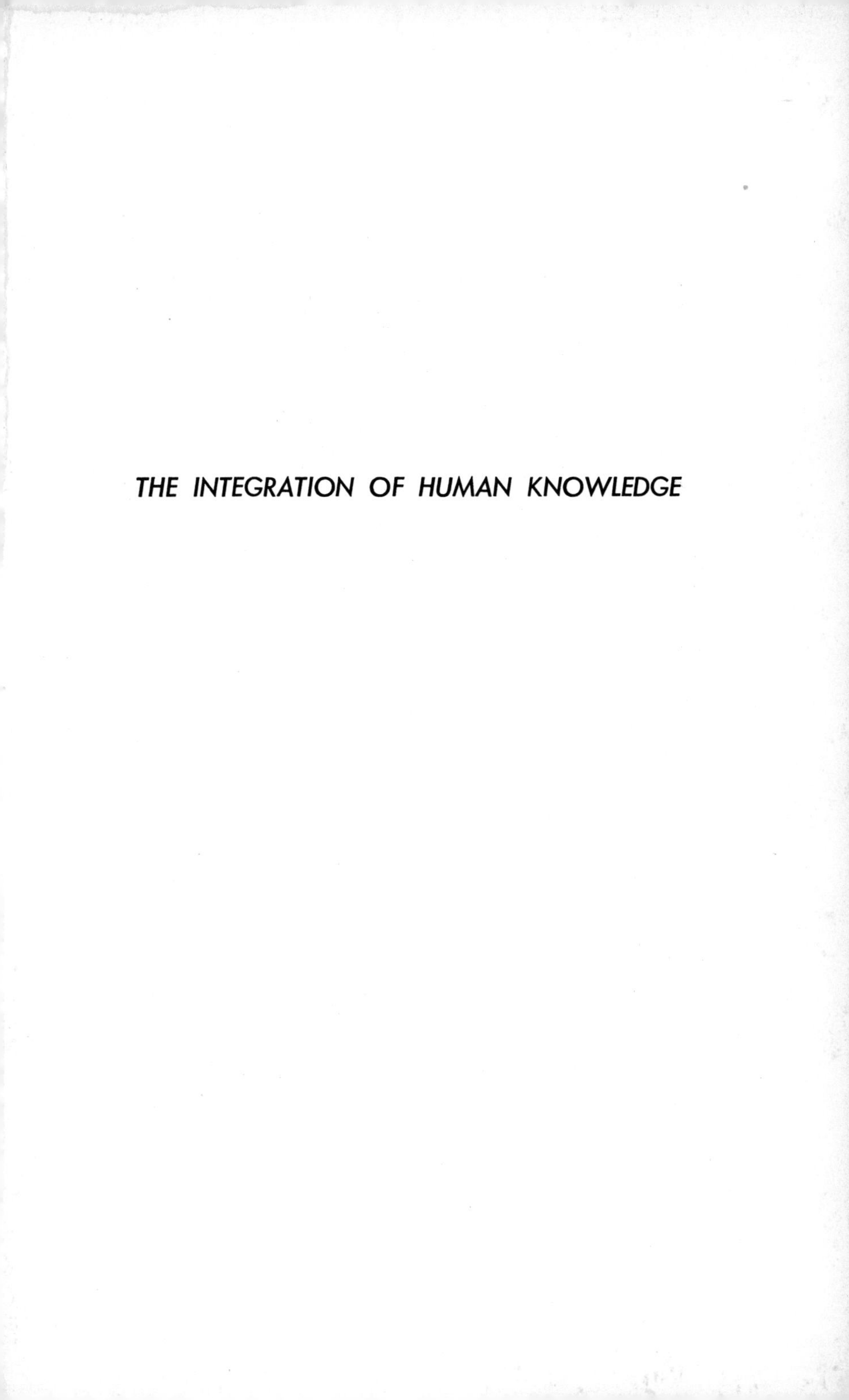

THE INTEGRATION OF HUMAN KNOWLEDGE

DIAGRAM I

A MATHEMATICAL THEME IN DESIGN

THE INTEGRATION OF HUMAN KNOWLEDGE

A Study of the Formal Foundations and the Social Implications of Unified Science

by

OLIVER L. REISER

Professor of Philosophy

University of Pittsburgh

extending horizons books — Porter Sargent Publisher — Boston

FOREWORD

Mr. Reiser has undertaken here to cope with the well-nigh impossible, to give shape to the unthinkable and to venture far out into the unspeakable. He has accepted hence to run risks commensurate with the enterprise. On the other hand, the wide-ranging and passionate attention that he has been giving over the years to all the new avenues of thought may ensure this book's usefulness as an exploratory survey.

As happens in such undertakings, the author is bound to know in part, and to prophesy in part. In what comes of knowledge, he may find, time and again, scornful scientists prompt to question his statements, and irate philosophers no less. *Habent sua fata libelli*, and one must leave him to face the test. When he comes, however, to deal with the shape of things to come, his words are no longer open to challenge. As a witness of our times, he can evoke only sympathetic interest in the historian of ideas, and it is strictly in the latter capacity that I will allow myself some comments.

One such witnessing, or shall we say prophecy, concerns the emergence of a new world religion based on scientific humanism, which should gradually replace — or integrate — the existing ones. The critic is reminded here, inevitably, of Comte's Religion of Humanity with the "great Fetish" at its summit. This one, however, is far more ample and cosmic-minded, as befits our age of astrophysics. The kinship with Stoicism, which the author brings up, is undeniable. It shows also historical perception. In the solitary ordeal of the concentration camps, the most frightful of our times, those who had to find a faith in order not to be broken emerged with some kind of stoic religiosity that they had worked out by themselves. Such a faith might well rediscover the cosmic overtones of the ancient one without coming into conflict with the scientific consciousness of our time. It would certainly take considerable distance from the present institutional religions, such as they are, and as they have taken curiously to justifying their existence from the behavior of men in foxholes, or from the need for some kind of social cohesive.

This preference for Stoicism is linked implicitly with another prophetic utterance of the author, namely that all good thinking proceeds from the assumption of the reality of a Cosmos, or shall we say, that the universe exists truly. This is quite interesting, for in today's thought no inference *from* the universe is allowed as secured. The universe has been taken for granted since time immemorial, and many strange conclusions deduced therefrom, but in good philosophy all that we may state about the universe is that it *is*, and in this we have not moved one step beyond Parmenides. The statement is strictly an act of faith in rationalism, with no formal or verifiable content. But surely, if it is so, then the contrary act of faith, the denial of a Cosmos, is equally allowable, and at least a novel one, which has led to interesting attitudes on the part of many penetrating scientific minds of this generation. For all we know, it is permissible to hold that what we call the Cosmos, like its historical analogue, is a case of ODTLCWA, or "one damn thing loosely coupled with another." It may be heresy, but it is not absurdity. To dismiss on this count the metaphysics of existentialism as "bad" is more excommunication than judgment. But then, from the top-level statement that "the cosmos is" have descended all the great rationalist myths and metaphors of being which are the very soul of science. By excommunicating acosmism, the author casts his option for those in the intellectual future of humanity. The choice is certainly significant.

It is, I think, in this spirit that we should understand his discussion of present-day theories, his refusals and his modifiers. They may not be critically tenable at many points, but as apotropaic gestures they are justified. Nor should he be thrown out of court for trying to subvert classic modes of thought with such futuristic devices as multimodal logics in which the formerly excluded middle is vindictively re-enthroned. I daresay we all feel something should be done about our current logic, or what goes under that name in the shaping of the large-scale commitments of our civilization. Policy-making thought in the West has shown itself increasingly unable to cope with the problems set by the power revival in ancient lands, and one need not cross the Mason-Dixon line to see how the mind can disintegrate when faced with impossible alternatives of its own devising. Dialectical thinking in the hands of newcomers seems to have had the historical role of a brief avenue of escape from the stiff Aristotelian dichotomy of black and white, right and wrong. With it usefulness now all but terminated, some other way of thinking should be found, less constrictive than the Hegelian Triad. Any attempt, even if not successful, is good in that it keeps the problem alive; one or the other may some day provide a lead. One such present lead comes to mind, that Mr. Reiser has omitted to mention but may find place in future editions of his book. I mean Piaget's fundamental researches into how propositional operations start out in our mind as a structural whole, which is also the form of equilibrium of the subject's operational behavior. "Genetic logic" may in time free us from the straitjacket of formal logic.

Some will say that what is good in this book is not new, and what is new is not particularly good. This is an indirect confirmation of the strength of the humanist position. By going beyond what can be reasonably secured, the author has run the risks of all extrapolators: he has ventured to peer into a future that can be neither visualized nor conceived in its actual complication. All predictions, in hindsight, appear rather simple-minded. But, like science fiction, they are exploratory forays from which one is too lucky to come back with a few, very few, unrelated possibilities. As for projecting future *integration,* that is surely, thank God, the most impossible task of all. The strength of the author lies really in his adherence to the past. Notwithstanding the modern jargon taken from the so-called social sciences, and some words like "behavior-stuff" which show a Spencerian nostalgia, Mr. Reiser's metaphysics still follow the royal road of pan-mathematism. The analogic deduction from geometry to metaphysics is as direct in his writing as it was five centuries ago in that of Nicholas of Cusa, and there is still in it, expressed in the varied and modern terminology that the Cardinal was searching for, the same sense of the infinite. The wealth of enticing symbolism contained in modern hyperspaces is used here with the true instinct, but is it not still the ancient "explication"? Are the images even so different? Beneath the logarithmic spirals and spins and rotations and divergences which befit the world of "electromagnetic man," we rediscover the archetypes of Kepler, the very same. We have a "response of the manifest world to the world of archetypal influences: Platonic solids, circles, spirals, and the higher patterns of spherical harmonics." We still have the same poetic intimations of "cubes and gyres" that Harun al-Rashid sought "in the great volume of Parmenides" as fancied by W. B. Yeats. We are still cradled in the foundational myth of Western thought.

The present, however, will not be satisfied with contemplation. It needs the *vita activa.* In fact, it gets it, under increasingly terrifying forms. Reiser's prophecies on this score are simply certain conclusions that others dare not draw. The coming integration of society with its new communications systems is seen, early in this text, as "the embryogenesis of a giant organism with a world sensorium." One begins then to wonder. Since our individual nervous systems remain what they are, I take it that Mr. Reiser is envisaging a machine to harbor that sensorium, or at best an ensemble of machines, with a coupling sufficiently loose to allow us to preserve our individuality in its crevices.

This is certainly scientific enough, but is it scientific humanism? Or is it an air-conditioned nightmare? Many of us who have tasted of Freud may have become sufficiently disenchanted with the psyche to look forward to the advent of a super-psyche as, at least, a new try. But would it transcend present man, or simply amplify him to an intolerable number of decibels? Would it be (to wonder about a simple issue) nicer? Or would it, like Laplace's god, spend its time forever remote from our concerns, calculating an indecently complicated universe? And what if it should develop, in the labyrinthine vastness of its mind, some dark little quirk which would turn it eventually into a destructive demon of galactic proportions?

The author, in his democratic optimism, seems to brush these doubts aside, but they keep haunting the rest of us. He disclaims, in fact, any future prevalence of the machine, for, as he says, there is the possibility that the mind can change its ideas about what being "logical" is, and that is something no machine can do. Yes, but supposing the machine refused to take orders?

The reason for comfort that I can perceive is not among those listed by author. It is that he himself, in his futuristic prophesying, has never moved from tested classical motifs throughout. In fact, here is a mind remarkably akin, across the centuries, to the learned and pious Proclus.

Some of us will remember a story by Anatole France, whose title is *Le Procureur de Judée.* Pontius Pilate, old and retired, is enjoying dignified philosophical conversation with his friends on the terrace of his villa. He agrees with their sad remarks on the decay of traditional religion. "But, gentlemen," he goes on "the spirit never dies. Some new faith is bound to arise, and I for myself venture to predict that in the next centuries Herakles will come into his own as the chief deity." Who knows, one of them objects, we never can guess what strange ideas may crop up next. Did it not happen to Pilate himself, many years ago, to have to deal with some poor young man or other in his province who fancied himself to be a god and had to be suppressed? "Is that so?" says Pilate in puzzlement. "I cannot say that I remember."

The weary irony of Anatole France may have missed the point: that in the end Pilate's prediction would turn out to be right. For lo, hardly a generation has passed, and Herakles is rising above the mists of the future as the new god.

"In our coming electromagnetic civilization . . . the Oriental and Occidental hemispheres would appear as the two halves of an earth-armature that is spinning out patterns or images over the proliferating ganglia of a giant planetary humanism . . . creating the *guiding fields* for the emergence of an electromagnetic society of the future. From this point on, the job calls for the special knowledge of social engineers, as Dr. John Q. Stewart points out. . . ."

Even without Dr. John Q. Stewart pointing it out, we knew what was coming and we did not like it. But let not that confuse the issue. That world organism endowed with a world cogitatorium, indeed with semi-divine attributes, ready for enormous adventures, is that not Herakles himself come into his own?

The idea of a Herakles, liberator of Prometheus, who might supersede the gods if he only knew how to handle himself, had been very present as a half-repressed symbol to the Greek tragic poets. It moves now into focus. His tasks are still very much ahead of him. The hellhound Cerberus, in the guise of the Unconscious, is still snapping at our heels, the Augean stables are a perdurable state of fact, the Hydra raises its renascent heads from more than usually pestilential marshes. Herakles is still how the poets saw him, strong and willing, but not very bright. Grown to planetary proportion, reaching out now into cosmic space, he is immeasurably stronger than they could imagine. But he is not much brighter. Let him not indulge in dalliance with Dr. John Q. Stewart; let him beware of sitting down to dinner with the Hydra.

GIORGIO DE SANTILLANA

M. I. T.
Cambridge, Mass.
September 13, 1958

TABLE OF CONTENTS

INTRODUCTION

INTRODUCTION

"In the conditions of modern life the rule is absolute: the race which does not value trained intelligence is doomed. Not all your heroism, not all your social charm, not all your wit, not all your victories on land or at sea, can move back the finger of fate. Today we maintain ourselves. Tomorrow science will have moved forward yet one more step, and there will be no appeal from the judgment which will then be pronounced on the uneducated."

— Alfred North Whitehead

"It is essential that education come decisively to grips with the world-wide crisis of mankind . . . higher education must share proportionately in the task of forging social and political defenses against obliteration . . . superficial curricular tinkering can no longer serve. . . . The crucial task of higher education, therefore, is to provide a unified general education . . . The means will have to match in boldness and vision the magnitude of the problem."

— President Harry S. Truman's *Commission on Higher Education for American Democracy*

"In this country we emphasize both liberal and practical education. But too often it is liberal education for one, and a practical education for another. What we desperately need is an integrated, liberal, practical education for the same person."

— President Dwight D. Eisenhower, June, 1955.

In bold relief the above quotations sketch the dimensions of modern man's problems. The world we hold so dear, — man's birthplace, his present habitat, and ultimate cemetery, — faces the ghastly prospect of an imminent and universal doom, unless we humans can muster the energy and intelligence necessary to create a World Philosophy as the mental foetus, a World Sensorium as the mature organ, and a Planetary Democracy as the action-patterns, of an emerging universal civilization. If we fail in this, all mankind may go down to defeat. In this time of divisive tendencies within and between the nations, races, religions, sciences and humanities, synthesis must become the great magnet which orients us all. But cultural coöperation and social integration must have a basis in a common nucleus of methods, concepts, and aspirations, — that is the overriding thesis of this book devoted to the search for techniques for the integration of all human knowledge.

Mankind has reason to be impatient with the failure of its thinkers, prophets, seers, and teachers. They have not provided the purposes and plans for the conscious control of human evolution. Observe the tragic impasse, as this is revealed in the shortcomings of science, religion, and philosophy.

Consider first the plight of society under the impact of science. Surely one of the fundamental difficulties of our world is that while the scientists are racing toward their specializations, they are failing to do their part in the recreation of social institutions to protect mankind from the harmful uses of scientific knowledge. If, as the advertisements inform us, we should "thank science for the miracle drugs of modern medicine," by the same logic we should also "thank science for hydrogen bombs and fallout and the techniques of biological warfare." Scientists have not greatly helped the world to humanize science and socialize technology. But most tragic of all, *scientists have not done what is possible toward integrating the bodies of knowledge created by science into a unified interpretation of man, his place in nature, and his potentialities for creating the good society.* Instead, they are entombing us in dark and meaningless catacombs of learning. Scientific knowledge must now be simplified and integrated; through a supreme effort the vast stores of unified and unapplied (or misapplied) principles must be integrated into a meaningful philosophical synthesis.

And what does modern religion contribute toward this program of salvaging the great human adventure? One of the interesting developments in contemporary society is the so-called 'return to religion.' This flight to the organized religions, as confirmed by the statistics on increased church membership, seems more to reflect the wide-spread fear of peoples than any abiding search for spirituality.

As the perils of thermonuclear warfare hover over us, there is increasing social pressure on the population to return to God and the churches, — as if they were the same! There is reason to believe that the turning toward the organized religions expresses the desire for security in a shaky world. The assumption seems to be that since we are a godly people, and our political enemy is materialistic and atheistic, therefore the ultimate decision in the battle will be ours. This is fatuous. Certainly, the earth-circling sputniks the Russians have put into orbits are a timely warning, — but not the kind of omen the authoritarian religions have seen in it. Adherents of the Faiths repeat the ritual: if our science cannot save us from destruction, our spiritual superiority over Communism will win the victory. Here we see the mental tranquilizer effects of the revealed religions which look to a miracle for man's salvation.

Whether it be the Fundamentalism of Billy Graham or the subtle Christological reinterpretations of Professor Paul Tillich, as set forth so profoundly in his *Systematic Theology*, the brute fact is that a theology based on the uniqueness of Christ is obsolete. But then Professor Tillich is no friend of the organized churches, and perhaps he would not oppose the thesis that the churches are spiritually bankrupt.

Contrary to this Epimethean viewpoint, the present volume will urge that we reach for a Promethean morality based on a modern cosmology and culminating in a planetary ethics. The troubles of the world are intellectual no less than spiritual and can be alleviated by perfecting a world philosophy. This common search should provide a higher plateau of coöperation enabling us to transcend the otherwise hopeless conflict of godless communism versus Judæo-Christian supernaturalism. In a word, the real problems are philosophical, — not primarily political, economic, religious, military, or technological. The failure of our world is the failure of philosophy.

Such are the social malfunctionings of science and theology. Now what is the situation in philosophy?

Not all philosophy has abdicated its historic rôle of providing the synoptic view which is unified knowledge. But much of current philosophy is seeking ways of escape from the laborious job of achieving the dynamic synthesis, which is wisdom, by taking refuge in Logical Positivism, Existentialism, and the newest diversion, Language Analysis, especially as this is purveyed by Oxford University scholars. An excellent account of this development is supplied by G. J. Warnock's volume, *English Philosophy Since 1900*, published by the Oxford University Press(1958). Students from all parts of the world (including the writer) visit England to study at first hand the expositions that are available there.

Among the British advocates of the notion that the task of philosophy is to analyze the meanings (uses) of words in language are Professors Gilbert Ryle, John Wisdom, R. M. Hare, J. L. Austin, and

F. W. Strawson. In his survey of this way of 'doing' philosophy, Mr. Warnock indicates that much of this approach stems from the work of Professor G. E. Moore, who inspired the belief that "the business of philosophy is clarification and not discovery; that its concern is with meanings, not with truth; that its subject matter is our thoughts or language, rather than facts." The informed reader will note the similarity of this viewpoint to the program of Logical Positivism as interpreted by A. J. Ayer. In his book, *Language, Truth and Logic*, Professor Ayer argues that the philosopher is not directly concerned with the physical properties of things, but is concerned only with the way we speak about them, — "the propositions of philosophy are not factual, but linguistic . . . they express definitions or the formal consequences of definitions," as Ayer puts it.

Obviously, this notion that verifiability applies only to scientific propositions provides no place for the conception of philosophy as a synthesis of our scientific knowledge. When I visited England recently (1958), I inquired of one of these Analysts what he thought of an attempted revival of Herbert Spencer's conception of philosophy as a synthesis of the sciences, — and he scoffed at the idea. Such is the dreary state of affairs of philosophy in some parts of the world. I shall have more to say about 'analytical' philosophy in the following chapters; here I can only opine that this latest form of 'descriptive semantics' is essentially uncreative, — even though valuable as a purgative of verbalism in philosophy, — and represents a passing phase of the subject. It is my hope that philosophers will soon return to their major function: putting into a unified world-view the findings of the natural sciences. The budding promises of scientific synthesis which were emerging twenty-five years ago were killed off by the chilling frosts of the anti-speculative winds of the analytical schools spawned in the cold climate of ice-age positivism and still putting the deep freeze on philosophy through the frigid waves of the new Oxford movement. But the great thaw is perhaps due, and philosophy (let us hope) will once more blossom forth in a summertime of fertility and fragrance.

These foregoing reflections aim at setting forth in clear outline the nature and the urgency of the contemporary problems of philosophy and education. At present the emphasis on *general education*, referred to above in the Truman Report, is certainly commendable. But this is only a beginning, as is pointed out in Chapter II. The thing that we must constantly bear in mind is that the aim of education is not only the problem of generating pious aspirations and benign attitudes through a study of the 'humanities,' — *it is a matter also of giving meaning to materials by relating them to the sum-total of human knowledge that is available in our time.* This means overcoming the fragmentation produced, not only by departments, but by the so-called distribution fields. More specifically, such a program for higher education demands the development of courses wherein the interactions of the sciences, the religions, the arts, and man's social institutions, are studied in ways that encourage students to seek and find their own highest visions, thus promoting inner unity and social harmony.

Such a project is outlined in my address at the University of New Hampshire Workshop, sponsored by the Foundation For Integrated Education (1948). This address was printed in the Proceedings, *Issues in Integration*, under the title, 'A Temple of Learning.' Here the conception of three levels of the Temple of Knowledge was outlined, namely, (1) the first level of the Foundations of Knowledge (logic, mathematics, scientific methodology); (2) the second level of the Natural Sciences; and (3) the level of Wisdom and Social Guidance. This third level is the level of synthesis, the level of inclusive generalizations about man and society, the level we must attain if we are to formulate plans that have broad social significance.

This plan for the unification of knowledge is presented in Chapter II of this book. Here, as the reader will soon observe, we have the above-mentioned three-level structure for the organization of knowledge. It is obvious that every study of conceptual synthesis must be selective. What appears here represents what I believe is most important. Frequently, also, the exposition will seem to be 'slanted,' and this of course reflects the special interests of the 'integrator'; sometimes it is a clue to my own limitations. There is bound to be unevenness in treatment, and one can only regret that it is not possible for any one individual to give adequate treatment to all important topics. Moreover, there frequently is overlapping in the handling of subject matters. This is especially true in the fields of semantics and cybernetics; but since the problems of symbolism and communication lie close to the heart of our modern problems, this is to be expected.

A leading principle which runs through the entire work is the thesis that there is no point in writing about the integration of knowledge unless the reader is given substantial evidence of the practicability of the project. I have therefore tried to provide a living example of what we are attempting as we move from one chapter to the next. The problem, in each instance, is a dual one: to outline the major viewpoints in the field being treated, and then synthesize the materials thus assembled in the forward moving integration of the volume as a whole. The reader may not find the particular pattern of integration here proposed congenial to his own ways of thinking, — a point of view described as a Scientific Humanism. The acceptance or rejection of this particular philosophy is not crucial. What is important is that the reader have an example set before him so that he may gain an understanding of what is meant by the 'integration of knowledge,' while at the same time sharing some of the exhilaration that goes with creative activity. Thus stimulated, he may be more inclined to do some integrating of his own.

At this point a word of warning seems in order. It must be kept in mind that the 'problem of integration' is not alone the over-all problem, *what does our modern knowledge as a totality mean?* This question must be broken down into more specific problems. I do not believe in a 'grand slam' resolution of all problems, — whatever their nature. I am in agreement with Ralph Barsodi's statement that the proposed integration of knowledge in each and every special field is futile; but a synthesis based on the use of materials, — facts, laws, and principles, — from all fields relevant to the philosophical problems being considered is practicable. The problems considered in the present volume are in most instances philosophical problems. Among them are the following:

1) How is scientific knowledge possible? What is the relation of the 'knower' to the things 'known'? What are the fundamental assumptions of all human knowledge?
2) What is man? Is he a 'machine'? Or is he a creature with an immortal soul? Or are there other alternatives?
3) What kind of universe is it that man inhabits? Is it governed by rigid causal connections? Or by 'chance'? Is there meaning and purpose within the cosmic processes?
4) What is man's place in nature? Is he here by accident or by design? Are there other intelligent beings on other planetary systems in the cosmos?
5) In the light of one's theory of the nature of the universe, biological evolution, and the nature of man, what is the best

kind of social system for man to inhabit? Is man free to recreate society? What is the place of human values in the cosmic scheme?

6) What is the answer to the challenge of totalitarianism? What is the best candidate for a coming world philosophy? Is it possible to synthesize a universal world-view?

Most of these problems will receive consideration in the present investigation. The reader may have his own preferred answers, and these may not agree with my own. This is not all-important. What is urgent is that we human beings, working together, make some headway in finding solutions to these comprehensive but crucial questions.

It should be clear from this that the present volume sets forth the broad outlines of a complete philosophy of science, from the formal foundations at the base to the highest synthesis which is wisdom for social planning. Here we attempt to weave into the form of unity the following major formulations: (1) a theory of the dimensional nature of thought-systems; (2) a solution to the problem of knowledge based on Brouwer's intuitionism and a system-theory conceived in non-Aristotelian fashion; (3) a novel theory of the creation of matter; (4) a theory of emergent evolution by way of archetypal synthesis; (5) a generalized theory of communication and a parallel resolution of the mind-body dualism; (6) the beginnings of an hypothesis for parapsychology to explain extra-sensory perception; (7) a conception of a planetary democracy in terms of a panpsychistic electromagnetic society as the next emergent level of synthesis. The manner in which these several related lines of thought are brought together to sustain each other in a complete cosmology will appear in due time.

The writing of this book has taken about ten years. During these years I have had the benefit of comments from numerous friends and critics. My greatest debt is to Mr. B. G. H. Vanderjagt, who has helped me work out the pantheistic philosophy here set forth. Beyond that, my thanks are due Dr. Albert Einstein for his encouragement in this effort at developing a form of pantheism which, as he put it, "is very near my own." I am grateful for helpful comments and criticisms from John Dewey, Harlow Shapley, Alfred Korzybski, J. R. Kirk, J. B. Rhine, Stuart Carter Dodd, F. L. Kunz, T. Weiner, Julius Stulman, Joseph Bunzel, Mario Lins, C. K. Bliss, George P. Conger, C. Judson Herrick, Frank Sutherland, C. West Churchman, John

Somerville, Lloyd Morain, George M. McKinley, Robert A. Clark, Samuel E. Gluck, Charles Francis Potter, Bebe Bruto, Blodwen Davies, G. W. Borecky, M. S. Kingston, A. Lowinger, and R. Piper. I am happy to acknowledge my indebtedness to these, and other, individuals, especially my students in philosophy over a period of three decades of teaching, so many of whom have helped me in the everlasting effort at clarifying my own thoughts.

Finally, it remains to be pointed out that while approximately two thirds of the material of this volume has not previously appeared in print, a third (or less) has been published previously. Chapter II contains material from an article, "Escape from Chaos," which appeared in the *Journal of General Education*, Vol. 6, 1948, 136–143; Chapter III contains my contribution to the symposium, *Operation Knowledge*, sponsored by the *AAAS* meeting in Philadelphia, December 1951, under the title, "Unified Symbolism for World Understanding"; Chapter V contains materials from an earlier paper on "Symbolic Logic and the Frontier of Social Science," *Psyche* (London), Vol. 16, 1936, 139–149, and my later paper, "Symbolic Logic, Cybernetics, and Semantics," read at the Conference of the International Society of Significs, meeting in Amsterdam in the summer of 1953, later printed in *Synthese*, Vol. IX, Nos. 5–8, and another paper, "Symbolisme, Semantique et Synthese Sociale," read at the fifth Congress for the Scientific Study of Symbolism, meeting in Paris in May, 1956; Chapter XI is an expanded version of my article, "The Field Theory of Matter in a Pantheistic Cosmology," *Scientia* (two parts), Vol. 89, 1954, Nos. 7 & 8. I wish to thank the editors of these journals for permission to use these materials. I am especially indebted to Mr. C. K. Bliss for his permission to use the materials which appeared in the brochure, *Unified Symbolism for World Understanding in Science*, including the Bliss Symbols, published by the Semantography Publishing Company of Sydney, Australia.

1

MAN AND HIS IDEOLOGIES

"It seems plain and self-evident, yet it needs to be said: The isolated knowledge obtained by a group of specialists in a narrow field has in itself no value whatsoever, but only in its synthesis with all the rest of knowledge and only inasmuch as it really contributes in this synthesis something toward answering the demand, 'who are we'?"

— Erwin Schrödinger, *Science and Humanism*

I. Man: The Planetary Species

Modern man suffers from an ambivalence of the spirit. During his moments of depression, the world about him seems to be completely lacking in wisdom — a chaotic jumble of tensions and frustrations. Philosophy, the beacon of progress, in such moments seems hardly more than a flickering candle, vainly struggling against the gathering darkness. Fortunately, this despair does not last. From some unknown source there comes a change of mood, a lifting of the human spirit — and courage is reborn. In the distance we seem to catch glimpses of light penetrating the gloom, portents of a brighter tomorrow. Is this merely a vain, illusory hope, or is there indeed a beacon to guide our course to the world of the future?

This question is of the utmost urgency to mankind, and thoughtful persons will see that it gives rise to other questions, equally in need of answers. What does man know of himself and of the universe he inhabits? How does he know it? What is his relation to that universe? Are there limits to human knowledge? How can man test his insights and confirm his visions? How can man synthesize his present knowledge into that meaningful totality which is wisdom? This last is more than a question; it is a partial answer for it tells us what we must do. It pledges us to investigate the foundations of man's knowledge for the purpose of unifying that knowledge into a comprehensive whole that we may the better fulfill the promise of evolution.

The doctrine of evolution is believed to supply the most satisfactory explanation yet available of the origin of the human species. Although there are many different philosophies of evolution, they all agree that the later and more complex forms of life developed from earlier, simpler forms by very gradual processes of change. For a period of about two billion years, life evolved from its beginnings in primitive unicellular organisms, ever changing, becoming more and more complex, until, at long last, man made his entrance upon the stage of planetary history. According to present theories, *homo sapiens* appeared about a million years ago.

During the early stages of his existence, the human creature made little progress. For countless millenia, paleolithic man and his successor, neolithic man, eked out an uncertain existence barely able to survive. However, his later domestication of plants and animals enabled him to advance beyond the nomadic life of the hunter to the pastoral and agricultural modes of life. This proved to be an important step in man's evolution for it resulted in a considerable increase in human population and the development of villages. Thus, paleolithic savagery and neolithic barbarism were superseded by the earliest civilizations.

Three important and contemporaneous early civilizations arose more than four thousand years before the Christian era, between the Tigris and Euphrates rivers, along the banks of the Nile river in Egypt, and beside the Indus river in India. The Babylonian and Egyptian civilizations are especially significant for their contribution of the arts, crafts, and technologies, the forerunners which paved the way for the later development of science.

Following these, came the greatest of the early civilizations — that of the ancient Greeks. These people, who called themselves Hellenes, were Aryans from the north who, sometime after 2,000 B.C., over-ran the peninsula of Hellas and intermarried with the original inhabitants of the region. They then proceeded to build the civilization which culminated in Periclean Athens, where science and philosophy received their greatest impetus. The Hellenic culture gave rise to such men as Pythagoras, one of the pioneers of mathematics, astronomy, and philosophy; he and the many other Greek philosophers gave the Western World the beginnings of atomic theory, evolutionary theory, democracy as a form of government, and far more. The life of reason, philosophy, and science were so highly developed by the Hellenes that, when they were captured by the Romans, their culture dominated that of their captors. The medieval period which followed the Graeco-Roman era was comparatively barren; some of the creative drive of the life of reason was lost during this period and was not regained until the Renaissance closed the middle ages and opened the modern era.

Thus originated the astonishing epic of scientific progress — surely the most revolutionary of all man's attainments. The discovery and application of knowledge to modify the world is the outstanding fact of human history. Science is transforming our world at an ever-accelerating rate. The flash of science across the horizon of history, like that of a comet rushing toward an unknown destiny, inspires us with awe and even dread. Man, the planetary species, possesses the earth. Although he lives on land, he plumbs the ocean depths and navigates the air lanes. Potentially, he is the cosmic species, living in an environment as vast as his imagination can encompass. Even now, mankind is stretching its tenuous pseudopodia across trillions of miles of space to penetrate extra-galactic universes. How has this come to be? What specific "organ of civilization" has appeared within the framework of human anatomy to make possible this new knowledge and power?

II. The Spiral of Protoplasm

Such a perspective as we seek is provided by Major William H. Wenstrom in his book, *Weather and the Ocean of Air*. Here the author, like a contemporary Jules Verne, dreams of the time when man in a rocket may escape his place of bondage. Space-conquering men will penetrate to the regions where the blue deepens into violet, and the violet turns to darkness, while "against the blackness of empty space planets and bright stars shine with steady brilliance like enormous and remote lamps. . . . Against all this infinite pageant the giant sun glares blue-white . . . and far beneath is the broad earth, expanded to new horizons, haze-wrapped and cloud-littered . . . evidently a part of a greater cosmic scheme, viewed for the first time from the mythical slopes of Olympus."

To imagine the world as a globe swinging in emptiness, from afar — above the earth's north pole, for example — yields a perspective which indeed is helpful if for no other reason than to fix in our minds the relations of cartography which this extra-mundane emancipation makes possible. The planetary stereoscopic view of Major Wenstrom, salutary as it is in the enlargement of our spatial perspective, suffers however from a flaw in that it reflects a picture of the world as a static entity. A rocket-eye view of the earth does not convey to us the temporal span of our planet as a being with a history. As an organ in time, the living earth is a repository into which the total effects of the past are embodied. In its earthquakes, the earth vibrates with the whole of its past. A geological memory reverberates within our present planetary-political relationships.

Viewed in the dimension of time, our world can be telescoped into a series of geological eras stretching from the premillenial dawn of three billion years ago to the present travail of a humanity struggling ever-upward. Earth history is interwoven with a pattern of life, a woof and warp of vital threads which knit the floor of the earth with a streaming trail of protoplasm as it climbs from the sea below into the sky above — a fabric of living tissues crosswebbed with earth-history, culminating in a pinnacle of cephalization in the last era, the psychozoic age of Man. The earth-organism has built a tree of life, with a nest of sensitized cells — human personalities — proliferating in the upper branches, and now the birdmen of evolution are leaving their old haunts to probe the vaster universe in all its dimensions of space and time.

III. Man's Needs: Biological and Spiritual

The question, of what it is that confers upon man his supremacy as the 'planetary species,' poses consideration of the more obvious features that characterize the human species. According to anthropologists, the differentiating traits of man are these: upright posture; binocular vision; versatile grasping equipment; lack of rigid instincts; and a retentive brain with capacity for abstract thought and articulate speech, i.e., the use of languages and symbolisms for purposes of communication. Some of these characteristics man shares with his animal ancestors (e.g., binocular vision); but, taken all together, they enter into man's unique gift of creative imagination: man alone among the animals is able to create and transmit culture.

Now it is obvious that religions, philosophies, and the sciences, as products of the human spirit, arise out of man's superior intelligence, his unusual capacity to learn by experience and to utilize this accumulated knowledge in the solution of the new problems that arise in an ever-expanding environment. Because of the inheritance of those mutations which have resulted in the human type, the human being as presently constituted has certain fundamental needs. Some of them he shares with his animal ancestors — the higher primates, for example — such as the need for food, shelter, and defense against enemies. These cannot be neglected if the species is to survive. But beyond these, as a member of a human social group, man has what are variously termed intellectual, or cultural, or spiritual needs: As a member of a human group, he requires a moral code — a way of life and a notion of the 'good society.' And as a thinking creature with human curiosity, he requires a world-view, or *weltanschauung*, a theory of the kind of universe he inhabits, the forces that control that universe, and his relation to those forces.

In the cultural history of man, these two needs have been closely tied together and have constantly interacted. In a general way one may say that in primitive societies man's need for a moral code is taken care of by the customs or folkways of the group; while the need for a world-view is satisfied by the mythologies and theogonies which all primitive groups seem to possess, and which 'explain' the *why* and the *how* of the processes of nature.

Students of anthropology recognize that in the 'animistic' system of primitive peoples the phenomena of the world are ascribed to the purposes of spirits, or personified forces. Later on, when the polytheistic religions replace the cruder animism, the gods or spirits are thought of as superhuman creatures with the intelligence and emotions of men. Thus, in his anthropomorphic manner, man humanizes the outer world. Primitive religions and forms of magic are based on fear of these supposedly superhuman forces in nature. Desire to placate these powers and secure their good will is responsible for the magical incantations and sacrifices and taboos. Later, when the monotheistic religions came into existence, there also emerged a recognition of uniform and predictable patterns. Thus to some extent the monotheistic religions paved the way for the appearance of science and philosophy, and vice versa.

Today ethical monotheisms and the various philosophies of the world exist side by side. At the present time, therefore, man's need for a moral code (ethics) and a worldview (cosmology) may be satisfied in either of two ways: (1) by the historical religions which are at hand and which combine a moral code and a cosmology; or (2) by a system of philosophy, which does the same thing. In the first instance the individual takes over a ready-made philosophy, and in the second case he constructs such a system for himself. That is to say, from the present viewpoint any one of the great historical religions is simply a standardized philosophy which has been transformed into a 'creed' and a set of 'dogmas' perpetuated by a social institution called a 'church.'

The founders of the world's great living religions, such as Hinduism, Judaism, Buddhism, Christianity, and Mohammedanism, were then philosophers — geniuses who experienced profoundly and reflected deeply upon the problems of human existence and man's relation to the 'higher reality' which brought him into being. Unfortunately, however, the penetrating insights of these philosophers, who in the course of time turned out to be the founders of new religions, were formalized into stereotyped rituals and inflexible doctrines. In brief, a religion is born when the philosophy of an ethical genius — Jesus for example — is converted by the disciples and followers of the master into an 'orthodoxy' which is then perpetuated by those who come later and organize it as a creed or religion. When this happens, the philosophy invariably loses something of its original insights and ultimately it may become another fossil. The human mind in its restless search for the richer life tries to maintain the ethics and the worldview as they were originally given, yet many 'living' religions have turned into stultified, institutionalized, authoritarian systems which look backward to some 'revealed' truth of a world that is no more.

Just because they look to the past for their eternal verities, the authoritarian religions preserve the characteristics of the time and the place of their origins. Such religions are functions of the latitude and longitude, the local circumstances, of their birth. For example, Orthodox Judaism, Islam, and Christianity, have preserved the supernaturalism of the prescientific world of the Arabian desert and the Palestine of bygone millennia.

This historical background states one factor that is responsible for the crisis in our civilization; in our Western World the traditional

Hebrew-Christian synthesis is fast losing its validity, and for this reason our world is drifting into an ideological vacuum: the foundations of religion are crumbling before the trumpets of modern knowledge — like the walls of Jericho — and we do not formulate a world-view to take its place. One may expect intelligent people of today to question a moral code tied to an archaic, and supernatural, religion of yesterday, even though the ethical genius who synthesized the world view enunciated sound principles of human relationships.

IV. Persistent Problems of Man

Over the centuries both religion and philosophy have constantly interacted, and each has been formative of the other, so that to understand the one requires introducing insight of the other. Then too both serve the same psychological function or purpose for human nature. Each provides an answer to the two fundamental problems of human life — the problem of the meaning and the place of man in the cosmic scheme, and the problem of the best way to live within the ethnic group which furnishes man his cultural home. Thus insofar as people abide by guiding principles from a philosophy or a religion, they live according to a set of ideas, the marked difference in the two situations being the extent to which people currently have scrutinized and chosen their beliefs.

A complete and functional philosophy may be said to answer the following needs: (1) A *cosmology:* a theory of the universe and the forces that rule its behavior; (2) An *ethic:* a moral code and theory of the good life; (3) An *epistemology:* a theory of knowledge to explain the origin and the validity of the beliefs we hold to be true.

In the present chapter we are concerned primarily with the first and second of these. In the later chapters I shall deal at length with the third, which is the problem of knowledge, indicating how our epistemological theory is related to cosmology and ethics.

The task of constructing a cosmology — a 'model of reality' — is a descriptive enterprise. One's cosmology is one's theory of the universe *as it is.* What kind of cosmos is it that man inhabits, and what are the forces that govern the events that occur? Is it chance that rules? Or purpose? Your 'cosmology' is your answer to such questions.

The second enterprise of philosophy, that of constructing a theory of the 'good life' and the 'good society,' is concerned with personal ideals and social values — a theory of how men *ought to live*, if they are to achieve their highest potential. This is where 'values' come into the picture. In recent years there has been much discussion concerning values, and some individuals have talked about values as if they were 'things' to be possessed, like coins in one's pockets. Here the ancient fallacy of the 'hypostatization' of functions has a tendency to creep into one's thinking.

In *A General Theory of Value*, Ralph Barton Perry defines a value as "any object of any interest." This definition allows for psychological processes whereby we manifest our preferences or 'desires,' and thus allows us to take cognizance of the fact that a value is an abstraction from a class of 'choice responses,' and not some discarnate entity floating about. One's value-system, therefore, merely represents one's scale or hierarchy of preferences: if you could mold the world a little closer to your heart's desire, what kind of social universe would you choose to create?

Fundamental to the present view is the notion that an ideal society cannot be formed in the absence of a cosmology. Here I agree with the approach of Edmund W. Sinnott as set forth in *Two Roads to Truth:* "Moral problems will never be solved unless they are treated as part of the structure of the universe." This means, I take it, that one's conception of the world *as it ought to be* must be related to one's conception of the world *as it is;* i.e., an ethics should be grounded in a cosmology.

Some reflection on the fate of the utopian dreams of the past indicates that a system of ethics may fail for one of two reasons: (1) It may try to compel people to do what they can't do, human nature and society being what they are; (2) It may try to prevent people from doing what they must do, human nature and society being what they are. If, for example, biology teaches us that the fulfillment of sex gratification is a necessity, we may as well provide 'normal' or socially acceptable ways of satisfying this drive.

In a well-rounded philosophy, not only the biological sciences, but also the physical will come into the picture. That they can is illustrated by the appeal which some scientists have made to Heisenberg's uncertainty principle as a basis for human 'freedom of choice,' and the manner in which Eddington and Jeans have found confirmation of idealism in recent developments in physics.

Without resting our case on the foregoing examples, and without assuming that the appeal to history will settle the matter, one may add some measure of plausibility to our thesis relating ethics and cosmology by reference to some great systems of philosophy. These systems may be considered as represented in schematic form in their evolutionary context as follows:

Cosmology	*Ethic of*	*Emergent System*
Theory of Nature Archetypes	Plato's Republic	Platonic Mysticism
Materialism	Hedonism	Greek and Roman Materialism
Pantheism	Cosmopolitanism	Greek-Roman Stoicism
Hebrew-Christian Supernaturalism	Ethic of Jesus	Christianity
Dialectical Materialism	Ethic of Communism	Marxist Materialism
Naturalism	Social Hedonism	British Utilitarianism American Pragmatism

This list of the systems of philosophy, although incomplete, is representative of a variety of viewpoints. In all older instances and up to the recent systems, there is an intimate association between cosmology and ethics. Let us observe how this works for each system and consider the interlacing of ethical ideals and cosmology.

(I) PLATONIC IDEALISM:

Plato's philosophy is based on the dualism of an 'unreal' world of sense experience, changing and imperfect, and an eternal, changeless, and perfect world grasped through reason. The eternal and perfect world of Platonic *Ideas* (later termed 'archetypes') furnishes the patterns for particular things found in the world of sense perceptions. This cosmology, which Plato sets forth in the *Timaeus* and other Dialogues, was borrowed in part from Pythagoras.

In Plato's philosophy man's highest mission is to discover and contemplate the changeless and perfect *Ideas*, thus escaping the unreality of an illusory world. Accordingly, in Plato's *Republic* mathematics as the science of *universals* is held to yield the highest kind of knowledge, while the poets and artists are banished because they direct our attention to the unreal copies of the eternal patterns. This otherworldliness of Plato's ethics is further exaggerated in neo-Platonic philosophies, such as that of Plotinus. It reappears in the asceticism of Saint Augustine, who was first of all a Platonist; the morality of his *City of God* is reminiscent of the ethics of Plato's *Republic*, — in both cases, for example, there is condemnation of sex appetites and carnal desires. Much of the monastic idealism of Western culture can be traced to the puritanism of St. Augustine and St. Paul as forms of the Platonic influence.

(II) GREEK AND ROMAN MATERIALISM:

Our second type of ethical-cosmological system is the materialism which made its appearance in ancient Greek and Roman philosophy. Here we have in mind the philosophy of the Athenian, Epicurus (342–270 B.C.), a hedonistic ethic which teaches that pleasure is the only proper goal of life.

As originally presented, the Epicurean ideal of the good life is that shared by an intimate group of kindred individuals with cultivated tastes who enjoy together the intellectual and aesthetic 'pleasures of the mind,' and shun such external entanglements as politics and business.

Following the death of Epicurus, his materialistic philosophy was transplanted to Rome, where it degenerated into the doctrine of pursuit of sensuous pleasures: "eat, drink and be merry, for tomorrow we die." This deterioration was to be expected, since there is nothing in the Epicurean ethics to place a moral restraint against 'burning the candle at both ends.'

Since those early days of Roman Epicureanism, a materialistic ethic based on the atomistic cosmology of Democritus, materialism has had a bad reputation. It is usually considered to be a philosophy with low moral standards, and we frequently hear of the paradox of the moral materialist, — the materialistic individual whose conduct is better than his theory calls for. Today the Marxist materialists would doubtless deny the existence of a 'paradox' although it is interesting to recall that Karl Marx wrote his doctoral thesis on a phase of this philosophy.

(III) STOIC PANTHEISM:

Stoicism as a philosophy was founded by Zeno the Stoic, a student of Cynicism who lived about three centuries before Christ. This is not the Zeno who invented the famous 'paradoxes of motion.' Stoicism included among its followers many renowned Roman figures — Epictetus, Marcus Aurelius, Seneca, Cicero, and others.

The Stoic ethics was based on the cosmology of *Pantheism*, to use a later term invented by John Toland. It taught, for the first time in the Western world, the doctrine of the brotherhood of man. Our own English and American theory of 'natural rights' derives from cosmopolitanism of Stoicism, and comes to us through Roman law, Christianity, and philosophers like Hugo Grotius — all influenced in a considerable degree by Stoic teachings. The Stoics made a distinction between two kinds of laws: (1) *jus civile*, the law of the community, which was ultimately based on customs; and (2) *jus naturale*, natural law, which was not a matter of custom or tradition, and therefore should be applied to all human beings. Since men by nature are equal, all being 'sparks of the divine fire,' the good society would treat them as equal, and social reforms should aim at wiping out the conventional class distinctions.

In the course of time this Stoic Pantheism was replaced by Christianity — as indeed were all the pagan religions and philosophies that had existed before the Emperor Constantine pronounced Christianity the official religion of the Roman empire. Pantheism was revived by Giordano Bruno who was burned at the stake in Rome in the year 1600 for advocating the new Copernican cosmology, and was to be further developed by Spinoza, Goethe, Emerson, Keats, Einstein, and others. In his study of *Democracy in America*, Alexis De Tocqueville predicted that Pantheism would eventually become the prevailing religion of the United States.

(IV) Christianity — Orthodox Variety

The doctrines of Christianity are, of course, the creeds of the Christian churches as based upon the supposed teachings of Jesus, and now embodied in the Four Gospels of the *New Testament*. Much of this rests upon the foundations provided by the antecedent Judaism of the Hebrews. The orthodox creeds of Christianity usually include the following: (1) the Special Creation theory of Genesis, though this no longer necessarily excludes the possibility of a belief in biological evolution; (2) the *Fall of Man*, the dogma of "original sin," that in Adam all men sinned; (3) the *Divinity of Christ*, the Messiah, whose vicarious atonement wiped out the collective guilt of mankind; (4) the doctrine of the *Trinity;* (5) and the doctrine of the *Day of Judgment*, based on the supposed immortality of each human soul, which receives its eternal reward in Paradise or eternal punishment in Inferno.

Obviously the Christian doctrines presuppose the supernaturalism which was prevalent in the world views of the pre-scientific era. The dogmas of the Western or Roman branch of the Christian Church (as opposed to the Eastern Orthodox Church) were perfected by the Church Fathers (Patrologists) and reached their highest degree of systematization in the Thirteenth century in the *Summa Theologica* of Saint Thomas Aquinas. This Thomistic or Scholastic synthesis was pronounced to be the official philosophy by Pope Leo XIII in the year 1879. In our day, Thomism is persuasively expounded by Jacques Maritain and other representatives of neo-Scholasticism.

The Protestant branch of the Christian Church, brought into being by Martin Luther, rejects certain doctrines and rituals of Roman Catholicism. For example, there are only two sacraments, baptism and communion, and even these have a modified significance.

We have indicated that the Christian eschatology and ethics are based on the supernaturalism of Old Testament Judaism. The "Dead Sea Scrolls" demonstrate this, if proof were needed. In the course of time, however, one important formulation was added to this Hebraic-Christian cosmology. The inherent supernaturalism of Christianity was later tied in with the Greek geocentric theory of the universe as first set forth by Eudoxus and Aristotle and subsequently perfected by Ptolemy of Alexandria. In this Ptolemaic-Christian cosmology the universe, finite in size, came into being with the first act of Creation by Jehova some few thousands of years ago (4004 B.C. according to Bishop Ussher), with the earth as the fixed center of the system of planets and stars that revolve around it. In this earth-centered, man-centered universe, the heavens are above us (even though the world was known to be round) and hell is beneath our feet. Only after a bitter battle with those who embraced the new heliocentric cosmology of Copernicus, the Church finally did renounce the geocentric theory. It should be remembered, however, that in this conflict between science and theology the attitudes of Martin Luther and John Calvin were no more favorable to the Copernican theory than was that of the Church at Rome. It is true that the Lutherans did not put Copernicus to the stake, but the Calvinists did burn Michael Servetus in Geneva.

After giving up the Aristotelian-Ptolemaic conception, the Church at Rome was without a cosmology, until the exploding-expanding universe of Canon Georges Lemaître was recently approved by Pope

Pius XII. In a widely publicized statement,[1] the Pontiff informed the scientists of eight nations meeting under the auspices of the Papal Academy of Science that scientific developments not only give evidence of the existence of God, but indicate also that God created the universe approximately five billion years ago. A number of astronomers, without being adherents of the Roman Catholic faith, have helped perfect this conception of the expanding universe. And so, once more, the Roman Catholic Church has a cosmology, quite different from the old Ptolemaic theory, but nevertheless a unified view which gives it a philosophical advantage over the splintered theologies of the Protestant churches.

(V) MARXIST MATERIALISM AND COMMUNISM:

The communism of Karl Marx (1818–1883) stems from left-wing Hegelianism. Marx took Hegel's formula for dialectical idealism, the idea that history represents a movement from one position to the opposite extreme by a principle of action-and-reaction, thesis-and-antithesis,— and converted this into a philosophy of history. The economic or materialistic interpretation is known as *Diamat*, an abbreviation of Dialectical Materialism.

A number of other elements enter into the composition of the Marxist philosophy. The Hegelian formula of thesis-antithesis-synthesis, which becomes the doctrine of 'class conflict'; Feuerbach's theory that the idea of God is a reflection of social ideals, which is translated into the Marxist notion that "religion is the opiate of the people"; the French socialist theories as elaborated by Proudhon and Saint Simon; and Marx's own observations on the effects of the Industrial Revolution in England — all these constituents enter into the Marxist synthesis. Marx and his collaborator, Friederich Engels, produced the *Communist Manifesto* in 1848. This revolutionary program was further developed and applied by Nicolai Lenin and Joseph Stalin; the latter's work, *On Dialectical and Historical Materialism* (1940) ,was a substantial contribution to the socialism of the Soviet Union.

But always, throughout its development, the Marx-Lenin ideology was (and still is) based on the doctrine that the material world alone is real, and material conditions are therefore the basis of life and its expressions. However, we are warned by careful students, one must not naively assume that the 'historical materialism' of Marxism is completely synonymous with metaphysical materialism. There are ideas common to both, in being atheistic in principle, for example. But there are also important points of difference.[2]

(VI) British Utilitarianism and American Pragmatism:

Utilitarianism as a philosophy developed in England about the time that Marxism was beginning its meteoric career. To some extent both are responses to the challenge of poverty and unemployment which were intensified by the Industrial Revolution. The difference between them is that Utilitarianism believed that the conditions of men could be improved by political reforms, such as Bentham and Mill advocated, whereas the Marxists held that neither political nor economic reforms could fundamentally improve the human situation — only violent revolution could usher in the classless society.

Modern Utilitarianism was the gospel of social hedonism, as contrasted with the ancient form of hedonism, Epicureanism, which was individualistic. The formula of the Utilitarians, the "greatest happiness of the greatest number," was later employed by Franklin D. Roosevelt to explain the objectives of the "New Deal." This humanitarian utilitarianism was based on a naturalistic and empirical pattern of thought shared by British philosophers as John Stuart Mill and by such American philosophers as William James and John Dewey. While Friedrich Nietzsche would have no part of Utilitarianism, exclaiming in his most caustic tones: "Only an Englishman desires to be happy"; most of us in the democratic camp would agree that social hedonism served a useful purpose in developing a humane society, even though the utilitarian ethics is no longer acceptable as a philosophy.

(VII) Logical Positivism or Empiricism:

The currently influential movement known as Logical Positivism or Logical Empiricism is an anti-metaphysical viewpoint that revitalizes the Positivism of Auguste Comte, with some important modifications. Contemporary Positivism takes over from Comtean theory the three levels of explanation: (1) *religious level* — animistic and polytheistic; (2) *metaphysical level* — non-empirical entities; (3) *scientific level* — positivistic explanations. On the third and last level, science merely describes *how* things happen, and gives up the attempt to explain *why* they happen. The first two types of explanation are teleological in nature, while the third is non-teleological, in terms of the language of 'physicalism.'

As in Dewey's Instrumentalism, Positivism has little in the way of a cosmology; at least it does not possess a philosophical theory of the universe which comes by way of a speculative synthesis of the sciences. The Positivists accept whatever the special sciences may teach us: astronomy gives us an account of the nature of the stars and the galaxies; biology reports to us on the nature and the evolution of living things; scientific psychology formulates the principles of human behavior; and so on. But there is no overall unification of these conclusions into a comprehensive world-view.

Positivism and Instrumentalism are based upon a naturalistic foundation, and they are both committed to the use of scientific methodology. But for the Positivists there can be no 'science' of ethics, whereas the followers of Dewey would insist upon the thesis that reason has an important place in the formulation of a theory of the good society. The Positivists hold with respect to the past that the study of morals is merely cultural anthropology, and with respect to the future, that ethical preferences are simply the result of wishful thinking. This, at any rate, was the viewpoint of the Vienna school of Positivism. Since the tragic days of Nazi domination, however, the Positivists now agree that they must have something constructive to say on ethics, and so in more recent years the social and humanistic emphasis has made itself evident in the developing positivistic philosophy. This is observed in the recent writings of Philipp Frank of Harvard University and Herbert Feigl of the University of Minnesota.

(VIII) Atheistic Existentialism:

The two outstanding answers to the ethical problems of man which have attained prominence in the last several decades are neo-Scholasticism, already discussed, and atheistic Existentialism. The remarkable thing is that while they are antithetical in many ways, they both suffer from a common limitation: lack of confidence in the ability of human intelligence to create a good society for mankind.

The neo-Thomist movement for the past seventy-five years has been directed toward diverting education into Scholastic channels of metaphysics. This revival of medieval Aristotelianism, fused with Christian theology, would lead men's minds into the hierarchical institution which allegedly goes back to Saint Peter for its inception.

But the Thomist approach lacks confidence in scientific method as the only means for discovering the truths that make men free. By contrast Atheistic Existentialism, which suffers from a bad metaphysics,— just the opposite of the Aristotelianism of Scholasticism,— holds to a notion of freedom and contingency which culminates in an individualistic 'cosmic nihilism' as an end product.

If we begin, as do the Existentialists, with the proposition that 'being' is always individual and indeterminate, of course the ephemeral and contingent world will not conform to the patterns of changeless essences (universals) which the Platonists and Aristotelians posit in order to interpret the world. If *existence* is not formed through *essences*, but essences emerge from existence, it follows that man can have no fixed nature or goals. Accordingly, life has no antecedent meaning, and the only significance that can emerge is that which man may be able to generate out of his own freedom.

All this, no doubt, sounds rather plausible to a weary Europe for many decades tortured by wars and the clash of ideologies. Heidegger in Germany and Sartre in France exercise a curious leadership over mental refugees who have lost their bearings. Man, the Existentialists inform us, is catapulted into a world he can neither comprehend nor master, condemned to his 'dreadful freedom,' weighted down with sorrow (*sorge*), and knowing only anguish and despair. Doomed for as long as he lives to know nothing but nothingness, face to face with *das nichts*, where can man find any constructive program?

From the viewpoint of a Scientific Humanism, Existentialism is no more satisfactory as a philosophy than is neo-Thomism. The Existentialist is sensitive to human tragedy, but he is insensitive to the persistence of logical forms and mathematical patterns in nature and human evolution — such principles of *isomorphism* as the gestalt theorists have studied and the principles of *polarity* that are revealed by field physics and organismic studies in biology, psychology, and sociology. Existentialism is fundamentally a literary gesture toward life; it has not been cross-fertilized by contact with the social sciences and philosophy of nature. In a word, Existentialism has no cosmology worth talking about.

In the last three systems we have examined — Utilitarianism, Positivism, and Existentialism — philosophy is detached from religion and from cosmology. The result is that moral principles are grounded neither in God nor in Nature — indeed they are groundless. In these philosophies Man maneuvers his precarious existence on a level of behavior that is headless and footless — apparently only the stomach and the heart are essential to driving the human race on its goalless course.

This is the situation as we find it. Desperate indeed! The growth of science has given man power, but little wisdom. Cultural relativism has encouraged the drift toward moral skepticism. Two world wars have left the human family tired and cynical. Even atomic energy developments are more frightening than encouraging. What can be done in such a period of disillusionment and moral confusion?

If we agree that we are living at the close of one period in human history and the beginning of a new era, the first thing required for the building of that new era is an acceptable method of procedure which we can all employ in fashioning a philosophy which will contain a universal ethics based on a firm naturalistic cosmology. Now what is this ethics of belief which can and must supply the methodological principles for world unity? Here is my own best answer.

V. The Ethics of Belief in Science, Religion, and Philosophy[3]

In an era of tensions arising from differences in religions, nationalities, colors of skin, and social classes, many human beings are resorting to violent forms of social action to make their views prevail. They are resorting to unreasonable ways of establishing their 'truths.' To slow up and eventually stop this drift toward unsanity, the thoughtful persons of the world need to formulate an ethical code which, if it can be made an effective part of educational processes, may serve to lessen the virulence of the fanaticisms and even dissipate the delusional systems which have been produced.

In order to construct a common basis of reasonable beliefs we must agree upon a methodology for arriving at our truths. As a step toward the formulation of a set of ethical principles, the following propositions are offered. It may be that others have proposed similar principles; but in the literature it seems that Karl Pearson's *Grammar of Science* and Bertrand Russell's *Skeptical Essays* are among the few volumes which provide anything approaching an adequate discussion of this important topic. The essential principles may be segregated into two sets of postulates, as follows:

I. Postulates with Individual Reference:

1) Fallible, painstaking, but self-corrective human intelligence is the only reliable tool that man possesses for the discovery of the truths about nature, man, and society. As we shall see, *insight* has its place in the knowledge process, but this is not independent of human experience and abilities. Nothing is so wonderful, so mysterious, so sacred, but that man can experience it and incorporate it within the framework of human understanding.
2) Freedom to know the truth is a basic right of every human individual. Willingness to seek out, accept, and transmit the truths of human knowledge is a basic moral obligation.
3) The highest moral obligation is the obligation to be as intelligent and well-informed as one can in terms of one's biological heredity and social environment.
4) The right to explore for ourselves the avenues to truth implies a respect for this same right in others and the duty to assist others in this same search for truths. A socialism of ideas is proper here.
5) The sum-total of human knowledge is the property of the human family, and no individual, group, or institution may claim or possess secret knowledge which it is unwilling to share with others.
6) The right to use truths from the common fund of human knowledge implies an obligation to contribute something in return.
7) In areas where experts alone understand what knowledge there is (e.g., physics, medicine), the layman should be guided in his acceptance of factual information by what the experts are agreed constitute the verified propositions.
8) Every scientist has an obligation to understand the social forces which surround and influence him and to interpret the consequences of his discoveries in terms of the human implications and social impact of scientific knowledge. The obligation of philosophical synthesis rests upon everyone.
9) Where it is impossible to apply reason, or where the person holds opinions not based on reason (i.e., he holds opinions in religion, metaphysics, the arts which are based on claims to non-rational sources of knowledge — such as 'revelations'

and 'intuitions') *and where those opinions cannot be demonstrated to prejudice social actions for better or for worse*, the person is entitled to the 'will to believe.' The 'pragmatic test' has validity in areas where there is no verified knowledge, as with beliefs about God, immortality, beauty, and the like. But theological views about birth control, and the like, *do* prejudice social action for better or for worse and therefore cannot be accepted as 'true' when they have not been established to be true.

10) We may infer the truth of new propositions from established knowledge when the 'new' is in harmony with the 'old.' But when an investigator announces new 'truths'—in Parapsychology, for example—which are inconsistent with established knowledge, the burden of the proof rests upon him. However, every hypothesis is entitled to its day in court. Every alleged truth offered by an investigator is entitled to an objective presentation and a fair hearing. Frequently beliefs which were seemingly inconsistent with the accepted knowledge of the age have later turned out to be correct, but here again, it is the expert—chastened perhaps by experience—who is to judge whether any given item of belief can be integrated into the progressively expanding body of knowledge.

II. POSTULATES WITH SOCIAL REFERENCE:

1) A democratic society is the only form of government that is ethically justifiable. One should obey the laws of the state because, through our elected representatives, one helps to make them. One always retains the right to advocate changes in existing laws. Minority groups have their right to be heard.

2) If a person voluntarily accepts the benefits of social living, he assumes obligations with respect to the perpetuation and improvement of that democratic society. "Every right implies a corresponding duty"—for example, the right to freedom of speech, thought, and movement, implies the duty to respect this same right in others.

3) Political revolution is ethically justifiable whenever it is clear that the processes of democratic government are nonexistent or have been suspended.

4) A democratic society is one wherein the results of human intelligence are most readily accepted and put to social use — that is, it has the least 'cultural lag.' Here the methodology of science, based on reasonable persuasion, is operative. Democracy is scientific method in action, and science is the very genius of democracy.
5) In a democracy everyone has a duty to render service for values received, but what form this 'payment' shall take should be left to the individual to decide. For example, no scientist should be coerced into research for military purposes. If a research worker freely enters into projects involving national security, he voluntarily accepts the obligation of 'secrecy' with respect to classified information. Secrecy, however, is undemocratic in principle, and no scientist devoted to democratic ideals can accept the limitations of work in areas of classified knowledge.
6) If a researcher chooses to withdraw from programs which violate his sense of morality, this should be possible without jeopardizing his social status or civil rights.
7) Authoritarianism, whether political, religious, or ideological, has no place in a democratic society. Therefore the principle of separation of church and state is required. No person or institution has the right to determine what human beings shall think. Nondenominational schools are the proper instruments of democratic society.
8) Any system of belief which circumvents the ethical obligation to help attain the 'good society' in reasonable ways is repudiating the historic role of intelligence. 'Power politics' is wrong, whether employed in religion, science, or politics.
9) Freedom to communicate via books, radio, television, the press, and private conversations, is an essential of a democratic society. Book burning and brain washing are signs of totalitarianism. The accumulation of knowledge is justifiable only as a part of the preservation of the democratic way of life.
10) The proper climate of democracy is not merely intellectual and political — it is also economic. The 'underdogs' and the 'have-nots' should be assisted by those who have the material and intellectual resources to provide the requested aid. Democratic nations have ethical obligations with respect

to non-democratic nations, and these must not be carried through by threats of force or forms of violence. The United Nations Organization is the best instrument of international coöperation.

Perhaps this is a beginning for what may in time become a universal ethics. In a moment I shall outline the substantive philosophy which seems to come from this procedural program. Meantime, a further word on this all-important topic of science and democracy.

VI. Scientific Method as Democracy in Thinking

The function of philosophy is still what it was in the days of Socrates and Plato: to seek wisdom and provide guidance. If we are to attain wisdom about man's ideal possibilities, we must return to the fundamental principle enunciated by Socrates,— teacher of Plato,— that truth, to deserve the name, must be the same for all and not dependent upon local peculiarities of race, religion, or province. The agencies in our world capable of providing such valid and universal principles are science and philosophy. Working together and using the same methods and tools, they are the only methodology capable of discovering and correcting their own mistakes. Since the resulting philosophy is primarily a philosophy of science, we repeat that the term 'science' has a dual reference. On the one hand, science is committed to a method of procedure; and on the other, it presents us with a body of propositions for our consideration,— the generalizations that are accepted by the experts who utilize this methodology. Here, then, we find the primary source for the factual content of a world philosophy of Scientific Humanism.

As we have noted above, science is democratic rather than authoritarian in its procedures. Both democracy and a scientific methodology hold to the proposition that no human individual or institution has the ethical right to dictate to men what they shall think. Science presents its findings and interpretations, and asks in the name of reason that men reflect on these conclusions. There is no coercion here. Even when it is urged that there is a morality inherent in scientific methodology — that we have here the equivalent of an objective theory of value — this does not mean that these principles are to be superimposed by a chain of authoritarian controls. Access to information, free debate and persuasion, must remain the instruments of a scientific method and a democratic ethics. Freedom to know the truth and communicate it to others is the basic human right, and all other rights are derivative. Science, therefore, is the very genius of democracy, and without the use of the method of reason democracy is impossible. Accordingly, democracy is far more than a political system — it is a way of regarding the universe and man.

Given scientific method as the only method for discovering true propositions,— laws of nature and of human nature,— what shall be the content of the resulting philosophy? Because Scientific Humanism is, above all, an effort to see life as a whole, it is inclined to regard the traditional European tendency to think of man, society, and the universe in terms of independent elements as the source of much of our present confusion. In our fragmented ways we humans now regard the heavens above and the earth beneath as unrelated, absolute things; we have separated continent from continent, nation from nation, race from race, class from class; we have evolved many languages; and when, finally, we created disciplines of science, we divided the resulting knowledge into 'fields,' separating physics from chemistry, medicine from psychiatry, geography from politics, education from life, work from leisure, morals from endocrinology, soul from body, and so on. Until at last our 'universe' is no longer a universe — it is a dismembered aggregate of chaotic entities studied by piecemeal analysis.

Yet this fragmentation is the work of man, due to his creativity. These specialized approaches to man, nature, and society were good in their time, and necessary to the accumulation of facts and principles. But abstraction and isolation are not ends in themselves. Synthesis, seeing things together and in their interrelations and as wholes, is the goal of understanding. Scientific Humanism is concerned to show that however diverse the results may be, there is a regularity behind the patterns of events and there is sound hope of the integration of knowledge to be reached by coördinating our efforts in seeking the comprehensive perspectives. This faith in the possibility of the conscious control of human evolution is necessary if we are to stabilize the world of the future.

Faith in one form or another is essential to human existence. Because this is so, science has done harm in taking away from people their chief source of stability, faith, while yet giving them nothing to take its place. By washing their hands of the problems of religion and philosophy and condemning the churches for what they *are* doing, those scientists who are mental isolationists share responsibility with the churches for increasing the confusion in our lives. It is somebody's job to reëducate faith by providing the integration of knowledge within and between our learned professions. Such a synthesis could be brought into being by *UNESCO*, were it not that it is snarled up in power politics. Perhaps we need a World University, a non-political institution created for educational purposes. Here it should be possible to formulate the integrative principles in economics, sociology, psychology, politics, and anthropology, which would supply the basis for a modern, universal, naturalistic ethics.

Thoughtful persons frequently have pointed out that man does not live by bread alone. One of the over all drives of man is the need for a world view, a theory of the wider universe, to provide the cosmic setting for the human adventure. Historically, ethics and cosmology,— a theory of the good life and a world view,— have, we find, been linked together. Today, as we have also seen, some philosophers are suggesting that this historical nexus should be severed. Why not develop a moral theory without a cosmology, they inquire? According to the present form of Scientific Humanism, this proposed divorce of ethics and cosmology is not sound. In a well rounded philosophy these two cannot be dissociated. Moreover, there *is* a cosmology already available which meets the requirements of science and man's deepest yearnings. This is the cosmology of Pantheism, a world-view introduced into Western culture by Stoicism and exfoliated by Giordano Bruno, Spinoza, poets like Shelley and Emerson, and contemporary scientists like Albert Einstein.

In earlier centuries man felt at home in the universe. Today man suffers from forlornness,— as the Existentialists say,— because he feels cut off from nature. Now Pantheistic Humanism corrects this man-centered isolationism with a sense of cosmic kinship. To be sure, we must not project our parochial formulae and earth-bound sentimentalities into the vast universe of galaxies; but neither should we waste our years in sadness over the absurdity of man's existence as a conscious creature in an insentient world of atoms. According to Pantheism, the immense reaches of time and space and matter are the mensurational limits of an infinite and eternal cosmos, a universe in which God and nature are welded together in indissoluble union. Thus while there may (or may not) be a cosmic response to human aspirations on the emotional level, we do have reason to believe that man and nature have a common denominator of order — a human and celestial harmony of mathematical relations such as Pythagoras dreamed about long ago.

Without this Pythagorean-Stoic philosophy to pave the way, Christianity could never have won acceptance as the religion of the Roman empire and Western world civilization. Eventually Christianity displaced the noble pagan philosophy which had helped to gain for the new arrival general approval and acceptance. Now the world's debt to Pantheism should be paid. Today science and philosophy, working together, are in a position to restore this world view in some of the major theses of this emerging philosophy:

VII. Some Theses of Pantheistic Humanism

1. Behind our perceived universe of material things in space and time there is a *Cosmic Field of Energy*, infinite, eternal, uncreated, and indestructible. (See *Diagram* II, p. 35). Within this universal and undifferentiated ocean of energy there is a Supreme Imagination which, by way of the *Cosmic Lens*, acts as a focusing and guiding field of influence in controlling the creation and evolution of matter. Thus, high above the local gods of our earth's regional religions, there is a Divinity, an immanent guiding field, maintaining the balance between the visible or *manifest* world and the invisible or *unmanifest* world (as required by Einstein's equation for the equivalence of matter and energy, $E = mc^2$). This guiding influence organizes matter into the forms of evolution, from the inorganic to the organic world, from atoms to human beings.

2. Since God is not a personality distinct from nature, 'miracles' and 'special providences' as violations of nature's laws cannot occur. Therefore, there are no revealed religions, and the doctrine of the verbal inspiration of scripture has no foundation in fact. The Supreme Imagination appears as an invisible field of influence permeating the visible physical universe, but since this impersonal and divine influence can never in man's thoughts be any greater than man's capacity to envisage, man will become more like Divinity as he reverences and increasingly understands the infinite and everlasting cosmos in which all things live and move and have their being (to use a Stoic phrase which Christianity borrowed).

DIAGRAM II

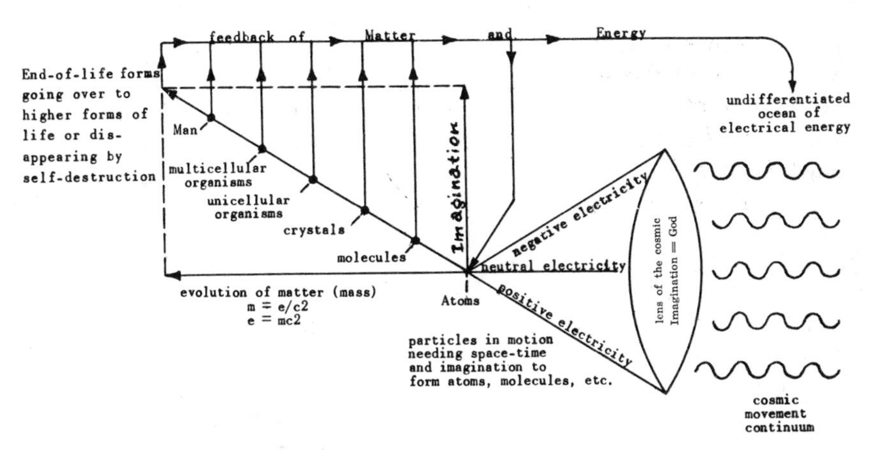

In Pantheism "God" is man's name for the Guiding Field or Cosmic Imagination by means of which undifferentiated energy is focused in nodal points in space-time, subsequently to evolve under the influence of guiding fields on higher levels.

3. There is no 'sacred' literature; there is no special religious experience; there are no chosen peoples; and sin as a violation of the laws of God as revealed to some prophet is sheer superstition. The clergy have no private contacts with supernatural powers, and they have no unique status as the interpreters of god's will.

4. Human consciousness in its awareness, and in its time-spanning properties, is man's most immediate experience of the cosmic guiding field in its organic expression. The invisible Supreme Imagination which guides the course of evolution in the visible physical world is a non-moral force, it is neither good nor bad, *until it reaches up into human consciousness to appear as integrated personality, at which point the Cosmic Energy acquires moral attributes.* If there are other universes — planetary systems with living and conscious creatures inhabiting them — there, too, problems of moral choice will arise. But here on this earth man alone is the bearer of that god-like quality of creative imagination which is the precondition for moral behavior.

5. Since a Pantheist does not pray to a personal god for special favors, he must seek for human 'salvation' through the 'therapy of knowledge.' The Pantheist cannot go to war because some god com-

mands it, and if someday man brings peace to the world, it will come as a result of the fact that man is endowed with the divine quality of creative imagination and has forged a social lens for constructive social synthesis. But if a Pantheist cannot be lured into virtue by promises of everlasting life in paradise, neither can he be tormented by fears of eternal punishment in hell. In a word, the sources and sanctions of the good life are natural from beginning to end. Man must fashion for himself a social lens for collective vision; but the potentialities of human nature are much richer than the materialists, ancient or modern, are willing to admit.

VIII. Archetypal Man: Avatar of Synthesis

The one thing that Existentialism can contribute to a Scientific Humanism is the idea that man can be free, if he earns and exercises that freedom, that is, utilizes the measure of freedom that resides in him to create the new humanity. This brings us to what may well be the supreme problem of modern culture: *what image shall man make of himself to provide the morphogenetic forces for the world of tomorrow?*

Human evolution may occur on three levels: physical, mental, and moral. So far as neuro-anatomy can discern, there has been little change in the human brain for tens of thousands of years. But this does not rule out the possibility of further changes in the future. In the meantime, the best hope for the creation of the new humanity seems to lie in the improved integration of aspects of personality which now are at war with each other. If reason and emotion, intellect and feeling, the head and the heart, can be brought into synergic relation, we may create the music of human consciousness which has been called the cortico-thalamic integration. Here, then, we have the answer to the challenge of Existentialism and neo-Scholasticism: Scientific Humanism responds to the crisis by offering its concept of man — *archetypal man as the avatar of synthesis.* Our image of man is quite different from the "superman" of Nietzsche. The task of Panhumanism would indeed be difficult if we had to begin all over again; but hope arises from the fact that there isn't any human being who does not in some degree have the qualities that are required. To that extent every individual is potentially a member of the new humanity.

Accordingly, the overarching purpose of our investigation is to investigate how the emergence of a free society of friendly peoples can be attained. The basic prerequisite of a planetary democracy is a new synthesis of ethics, cosmology, and theory of knowledge. This is nothing less than the job of creating a world philosophy. In our own handling of this problem we shall seek to formulate a Cosmic Humanism wherein ethics and cosmology are joined by a bridge of understanding which spans the chasm, as some regard it, separating the physical and the spiritual worlds.

FOOTNOTES CHAPTER I

[1]See "The Proofs for the Existence of God," Address of Pope Pius XII to the Pontifical Academy of Science, published by the National Catholic Welfare Conference Publications Office, Washington, D.C. See also the *Washington Post,* November 23, 1951.

[2]On this problem, see for example Sidney Hook's article on "Materialism" in the *Encyclopedia of the Social Sciences.*

[3]These postulates are set forth in an article appearing in *Philosophy of Science,* 1956, Vol. 33 (October).

2

THE UNIFICATION OF KNOWLEDGE

"*Wisdom hath builded her house;*
She has hewn out her seven pillars."
— Proverbs of Solomon

I. Escape From Chaos

Gloomy predictions have been made about the future of the human race. Of these many prophecies one of the more plausible is that man will eventually bury himself under the mountains of factual data he is piling higher and higher with each passing year. In support of this depressing conclusion two converging lines of thought may be introduced. On the one hand, the modern university is so over-departmentalized that there is no longer any significance to what the university is doing. In his book, *The Higher Learning in America*, Dr. Robert M. Hutchins states:

"The modern university may be compared with an encyclopedia. The encyclopedia contains many truths. It may consist of nothing else. But its unity can be found only in its alphabetical arrangement. The university is in much the same case. It has departments running from art to zoology; but neither the students nor the professors know what is the relation of one departmental truth to another, or what the relation of one departmental truth to those in the domain of another department may be."

If this indictment is sound, the modern university has little reason for being, except for the ignoble purpose of turning out specialists who are entombing themselves (and the rest of us) in their dark and meaningless catacombs of 'knowledge.' Significantly, Dr. Hutchins is no lone prophet crying in the wilderness. Sir Richard Livingston (Oxford) and James B. Conant (Harvard) have joined their voices in the chorus;

for all their brilliance and diversification, universities lack inner unity of purpose, pursuing immediate ends with little thought of their ultimate goals in terms of contributions to the future well-being of mankind.

From a quite different point of view, Dr. Vannevar Bush observes that the sheer physical problem of providing space for the books which store up man's accumulating knowledge is reaching overwhelming proportions. Proclaiming science as the 'endless frontier,' Dr. Bush points out that the rate of growth is so rapid that it is creating a librarian's nightmare — not to mention a scholar's inferiority complex.

Evidently both Dr. Hutchins and Dr. Bush, each in his own way, are struggling between the horns of the same terrible dilemma of modern learning: without more knowledge we are lost, and with more knowledge we are overwhelmed. Each of these analysts, of course, has his remedy, and it will repay us to take note of them.

The "great books" project of Dr. Hutchins and Dr. Mortimer Adler has been well publicized. The University of Chicago served as an early testing ground for the experiment, which spread from there to other educational institutions. Using the *Syntopicon*, Dr. Adler's master-index-of-great-ideas, as a tool, the Hutchins-Adler solution is to provide the modern 'hierarchy of truths' necessary to order man's existence.[1] This *Summa Dialectica*, based on a 'hierarchy of essences,' will supposedly do for our modern world what the *Summa Theologica* of Thomas Aquinas accomplished in the medieval synthesis — and the world is thereby saved from intellectual and spiritual chaos.

Without benefit of metaphysics or theology, Dr. Bush tackles the problem from another angle. He offers the suggestion that the problem be solved by codifying knowledge (*Mimex* will replace the present crude systems of classification), encoding the knowledge on micro-punch cards, which can subsequently be decoded and utilized as occasion requires. Thus, if I may extrapolate, the graduate students of our coming universities will be manipulators of electronic devices and translate higher education into a game of academic pin-ball machines. Perhaps these two projects could be combined, in which case 'Mimex-Syntopicon' would become the Aladdin's lamp of knowledge in the decades that lie ahead! From our point of view, however, neither of these proposals really contributes much to the goal of integration, — the wisdom of reflective synthesis, — and the problem remains unsolved.

II. Mountains of Knowledge

Some idea of the immensity of the job can be gained by reading Dr. W. Grey Walter's book, *The Living Brain* (1953). In his closing chapter, Dr. Walter calls attention to a fact which we have already emphasized, that "the rate of accumulation of knowledge has been so colossally accelerated that not even the most noble and most tranquil brain can now store even one thousandth part of it." Thus our bewilderment mounts in rapidly widening spirals, perhaps following a Gresham's law of the economics of information to the effect that half-truths drive out full understanding.

The root of the trouble is that facts accumulate at a rate faster than our understanding of them. As Dr. Walter observes:

"Continuation of the sectarian process of specialization could only lead to one result, the creation of an irresponsible scientific priesthood, preoccupied entirely with its liturgy and its mysteries; and in due course, to a popular revulsion from scientific knowledge and a slump of scientific credit."

Here we have a clear recognition of the nature and size of the problem. Hence at the present time the human mind patently cannot encompass all knowledge even to the degree necessary to see one's own 'specialties' in their true perspectives. That is why, in a democracy, thinking must begin at the bottom. Top planning reduces progressively the number of persons whose work can pioneer along frontiers. One great aim of education should therefore be to provide the facilities for teaching the principles of thinking to masses of people so that, later on, they can function intelligently and creatively closer to the top in a highly specialized world.

The number of specialities is well toward twenty thousand, so Mr. Paul Mandeville, Director of the Library Research Conference, informs me. The subject matter of human knowledge is difficult enough to break down into classifications for shelving books and papers. This is illustrated by the Bell Telephone studies in classification, where the attempt is made to get specialities decently grouped under six thousand main classifications. It is even difficult to present schematically the break-down in separate industries. Moreover, each industry has its own language, often a rich and specialized one. The difficulty was recognized in the revision of the Kilgore bill introduced into the U. S. Senate in 1947. Here we find mentioned "a functional system of classification" to be worked out by the Office of Science and Technology in collaboration with the Library of Congress. According to Jesse Shera, head of the Preparations Department of the University of Chicago Library, the difference between the usual classifications of literature (according to titles, authors, and subjects) and a classification that is functional, is that the latter is basic to or inherent in the nature of such work. Libraries, it is pointed out, necessarily use a linear classification, while the relationship of literature to work is polydimensional.

Of course, the preparation of a functional classification of scientific and technical literature would be a monumental task. But if a *World Encyclopedia* a la H. G. Wells, which will be discussed later, could be edited so as to use a common language throughout, with articles classified functionally according to work and not according to a linear "tree of Porphyry" or Mortimer Adler's "hierarchy of essences," we would at least be headed in the right direction in our search for a way to the integration of all knowledge.

Obviously the present work, exploring the vast area of modern man's confusion, would never have been written in the absence of a considerable confidence in the feasibility of the task. Fortunately the art of synthesis is not a one-man enterprise. Already there are many scholars moving in a convergent march toward the common goal of the unity of knowledge. These seekers after synthesis are consciously trying to restore philosophy to its ancient and rightful status as the 'love of wisdom.' The mission of philosophy is still what it was for Socrates and Plato: the search for vision and guidance. The knowledge consists of multitudes of facts; wisdom is the insight into the relatedness of these facts to each other and to the central principles underlying man's conception of himself and the world in which he lives.

It must be admitted, however, that many of the pioneers of this development are moving forward under a common banner,—the standard of Scientific Humanism,—and that is the reason their adherence to synthesis makes possible an important program, built around a shared purpose and a nucleus of ideas. There is much to be gained by having a name to give these concepts coherent form and social reality despite the admitted danger in labels. A great deal of Scientific Humanism abroad in human affairs hasn't been named and recognized as a thought-form, something definite and intelligible as an authentic pattern. This emerging thought-form for a new age will grow and unfold with experience, but there is now at least a literature to which people can turn for a statement of principles which support their own impulses toward world unity. Thus Scientific Humanism attempts to provide the thought that should sire the action.

III. Education: Man's Last Refuge

If there is any lesson we may learn from recent decades, it is that education, like science, is a two-edged sword. The world is no better off, and indeed may be worse off, if the science and the education that shape the world are in the hands of those who have narrow interests and selfish motives.

Doubtless it is the recognition of that fact, namely, that physicists, chemists, and biologists are developing powerful instruments for weal or woe, the application of which can result in the destruction of all forms of life on a scale hitherto undreamed of, which has created the wide demand for reforms in education. Those who direct the educational policies of our institutions of learning now want an education that is likely to produce vision, understanding, and good will, not merely the narrow and specialized skills. They realize now that one fundamental shortcoming of our society is that while the sciences have been racing toward specialization, we have failed in the development of a broad social viewpoint and the creation of a set of institutions to ward off the harmful consequences of scientific advances. We have not humanized science, technology, and industry. And,— worst of all,— *the scientists produced by our universities have not been trained to synthesize the bodies of knowledge they master into a unified conception of man, his place in nature, and his potentialities for the good society.* That integration can no longer be postponed is clearly set forth in the *Report of the Harvard Committee on General Education in a Free Society*, which states: "The question of *Unity* has become insistent . . . the search continues and must continue for some over-all logic, some strong, not easily broken frame within which both college and school may fulfill their at once diversifying and uniting tasks." This thesis is supported by similar statements from many other educators who insist upon the need for a reorientation of our thinking, if mankind is to survive.

It is now generally conceded that our world suffers from a progressive breakdown of traditional culture patterns. The old institutions obviously cannot meet the needs of the new society created by science. Indeed, the very persistence of the old patterns of thinking makes the breakdown more certain. Beginning at the top with a conceptual (ideological) breakdown, this is leading to an ethical collapse, which in turn will accelerate the processes of social decay. We must stop this descent from conceptual, to ethical, to social confusion, before it moves to irretrievable economic, political, and finally military exhaustion.

Applied science has at the same time been shrinking the world physically into one community. Uncounted millions of human beings are for the first time brought face to face, and stare into each other's eyes with mingled feelings of surprise and resentment. The brute fact is that while the compulsions of industry and technology are driving human beings into a one-world society, *we are not mentally prepared for this next level of social integration, because we have not been able to derive the principles of a one-world society simply and directly from the controlling features of our present ways of thinking*. The failure of society is the failure of philosophy to do its job, and now the task must be tackled by all of us, working together, whether we be professional philosophers or not.

How have our schools lived up to these challenges of the atomic age? Surely one hopeful development is the current general education movement, an inspiration toward revision of the traditional attitudes and courses. In looking over the objectives of the new courses that many of our colleges and universities have set up, one finds such purposes as the desire to provide a common intellectual meeting ground for individuals of diverse backgrounds. This is all to the good. Let us have more such courses. On the level of graduate study, however, this is not enough. Presumably by the time the students are in the graduate school, and therefore quite mature, they should have assimilated the values of a general education. As I see it, the aims and procedures of general education, operating within the natural sciences, social sciences, and the humanities fields, and perhaps even across them, are to develop attitudes and methods useful for the cultivation of 'good citizenship' outside any subject-matter specialty. This type of education would still be adequate for the level of graduate study, provided the needs of graduate education presented no additional problems, and provided, also, there were the same three major distribution fields within which the students were expected to take their work, — which is frequently not the case. The high degree of 'specialization' in graduate study does not permit it. And that is where integrated education enters.

IV. General Education and Integrated Education

Wherein does general education differ from integrated education? Integrated education represents the conscious striving to produce content courses of ideas, based on the sum-total of human knowledge. That is to say, general education works *within* the distribution field areas in the hope of producing trans-departmental attitudes and skills. Integrated education is not content to stop at this point. It results in a difference by way of addition rather than subtraction. The aim of integrated education is to assist the student who proposes to major in some specific subject, to develop or formulate a body of ideas that will be useful in forming judgments and arriving at decisions which will have broad social consequences.

The potential leaders of our future society, in education, public health, politics, the sciences, and the rest, may benefit in having their attention directed toward the possibilities, facilities, and techniques, for the integration of knowledge, not only *within* the areas of their specialties, but *between* fields, as for example, physics and politics, biology and sociology, economics and politics, psychiatry and religion.

In our thinking on this subject we begin with the fact that many universities have the three distribution fields of the *natural sciences*, the *social sciences*, and the *humanities*. We know that these divisions are largely the product of historical developments which, in turn, have some basis in the differences in subject matter as these differences have been solidified into the content of these 'fields.' One present result of this development is the rivalry that has grown up between the sciences and the humanities, with the consequence that the members of the teaching staff in each field are now on the alert to defend their 'interests.'

The story of the conflict between classical education and natural science education need not be reviewed here. It is enough to point out that the social sciences, which might have served as a bridge of understanding between the natural sciences and the humanities, for one reason or another have not functioned in this manner. And so the rivalry is still unresolved, in spite of such efforts as Northrop's *Logic of the Sciences and the Humanities* to find a common ground.

V. The Sciences Versus the Humanities

It is my impression that this dualism of the 'scientific' and the 'humanistic' is at the root of much of our trouble, social as well as intellectual. If we could devise courses in integrated education which would cultivate a rapport between both fields, and within the same individuals who share both interests, the rivalry of 'art versus science,' for example, would vanish. It might be possible in time to build courses in the physics of politics as well as the politics of physics, the mathematics of art as well as the art of mathematics, the humanity of science and the science of humanity, and so on.

Of course, some oddities could result. There is the story told about the professor who gave two courses, — one on the history of philosophy and the other on the philosophy of history, — and to pass from the first to the second course, he simply took his notes and read them backward! This, of course, is not what we mean by the integration of knowledge. The psychology of philosophy is not the philosophy of psychology spelled backwards.

We have made the point that our present program of graduate studies is not good enough. As I see it, our next major enterprise is nothing less than the immense job of putting our specialized bodies of knowledge together to see what it all means, to get an overall picture of the nature of man, and the nature of the universe in which man lives, the possible interrelationships of man and nature, and a clearer conception of the best kind of society for men to live in, in the light of what the sciences and the humanities tell us about both man and nature. That is the most important intellectual task our higher education now has to face.

In order to attain some idea of what this may mean, — a preview of the sort of integration of knowledge which might provide the core for a unified education, — let us supply ourselves with some necessary building material from the intellectual history of the western world.

VI. The Social Background of Science

What we have in mind here involves a brief excursion into the field of the interaction of social institutions and scientific concepts. The idea to be presented is that science in its interests, types of problems, and even its explanatory concepts, bears some functional relation to the culture-patterns and institutions of the society in which that science grows up and survives. That is to say, science is not an absolute, self-sufficient atom of intellectual activity; it is a process and a product that occurs within a social context. This, of course, is not a new idea.

In the course of investigations in this field, showing that the specific explanatory concepts we employ in science have a discernible social background, one comes across Professor B. Hessen's "The Social and Economic Roots of Newton's 'Principia' ", a paper presented on the occasion of the Second International Congress of the History of Science and Technology held in London, and printed in the volume *Science at the Crossroads*, 1931. His article traces the relation between Newtonian science and the economic forces at work in the England of that period. The idea that there is an underlying connection between Newtonian dynamics and the general social conditions provides a most interesting interpretation. In this particular case the analysis represents a Marxist viewpoint as expounded by a Soviet delegate, and it presupposes the familiar Marxist approach that seeks to demonstrate how economic factors influence ideological formulations.

But further reflection on the part of a non-Marxist investigator reveals that we have here only half the story. The other half of the story brings out the manner in which scientific and even philosophical ideas recreate the social culture, in some cases giving rise to new methods of production. The validity of the other half of the story can be substantiated by reference to the thesis of J. G. Crowther as touched upon in his book, *Famous American Men of Science*. He points out that Newtonian mechanics had a significant influence on the framers of our own Constitution, partly direct and partly indirect, through such intermediate figures as Montesquieu.

The sanction of Newton's immense prestige was thus given to the notion of government as a self-regulating mechanism. For example, after God created the atoms out of which the universe is made, the laws of behavior were imposed by the supreme authority; therefore, the laws of nature were not mere human conventions, but inviolable, and so on. This conception permeated the constitutional law embodied in our form of government. Perhaps the most interesting feature of this development appears when we discover that the only physical scientist at the Constitutional Convention was Benjamin Franklin, and since Franklin's work was in the field of electrodynamics, he was not dominated by Newton's authority. For this reason Franklin was able to escape the legalistic formulations of the lawyer members of the Convention. Accordingly, Franklin managed to achieve a measure of skepticism about the system of 'checks and balances' which found sanction in the Newtonian type of explanation as carried over into social theory.

The foregoing considerations call attention to a very interesting problem. If it is true that social concepts and institutions control in some degree the nature of the explanatory concepts of science, and if science as a process and a product in turn recreates society, so that we have here a genuine case of reciprocal causation (the cyclical relationship now described as a feed-back mechanism), where does this leave us with respect to the proper relation between 'science' and 'society'?

It is true that this issue is not new to the world: pioneers in science,—men like Galileo and Darwin,—were familiar with it. Today the scope of the issue is broadened; no science is exempt. Currently the controversies of Michurin-Lysenko genetics versus Weismann-Morgan genetics, and the problem of the freedom of exchange of knowledge in the field of atomic energy developments, are among the more familiar phases of this debate in which political issues complicate scientific problems.

As one looks into the future,—say one hundred years hence,—one wonders what kind of society people are likely to be living in, in view of the impact of coming scientific developments. And what will science be like, if its explanatory concepts are subject to evolution? Shortly before he died, A. N. Whitehead was elaborating an 'organismic physics' and using such terms as the 'electromagnetic society.' Perhaps, then, some future Benjamin Franklin, or Whitehead, or Einstein, may give science a new twist that will reshape the form of scientific theory. Or, perhaps, will some future Alfred Rosenberg twist the framework of science to fit the form of some recrudescent fascism?

VII. Totalitarianism or Planetary Democracy?

We have seen that philosophy is the search for wisdom and social guidance. Synthesis of knowledge and understanding about the goals of life,—these have been and evermore should be the aims of those who think philosophically. This ancient conception of the function of the philosopher has led to the idea among laymen that philosophers suffer from grandiose delusions. Doubtless it is this 'system-maker's vanity' which explains why the subjects which philosophers deal with, and the visions of reality which they report, seem to belong to a world of phantasy. Philosophers, therefore, are frequently pictured as spinners of metaphysical cobwebs, distillers of stratospheric moonshine, whose abstract schemes have little contact with the world of reality and even less influence on the course of history.

Now a curious thing is happening. In the past, even the professional philosophers, for all their intellectual brashness, have hesitated to come out of the ivory towers and descend into the market places. It is almost as if they had accepted the derogatory opinions of the 'men of action' concerning their idle dreams. Accordingly, philosophers have hesitated to urge the need for a unified philosophy, — or have only half-heartedly hinted at this necessity. But now, however, people of the market place are going to the philosophers and asking for help. With this unexpected encouragement, philosophers no longer feel so presumptuous in their sense of 'mission.' The concept of a unifying philosophy, not only for American education, but for world politics, is a growing idea. It is in the air. Men of unquestioned integrity and ability are devoting themselves to the search for a democratic pattern of world civilization.

On the highest level, — that of world politics, — it is quite probable that one of the most powerful drives toward a 'world philosophy' comes out of the ever-present tension between Soviet Russia and the Western democracies. Here we have today's paramount problem and challenge: How shall this far-reaching conflict-pattern be resolved? Who can doubt that it is precisely because the Union of Soviet Socialist Republics (Russia) already has a program and a full-blown candidate for the world philosophy in the field, — the Marxist theory of Dialectical Materialism, — that other countries, for one reason or another not inclined toward this philosophy, feel the need for finding a rival philosophy? Thus far, the philosophy of democracy, and Christianity as a potential world religion, are the only other major ideologies in the running, but there are reasons for believing that both of these will need modifications before they can become viable embryos for the coming world philosophy.

It seems, therefore, that several conceptions of the world philosophy and its method of attainment are possible. One way to attain such a philosophy is to return to a viewpoint which in recent years has lapsed into disuse, but which, it appears to me, is pretty much what is required by our modern world with its complex and specialized bodies of knowledge. I refer to Herbert Spencer's conception of philosophy as the *synthesis of the sciences.* The outstanding objections to Spencer's enterprise can be met, and there are good reasons why the 'synthetic philosophy' should be revived. In seeking to salvage this system, I shall remodel the structure to render it habitable again.

VIII. World Philosophy and the Temple of Knowledge

This diagrammatic concept may be entitled A Temple of Knowledge. Analogous to a Greek temple, the schematism shows a structure of three parts rising to the crowning triangular pediment representing the following components:

Level I: *Logic and Scientific Methods; Semantics and Epistemology.*
Level II: *The Special Sciences.*
Level III: *Wisdom and Social Guidance — the level of World Philosophy.*

From the present point of view, *all valid philosophy is philosophy of science,* i.e., philosophy of knowledge. Level I deals with the fundamental assumptions and the basic methodology of all science. Level II deals with the specialized bodies of knowledge (facts, laws, principles) of the several special or natural sciences. Level III, Wisdom and Social Guidance, represents the broad philosophical implications and social applications extracted from our bodies of specialized knowledge and integrated into an archetypal synthesis, — the new earth and the new humanity. The first level represents what C. D. Broad calls "critical analysis"; the third level is the level of "speculative synthesis."

Our scientists and their students are at the present time on Level II. The pillars of the temple of knowledge, that is to say, the rectangles on the second level, are the fields of knowledge which result from applying the strategy of 'divide and conquer.' There is no science of nature as a whole; each science marks out a small area of the universe (its 'field') and studies it intensively. Many scientists confine themselves to their own narrow fields. One can be a 'specialist,' — a chemist, a biologist, an astronomer, — and not know much about neighboring fields of knowledge, except as, for example, a knowledge of physics and mathematics is a prerequisite to the study of chemistry. But, generally speaking, an individual may be a 'good' scientist without having much interest in other 'subjects' or even in the philosophy

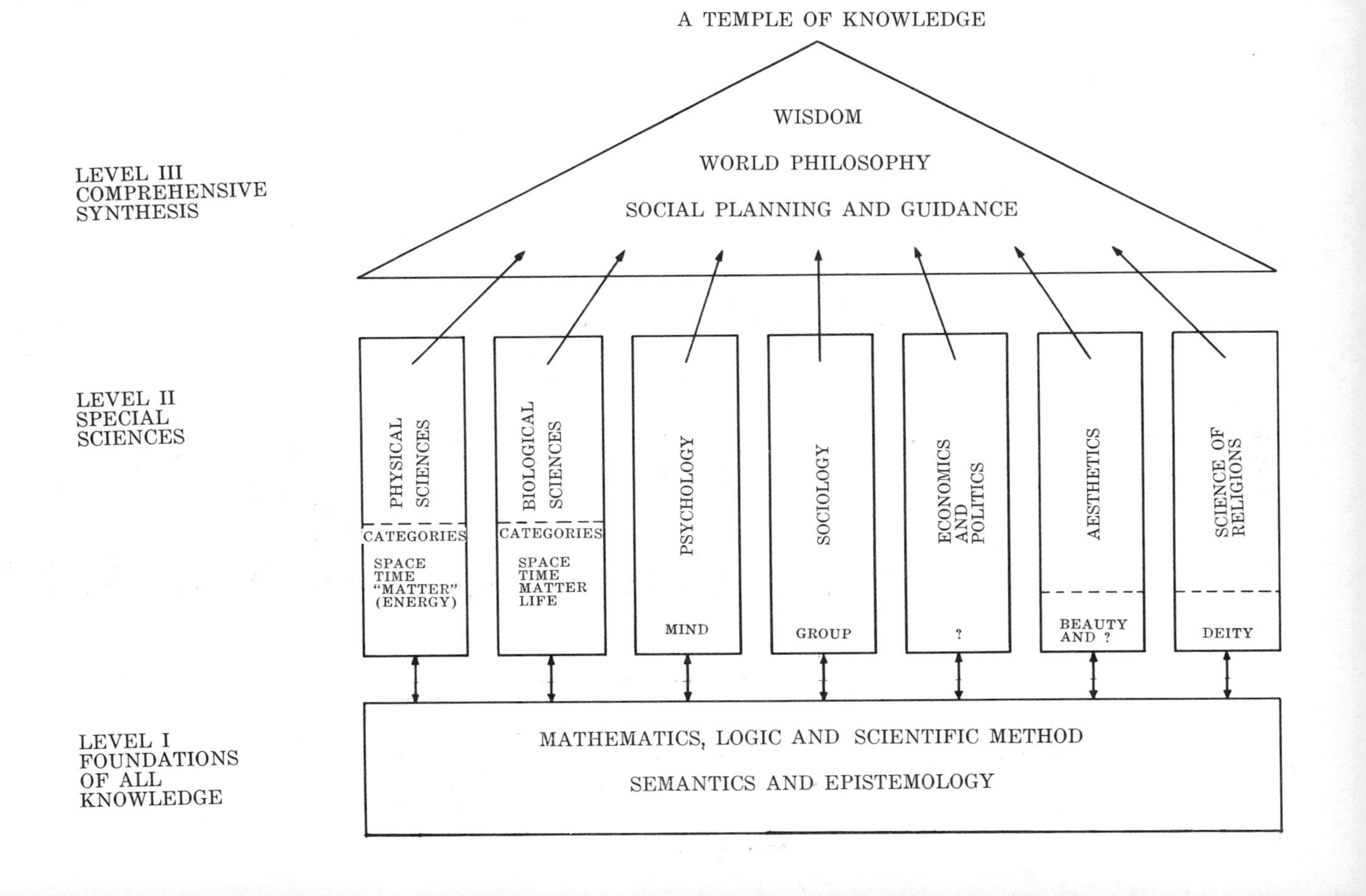
A TEMPLE OF KNOWLEDGE
WISDOM
WORLD PHILOSOPHY
SOCIAL PLANNING AND GUIDANCE
LEVEL III COMPREHENSIVE SYNTHESIS
LEVEL II SPECIAL SCIENCES
PHYSICAL SCIENCES
CATEGORIES
SPACE TIME "MATTER" (ENERGY)
BIOLOGICAL SCIENCES
CATEGORIES
SPACE TIME MATTER LIFE
PSYCHOLOGY
MIND
SOCIOLOGY
GROUP
ECONOMICS AND POLITICS
?
AESTHETICS
BEAUTY AND ?
SCIENCE OF RELIGIONS
DEITY
LEVEL I FOUNDATIONS OF ALL KNOWLEDGE
MATHEMATICS, LOGIC AND SCIENTIFIC METHOD
SEMANTICS AND EPISTEMOLOGY

of his own area, where the 'philosophy' would be investigation into the basic assumptions and overall implications and social impact of the sciences.

But if the scientist has a philosophical mind and a sense of social obligation, he will perforce move downward from his own (second) level to a study of the foundations of science, and upward to the third level where the problems of the implications of the specialized disciplines are considered.

Scientists who remain within their own rectangles of knowledge are not assets to our society. These are the narrow 'experts', frequently the empirical grubbers, who stumble upon truths in the sciences, but are not much concerned with the uses to which these discoveries may be put. Fortunately, they are a disappearing breed. Even the physicists have come to realize that the social control of scientific discoveries, — in the field of nuclear energy developments, for example, — are tremendously important. Indeed, in this respect the physicists are now ahead of their colleagues in the other sciences.

Having thus made some general remarks about the three levels, let us next examine more carefully each of them, beginning with the first.

IX. The Level of Logic and Scientific Methodology

We describe the Foundations of Science, Level I, as the level of Logic and Scientific Method. In this we include Epistemology, or Theory of Knowledge, and Semantics. Here we examine the fundamental assumptions or postulates of all science. These presuppositions and tools of all science fall into two main groups, as follows:

I. The Assumptions of All Science:
- (a) The "Laws of Thought."
- (b) The Categories of all Science, — Space, Time, Matter, Energy, Causality, and the like.

II. The Epistemology of Science:
- (c) The Epistemological Assumptions of Science:
  1. Uniformity of Nature.
  2. Independent Existence of an External World.
  3. Reliability of Sense Experience in Perceiving Nature.
  4. Correspondence of Inner and Outer Forms, so that a Matching of Concepts and Percepts is Possible.

Turning to the "Assumptions of All Science," it will be noted that on LEVEL II there are many sciences which have the suffix *ology* (e.g., Biology, Psychology), meaning that they represent *logic* applied to the factual material of that special field. The term 'logic' comes from the Greek word *Logos*, meaning reason and speech. So the science of anything is the reasoning about, or the logic of, that subject. But are the principles of reasoning the same for all sciences? Are they the same throughout all time? Or is the human mind still evolving, so that new 'laws of thought' may make their appearance and take their places in the battery of scientific tools? Are the three time-honored 'laws' of Aristotelian logic ultimate and everlasting? Or may they be superseded by other principles? The answering of such questions belongs to the first level of theory of knowledge. Whatever 'laws of thought' are set up, their acceptance becomes a part of the fundamental assumptions of all sciences which take them for 'granted.'

A second class of ideas required by science consists of the explanatory concepts and categories, — such as space, time, matter, motion, causality, and the like. In addition to these, required by all science, there may be new categories demanded by the 'higher' sciences, — biological and human social, for example, — such as the supplementary categories of 'life,' 'mind,' 'culture,' and so forth.

A third class of assumptions of science (c), consists of the epistemological assumptions of science. We have separated these from (a) and (b) for purposes of clarity, since they seem to be different in nature. Examples of such assumptions are (1) the *principle of the uniformity of nature* (that under the same conditions nature will behave in the same way); (2) the assumption of the *independent existence of the external world of 'matter'* (this is an 'assumption' which is not shared by the Christian Scientists, and idealistic philosophers like Berkeley and Sir James H. Jeans); (3) the *reliability of sense perception* (that our senses give us reliable information about the external world); (4) a theory of *the correspondence of the inner and outer forms* so that a matching of concepts, such as *number*, and external realities is possible.

It is evident that studies on the first level are incomplete. Many questions concerning the 'foundations of science' remain to be answered. Even 'scientific methodology' conceals some tricky problems: What is the essence of scientific method? Is it the same in all the sciences? Or does a subject like psychology add something to scientific method (*introspection* and the subjective elements of inner experience) which is not present in the uses of scientific methodology in the physical sciences? Is there a place for 'intuition' in science? If so, does this introduce a super-logical element into research? Is there a component of aesthetic appreciation in science? And are the tests of 'validity' the same in all sciences? Is all knowledge publicly verifiable? If so, what does this mean in terms of the uniformity of human nature? Is science ethically neutral? If not, what is the place of value judgments in science? These are problems that must be considered.

Now we pass to a consideration of the second level of our structure.

X. The Level of the Natural Sciences

The level of the special sciences, Level II of our structure, is concerned with limited bodies of knowledge, that is, systems of principles and laws which result from the applications of methodology to circumscribed areas of facts. How many such special or natural sciences exist is a moot question.

The dispute as to whether the social sciences, — such as psychology, economics, sociology, and the rest, — are 'really' sciences probably results from a duplicity of tests on the matter of what constitutes a 'science.' If one employs as a test of a science the applicability of 'scientific methodology,' doubtless the social sciences will qualify, even though it is admitted that in studying human relationships and social change it is more difficult to stick to the canons of objectivity and freedom from bias. But if one insists that a subject can be called a 'science' only when there has been formulated a body of laws making possible rather accurate predictions of what will happen in the future, then certainly the social studies are not sciences.

The goals of science are *prediction*, *control*, and *explanation* of the phenomena of any given territory; but even though the investigator employs the *methods* of science, the *goals* may not yet be attained in that field. Clearly the various sciences are in different stages. Differences in age, difficulty of achieving objectivity, ability or inability to control experimental data, and sheer complexity of materials to be studied, explain the relative differences in maturity of the sciences. Perhaps when sociology is as old as physics is now, it may have attained as much predictive power as physics presently possesses.

Perhaps the most significant thing about Level II is the inclusion of the sciences of aesthetics and comparative religion among the social sciences. Here we part company with Spencer's formulation, for Spencer had little interest in these areas. Spencer was right in rejecting the claims of religion to a knowledge *peculiar to itself.* But it is still true that anthropological studies of religion and Jung's studies of religious symbolism and experiences yield much scientific knowledge about man.

Similarly, the science of aesthetics, — the study of man's responses to 'beauty,' and other values, through his creations in the fine arts, — will tell us much about man and the universe in which man and his values have evolved. Studies in the fields of poetry, music, painting, the dance, and the other arts whereby man expresses emotions and ideas, should reveal much about human nature which the presently emasculated sciences of psychology and sociology have let slip through their fingers. A narrow behavioristic theory of scientific methodology which excludes the study of man's inner life, his subjective emotions, aspirations, hopes, fears, and strivings, is bound to produce a very impoverished sort of social science.

Now we move up to the third level of our Temple of Knowledge.

XI. The Level of Wisdom and Guidance

If there is one cultural commodity we need in our time, it is wisdom. Wisdom is knowledge applied for the purpose of guiding the course of social change along lines of human progress. Wisdom is knowledge that has been socialized and humanized. In technical language, we may say that wisdom is the effective utilization of bodies of factual information for normative goals of social evolution. Knowledge is not wisdom; but there can be no wisdom without knowledge. Intelligent self-development and social planning require the very best knowledge, plus insight into the proper goals of life.

If the maxim of Level II is 'divide and conquer,' the maxim of Level III is 'unify and understand.' It is on this level that our educational institutions are failing miserably. Our bodies of knowledge do not build up to anything dramatic and meaningful. Students are confused because their teachers lack understanding and comprehensive vision, and this, in turn, arises from the fact that there is no synthesis of knowledge.

How shall we make at least a preliminary attack upon this prodigious job of the integration of all knowledge? Before coming to grips with the question, let us glance at some of the difficulties that confronted Spencer when he faced the problem in his own day. In supporting our own approach, we shall have to consider the objections raised against Spencer's conception, and we should be fully informed of the difficulties of the task before we undertake it.

In trying to create a 'world philosophy' through the integration of knowledge into a comprehensive synthesis we should recognize that knowledge is a changing thing, growing by leaps and bounds in some instances, and any synthesis that may be set up will therefore be imperfect, impermanent, and fallible. In the case of Spencer, as his critics have pointed out, before the last volume of his synthetic philosophy was published, the first volume was out of date.

It is probably true that wisdom, — scientific knowledge interpreted for purposes of social guidance, — is an imaginative synthesis, and will therefore possess a lesser degree of certainty than the generalizations of the sciences (LEVEL II) upon which it is based. This is especially likely to be the case when the higher level synthesis involves value judgments which (supposedly) are not present in the descriptive propositions of the natural sciences. But in spite of the fact that this wisdom will be fallible, it will be the best possible synthesis we possess in the age in which our social programs are in use. Certainly it should be superior to the patterns now functioning on the basis of authority, vested interests, folkways, prejudices, and other ethnocentric motivations.

If it is true, therefore, that what we take to be 'knowledge' today is something that must be 'dated,' we need only a procedure for revising periodically the synthesis which is our social wisdom. To solve this problem, it will be helpful if, at the same time, we consider and link our solution to another and related question.

This related question grows out of a second objection which may be urged against Spencer's program. An obvious criticism of the attempt to create the highest synthesis which is wisdom for social guidance is that it is not possible for any one mind to comprehend all knowledge. Indeed, it is not even possible for one mind to master all of any one science. How then can one hope to encompass all knowledge? Francis Bacon's boast was, "I take all knowledge for my province"; but that was long ago, before knowledge had increased to the point where it would overwhelm a modern Aristotle, — could one but find such a universal genius.

The solution to the latter difficulty is simpler than one might suppose. We must admit that it may be that the 'great thinker,' in the mold of an Aristotle, or a Descartes, or even a Herbert Spencer, is a thing of the past. Perhaps Bertrand Russell is the last great genius of philosophy. If so, there will be no more great systems invented by individual minds. But this does not mean that great systems can no longer be built. We must learn the technique of group thinking. Our social wisdom must be the result of the pooled knowledge of many experts in their respective fields, experts who have learned how to collaborate in the difficult job of making broad blueprints for the future evolution of humanity. We must assemble the best minds of the world, put them in an academy where they will have the leisure, the facilities, and the social obligation of turning out a world philosophy. This world philosophy could be summarized and issued periodically in a set of volumes which would correspond to Wells's *World Encyclopedia*. The Academy I have in mind would not have political functions or connections; it would be organized for educational purposes.

Clearly there are two phases to this problem. On the one hand, there is the question: *how does the individual thinker pass from the second to the third level of the temple of knowledge?* In replying to this question, it must be pointed out first of all that (according to the present viewpoint) *nothing is added to methodology* in moving from the level of natural science to the level of social planning; there is a difference only in the type of question one is trying to answer. That is to say, 'moral values' are a part of scientific method as employed on the second level (i.e., intellectual integrity, passion for facts, the virtue of synthesis, and the like, are a part of the scientist's moral attitude and motivation); but given this drive, one may ask, *what is man?*, and that is a second-level problem for natural science. But one may also ask, *what is the best society for the scientist to live in?*, and that is a third-level problem of ideology. But the good society for the scientist is the society that is good for man as a citizen of a community wherein reason, working in the fields of science, philosophy, religion, politics, and the like, can flourish. I see no fundamental differences between the methodologies and motivations on the second and the third levels. The problem of forming a vision of the evolution of life here on earth is no different from the problem of forming a vision of the perfect society (any one of the several utopias); both *cosmology* and *ideology* are forms of philosophical synthesis.

It is true that there is a difference in difficulty of work in getting acceptable conclusions on the two levels, and this is related to the process of verification ('certainty'). Social wisdom is difficult to attain, and the more comprehensive (trans-departmental) one's conclusions, the more controversial they are. But from a psychological point of view the technique of synthesis is the same. Of course, the psychology of creative thinking is not well understood. For example, how does one build a cosmology? Out of the data of the senses the mind's eye forms visions, and these are the comprehensive theories of science. But the actual evidences for evolution (inorganic and organic) do not *prove* the theories; the 'proofs' come from an inner vision that perceives the laws of evolution. How shall we account for this faculty? The anthropologist stares at a fragment of a jaw-bone, and an ape-man comes to life. We observe a few stone implements and see a culture being born. How do the simple sensory stimuli cause us to reconstruct pictures of the past? Is there an eye of the mind imposed on the physical eye, which receives stimuli that are then enlarged so that the mental eye achieves a sweeping view through time and space?

These are difficult questions; and important ones. But they are not the only questions we are here concerned with. The second phase of the problem is also important: *how can society manage to function more effectively on the third level?* Here the institutional frame of reference comes into focus. Given the visions that always originate with individuals, what is required now is that society provide social institutions for the *therapy of synthesis.* I am not here proposing to socialize (federalize or collectivize) research. However, just because genius is spread rather thin in any society, top-level research must be done by small groups, and much would be gained by concentrating and coördinating the efforts of such groups. Here is where Foundations and Academies have their proper rôles. Whether the statesman, the business man, the industrialist, the labor leader, and the like, would pay much attention to the social wisdom thus made available to them remains to be seen. But at least such broad plans for the future evolution of the human race would be available to those who would be interested. As it is now, there is no vision, no wisdom.

XII. Operational Research and the World Brain

In his important little book, *The World Brain*, Mr. H. G. Wells pointed out that we are using but a small part of the economic and political knowledge that already exists. He deplored the ineffectiveness of modern knowledge and regretted that nothing was being done to draw our knowledge together into a comprehensive conception of the world. Realizing that we live in a world of unused and even misapplied knowledge and skills, Wells's answer to the challenge was to create a new social organ, the *World Encyclopedia*.

As Wells put it, "I am sketching what is really a scheme for the reorganization and reorientation of education and information throughout the world." The *Encyclopedia* "would be a world-wide organization to hold men's minds together"; and without this new institution "there is no hope of anything but accidental and transitory alleviations of any of the world's problems." This argument, forceful enough in the days when Wells presented it, surely has increased in strength with the passing years. For my part, I would add to Wells's formulation the thought that the scholars who produce the *Encyclopedia* should be everlastingly at work and that the results of their collaboration be constantly in process of revision as knowledge grows and that these results be issued periodically, perhaps every quarter century. This, then, would constitute the best human wisdom in any given generation.

Of course, it is easy to become discouraged in the face of the difficulties. But as a result of work during the war, we have learned some lessons in group research and coöperation. The development of the atomic bomb is the most striking example of this. But other illustrations are at hand in connection with what is now termed 'operational research.' According to Waldemar Kaempffert,[2] the term and the thing itself were invented by the British. The coördination of radar and anti-aircraft fire yielded results so satisfying that operational research was applied to every phase of war on land and sea and in the air. During the war zoologists, geneticists, mathematicians, psychologists, anthropologists, and physicists worked together in teams to solve problems.

Unfortunately, a method of attack which was brilliantly successful during the war is looked upon with suspicion during peacetime. According to Dr. Kaempffert, "university professors still cling to the individual *laissez-faire* method of research on the mistaken supposition that only thus can their freedom be preserved." With such a prejudice to struggle against within the fold of the scientists, it is small wonder that on a larger scale one finds all the frustrations of science which are discussed by J. D. Bernal in his work, *The Social Functions of Science*.

The argument over Operational Research is likely to continue for some time. The older scientists are inclined to oppose it because they feel that it is a restriction of freedom of research, — a kind of 'totalitarianism,' — in science. But the advocates of the group approach ridicule such criticisms, arguing that the operational researchers also believe in freedom, — an informed and responsible freedom. Indeed, it is becoming a sheer necessity of modern developments, as Professor David Green has pointed out in some detail.[3]

Perhaps present failures and frustrations of science might be more easily overcome if somehow we could convert the pursuit of truth and the integration of knowledge into a kind of 'religion.' But in order to accomplish that, one must first 'convert' the scientists so that they become devotees of this new 'religion of science.' And this brings us to another objection to Spencer's conception of philosophy as the synthesis of the sciences, the argument that science has certain 'limitations' which render it unfit as a guide in certain areas of human existence. Let us examine this criticism.

XIII. The 'Limitations' of Science

There are many individuals,—religious, educational, and political leaders, and even scientists,—who talk about the 'limitations' of science, as if there are some things in life which cannot be translated into verifiable and communicable knowledge. 'Life is more than logic,' might be a trite way to phrase the argument. From this point of view, the conception of World Philosophy (Wisdom) as a synthesis of the sciences is slanted too much toward the scientific approach, thus allowing too little room for the emotional, aesthetic, and religious factors in life.

In an indirect way we have already anticipated this criticism in proposing that such humanistic studies as the fine arts and comparative religion constitute an essential part of the natural sciences on Level II. The argument for an extra-scientific area not amenable to rational investigation has been stated and criticized by Robert M. Yerkes.[4] First Dr. Yerkes quotes the argument as it was stated by a

British scientist, and then gives his own reply. The salient paragraph appearing in *Endeavor* (the British journal) runs as follows:

> "It is, however, in the realm of qualities not susceptible of measurement of any kind that the scientific method — as far as it has yet developed — ought frankly to be recognized as inapplicable. An obvious example can be taken from the field of art. The scientific method can give a great deal of information on the chemical nature of pigments, on the wave length of the light they reflect, and on similar factors, but it is wholly unable to predict whether a picture will have aesthetic appeal to those who see it. Nor can the scientific method be of help in those problems relating to drama, literature, and the like, which involve qualities that cannot be measured and knowledge which is not communicable. In the wide field of human affairs the scientific method cannot be applied, even in the form of statistical analysis, to the problems in which events are influenced by the philosophical values of goodness, truth, and beauty, and emotions such as patriotism, fear, or political convictions."

According to Yerkes (and here I agree), this is a false view which should be contradicted emphatically. Actually, as Yerkes notes, what the British writer declares impossible is being done in the sphere of creative scholarship, and the remainder of Yerkes' article is devoted to a display of the evidence for the application of scientific method in the field of the social sciences.

The reply that Professor Yerkes gives is excellent as far as it goes. It might be added that the whole history of science is an example of the progressive reduction of the extra-scientific and the qualitative to mathematical handling. The recent application of topology (concerning which we have much to say) to the psychological field is an example of this. One might also cite the work of Jay Hambidge on *Dynamic Symmetry* and George D. Birkhoff on *Aesthetic Measure* as illustrations of what can be done in the mathematical handling of aesthetic standards.[5] Now for a few words on the possibilities of applying science in the field of ethical values.

XIV. Science and Moral Values

The question of whether science can provide a place for moral values has been much discussed. Bertrand Russell has argued that the field of values is closed to science. Along these lines, there is much said about science being more suited to the determination of *means* rather than *ends*, to the study of *facts* rather than *values*, to the description of *what is* rather than *what ought to be.* It is surprising to find religionists and Logical Positivists agreeing with this conclusion, even though the motivations in each case are very different.

Contrary to this view that 'facts' and 'values' are mutually exclusive, I hold that the realm of facts and the kingdom of values are ruled by a common sovereignty: we must learn to think compassionately and feel intelligently. That is to say, science is committed to a value-system. Accordingly, the alleged dualism of facts and values does not culminate in skepticism about the possibility of rational standards in the field of morals and politics. As previously indicated, in a democratic society we get the equivalent of an 'objective theory of value' in the processes of the democratic way of life, which have notable analogies to the methodology of science.

Experience also teaches us that many ethical-social arguments that arise could be settled by the gathering of more facts and by a better understanding of the factual knowledge we already possess. It may well be that with a better comprehension of the implications of things as they are,— what is called the 'logic of events',— we shall soon be able to say to men the world over: "Those of you who want to live line up on this side, and those of you who prefer death stand over there!" Surely when the alternatives can be made that simple, it will appear that the majority of humans will choose life rather than death, an economy of abundance rather than scarcity, health rather than illness, understanding rather than ignorance. Insofar as we already agree on some general ideals and objectives, we *do*, even now, have the beginnings of a world philosophy. And certainly there is abundant reason for believing that when people honestly try to find the truth and work together intelligently, they do progressively discover means for increasing the common area of understanding and coöperation.

This all adds up to the proposition that we humans never begin with a *tabula rasa* of values. Man, whether he be scientist, poet, politician, peasant, or philosopher, begins with commitments which are implicit in the facts of life,— in his biological constitution and social heredity. Because of this inescapable inheritance, we want life and a measure of order and security, balanced usually with novelty and adventure. In this sense, certain values are primary, while others are derivative. If this is correct, the proponents of the idea that science has no ethics, politics no reason, and art no morality, are fighting a losing battle against the extension of compassionate reason to all areas of human experience. It is for this reason that education is so important.

XV. Universal Knowledge and Education

The easiest and most obvious solution to the problem of a well-rounded development on the level of higher education would be to look at the 'profile' results of those who have taken the 'graduate record' examinations and recommend to those students who, let us say, stand high in the *humanities* and low in the *natural sciences* (or vice versa) that they make up their deficiencies by balancing their course of studies.

But this solution is not enough. It is not sufficient that students of economics or politics master some factual data of atomic physics, or for a major in electronics to be compelled to 'take' work in the field of the social sciences, good as that may be. What is required is that each graduate student, working with instructors who have this interest, should labor to put together information derived from different fields. This might encourage the *habit of synthesizing*, which the citizens of our world must cultivate if mankind is ever to attain vision and wisdom.

The perplexing problem of how to weave the threads of knowledge spun from the looms of science into the fabric of political and economic institutions is one we cannot put aside. On other occasions, I have argued the need for a World University, preferably sponsored by *UNESCO*. In some ways, this new social institution would resemble the World Institute of Mr. Julius Stulman, whose thinking about social problems has influenced my own views at a number of points. But in any case, before we can undertake to translate philosophical theory into institutional practice, *we must produce the body of wisdom which is the precondition for such social engineering*. And so we return to the need for courses that shall be concerned with the direction and control of man's future evolution on this planet. Faculty members in the graduate schools who have developed courses along the lines of integrated knowledge could offer such courses in a new department of integrative studies. For such limited ventures, no *World University* is required. In offering such courses, the instructors do not pose as 'experts on integration'; like their students, the teachers are seekers after the unification of knowledge. Any philosophy would be the culmination of this search as students and teachers carried on the relentless quest for that super-national, super-racial, super-party body of truth, the discovery of which has provided the incentive for all new science and philosophy since the time of the earliest investigators.

This last observation brings us back to those trans-departmental values which are the concern of all liberalizing education. The cultivation of a respect for the best of our cultural heritage is certainly one of the major aims we all profess to share. This tradition is now quite complex, but part of our Western World heritage is the slow and steady advance of a corpus of universal knowledge,—a tradition first enunciated by Pythagoras, Socrates, Plato, and Aristotle, and passed on by them to later generations. The finest flowering of the human spirit is to be found in this everlasting striving for universal principles in the fields of the arts, the sciences, politics, and philosophy.

The most awesome discovery of the human mind is the revelation of the reliability and harmony of the processes of the universe. Man's endless search for order, and the immense success that has attended this quest for uniformities, validate this confidence in the 'rationality' of nature. It is difficult to believe that there exists a body of truth on the basis of which the physical sciences can be built, but no corresponding body of principles about the nature of the human mind and about social evolution. Rooted in the assurance that there is an understandable regularity behind the manifold of events, Scientific Humanism holds forth the hope that a progressive synthesis of knowledge can be maintained through coördinating our efforts. Synthesis must become the great magnet that orients us all.

Our supreme need today is for 'operational research' on a planetary scale to create a world-level wisdom for all mankind. It is important to stress what we have already noted, that this enormous enterprise cannot be carried forward as a 'one-man' job. The reservoir of wisdom will have to be the product of the sustained efforts of sensitive and thoughtful individuals who have learned to work together in assembling the fragments into one comprehensive world philosophy. Part of this labor is to bring into closer harmony the high-level scientific concepts and the low-level use-enjoyment phases of life. As we shall see later, the program (in one aspect) is to bridge the widening gap between two kinds of symbolism: the symbolism of science communication and the symbolism for world understanding among peoples everywhere who are eager to tell other people that they, too, are human persons with needs, aspirations, and achievements. Let the reader not say of this study that it operates on two different levels of appeal! Unless it does that, and establishes a bridge between them, it fails in its purpose.

XVI. The Plan of Development

And now, having outlined in a broad manner the main features of our program for the integration of knowledge, it is our task in the remaining chapters of this volume to provide our own best example of the project we have insisted upon as so necessary: put together the separate pieces of the mosaic of human knowledge and see whether any meaningful patterns will emerge from the survey.

While we shall consider each level of the *Temple* in its proper turn, we emphasize that the demarcation of boundaries is somewhat artificial; we also repeat that on Level II there is constant interaction, vertically, and sideways from science to science.

It will be noted that in our scheme there is no place for 'metaphysics' as the 'science of being' as such,— the science of the generic traits of all existence,— the kind of subject which those who follow the Thomist tradition believe is foundational to all science. Metaphysics, I hold, is but another name for the Temple as a whole, and I do not see that the 'metaphysician' adds anything to what the sciences teach us, except that putting our present knowledge into the form of unity and seeing it as a whole may bring out certain overall features which are not evident in the details.

We therefore begin our survey of the organization of knowledge by studying first of all how symbolisms and languages enter into and give forms to the thought-structures in the areas of natural science wherein, as we believe, we possess knowledge. It may come as a surprise to discover that the problems of significs and semantics are treated as a part of the 'foundations' of knowledge, when for many investigators the science of communication is an empirical study which belongs on Level II, the level of the special (natural) sciences. This matter requires a bit of reflection.

The difficulty of deciding whether semantics is an empirical science on Level II, or whether it is a part of the formal foundations of

LEVEL I, arises from the fact that there is here a semantic question as to what semantics 'is.' The subject itself is complex, and perhaps the several aspects should be split apart. If we take language, or symbolism generally, for granted, we may inquire how one may use existing symbolisms more effectively for purposes of communication to gain objectives already established. Thus a minister of propaganda of a totalitarian society could discover and employ the most effective means to achieve the goals of the state. This is a 'scientific' procedure in the same sense in which the 'psychology of advertising' is scientific. But if one investigates the ways in which the forms of syntax, for example, of the Indo-European family of languages, influence the structure of thinking of new generations, we are dealing with the formal foundations of knowledge. The anthropologists are now telling us that every language is a philosophy, a way of looking at the world, since there are unconscious assumptions wrapped up in the structure of every language. For example, the 'subject-predicate' mode of speech of the Indo-European family of languages reflects a 'substance-attribute' type of thinking. One phase of this complex problem, the language and thought of the North American Indian, has been studied by Benjamin Lee Whorf[6] with interesting results. Papers dealing with the Oriental aspects are also becoming available. Now it is possible to learn something of Chinese grammar and logic[7], and Hindu logic.[8] All this material, properly interpreted will help us evaluate what is now sometimes termed the 'Whorfian hypothesis.'

If language-forms, which are a part of each culture, mold our thoughts, then they are to be considered as much a part of the study of the foundations of knowledge as the analysis of the logic and the mathematics we employ. But we must also keep in mind that there is a constant interaction between the several levels of our Temple. No level exists in its 'own right' or for its 'own sake,' but each exists for the others and as part of a total organization of knowledge. The base of the Temple does not exist for the base alone, but for the pillars and the entablature. Similarly, science does not exist merely for the sake of science, but for humanity's sake. To paraphrase Kant: ethics without logic is blind; logic without ethics is empty. Rudolf Carnap's claim that there is no ethics in logic stems from his adherence to the school of the Viennese Positivists.

To sum up: we begin with a study of the rôle of symbolism and language, rather than logic, not because language and symbolism are more important, but because they are more familiar, and also, as just indicated, because there is need for the study of *metalinguistics* as a preparation for all that comes later. We repeat this warning, however: when in the following chapters we deal successively with semantics, epistemology, logic, mathematics, and natural philosophy, we think of the *formal* part of science as an abstraction from the ongoing activities of living organisms participating in the creation of the several natural sciences. Thus while 'semantics' is a name for the science of communication, and so can be discussed as if it were a 'subject in itself,' in actual fact responses to symbols ('semantic behavior') was not at the outset an independent something or other, though now, by a process of abstraction from the 'arts' of communication, we can convert it into a 'science' in its own right. But this is also true of logic and mathematics, as will become evident when these topics come up for consideration.

FOOTNOTES CHAPTER II

[1]A statement of the nature and objectives of the *Institute for Philosophical Research,* in which Dr. Mortimer Adler's project will be pursued, is provided by the *Biennial Report* (1952-1954), issued by the *Institute,* now located in San Francisco.

[2]See his communication on "Organized Coöperation in Scientific Research," *American Scientist,* Vol. 36, 1947, 142-143.

[3]Cf. "Group Research," by David Green, *Science,* Vol. 119, 1954, 444-445.

[4]Cf. "The Scope of Science," by Robert M. Yerkes, *Science,* May 2, 1947, 461-463.

[5]For further literature about this problem, the reader may consult Joseph Schillinger's *The Mathematical Basis of the Arts* and my own article on "Music, Mathematics, and Cosmology," in *Main Currents in Modern Thought,* October, 1947 (reprinted in my volume, *Nature, Man, and God,* U. of Pittsburgh Press, 1951.)

Of course, this area of the interaction of science and art needs much more investigation. It is helpful to find that Prof. Richard McKeon, in an article on "The Nature and Teaching of the Humanities" (*Journal of General Education,* III, 1949, 290-303), indicates how any great work of science is subject to scientific, social, and humanistic analysis; while any great work of literature is also subject to scientific, social, and humanistic analysis. This is one way of helping to abolish the 'spite fences' that have been erected to separate these fields.

[6]On this matter see the volume, *Language, Thought, and Reality,* by Benjamin Lee Whorf (1956).

[7]Cf. "Notes on Chinese Grammar and Logic," by Yuen Ren Chao, *Philosophy East and West,* Vol. 5, 1955 (No. 2), 31-41. See also the comments on this article by Homer H. Dubs, *Ibid,* Vol. V, No. 2.

[8]On Indian (Hindu) logic see the volume, *Materials for the Study of Navya-Nyãya Logic,* Harvard University Press, 1951.

3

SYMBOLISM, SEMANTICS, AND SOCIAL SYNTHESIS

"It has never been in my power to study anything — mathematics, ethics, metaphysics, psychology, phonetics, optics, chemistry, comparative anatomy, astronomy, gravitation, thermodynamics, economics, the history of science, whist, men and women, wine, meteorology — except as a study of semeiotics."

— Charles S. Peirce, *Letter to Lady Welby*

I. The Integrative Power of Symbolism

Scientists are generally agreed that the use of symbols plays a key rôle in the formation of human nature. The ability to think in terms of abstract ideas and make use of symbolic substitutes for his inner thoughts and emotions, as well as for outer things and events, is a basic trait of the human animal. It is this which lifts man above the level of his subhuman ancestors. The language of spoken and written words is of course the best known of man's modes of communication, but there are others, as for example the symbolism of the dance, music, mathematics, and the rest.

Studies of the universality of symbolism teach us many things. As part of this study we may mention the comparative anatomy of symbolism, the migration of symbols, the integrative and disintegrative power of symbols, and other subdivisions of the subject. Man's capacity for what Alfred Korzybski terms *time-binding*, so succinctly described by S. I. Hayakawa as "the ability to organize social coöperation *at a distance* and to accumulate knowledge *over* generations of time through the use of symbols," is a manifestation of the symbolic function. But more than knowledge is conserved, — life itself is thus preserved and transmuted. Indeed, fear of death is perhaps only man's fear of 'excommunication,' — fear of loss of contact with social reality;

if so, then by way of the arts we attain a feeling of security: we communicate endlessly with other generations in the stream of time and thus achieve a kind of social immortality. Rather than serving as a substitute for reality, as a Freudian theorist might suppose, symbolism goes to the very heart of reality, — at least human reality.

Considering this, is it not permissible to suppose that symbols constitute a system of values of their own? May it not be the case that the symbols of the soul, — the myths expressed by the arts, — are the authentic and abiding carriers of enduring insights? Is it not true that in studying archaic cultures, it is not so much their systems of barter and trade, marriage and legal customs, and the like, as the artistic manifestations of their lives that appeal to the mind's eye? Is it too far-fetched to treat the delicate balance of art and life as a trustworthy model of the meaningful nature of primitive group life?

If indeed aesthetic experience is the archetypal pattern for communication by way of symbols, then one may look with favor upon the proposal, set forth by some investigators under the term of the *monogenesis of speech*, that in the early dawn of human history there prevailed a universal symbolism and that the vocabulary of this language was enunciated in the spirit of a universal brotherhood that embraced the community of man. Such an hypothesis of the 'psychic unity of mankind' would find some support in Carl Jung's studies of the symbolism of the alchemists, where it appears that nature speaks through the archetypal imagery of man's sublimated aspirations.[1]

But somewhere along the line things got out of joint. Language, which formerly served regional groups so well, became an obstacle to further communication and understanding. Just why the failure of social synthesis is so largely the result of the failure of symbolism in civilization is a matter in which the social scientist and statesman should be interested. The explanation of the breakdown is to be found in the subsequent developments of man's systems of communication. Today we find ourselves overwhelmed by the diverse symbol structures which are now embodied in the manifold cultures. The diversities of groups is associated with diversities of symbolisms which to those outside the group are frequently only so much 'semantic noise.' The diversity of languages which emerged from elementary speech and gesture communication is brought out in our Diagram IV, the *Possible Development of Languages* (page 71).

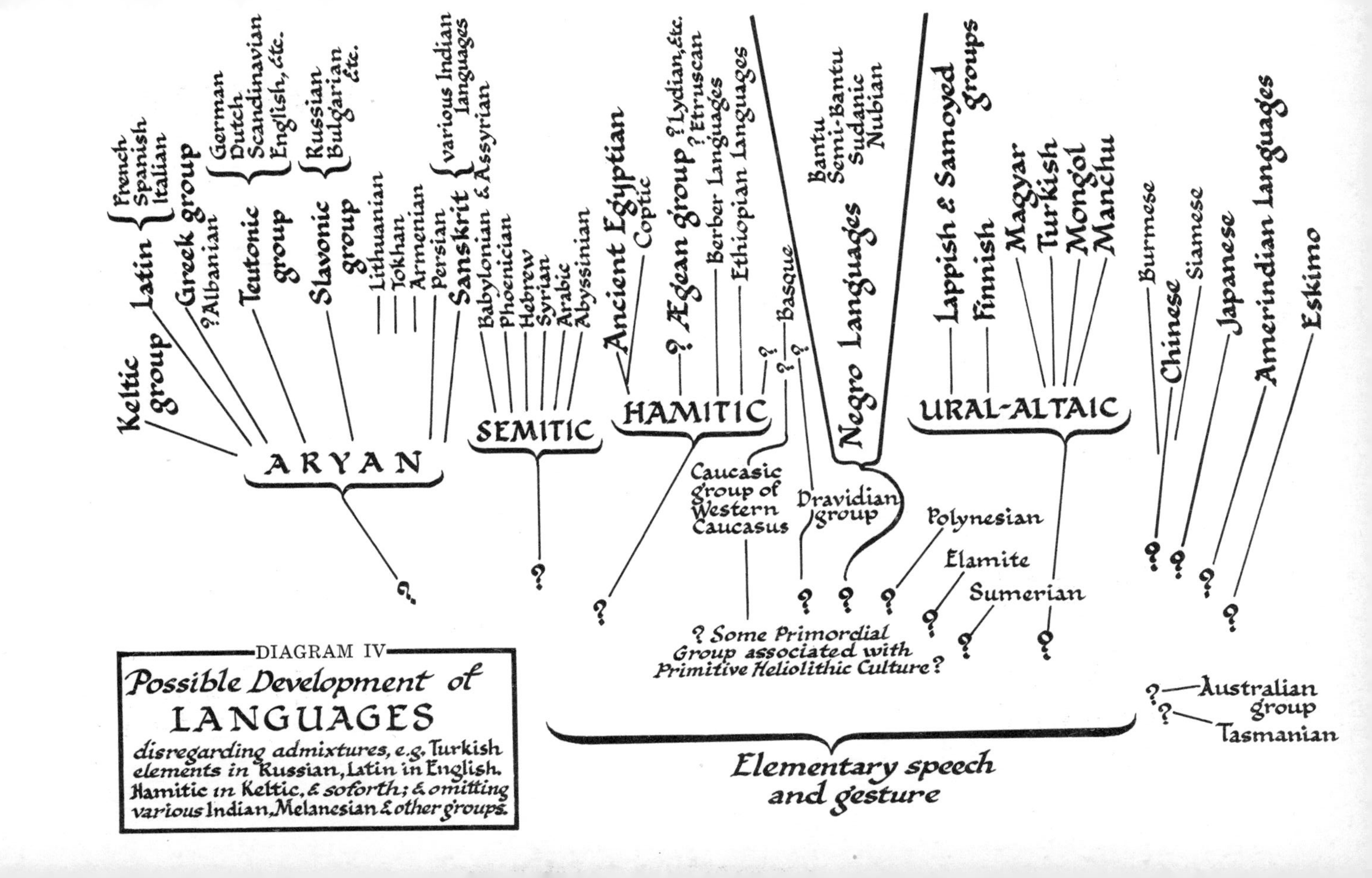

DIAGRAM IV

Possible Development of LANGUAGES

disregarding admixtures, e.g. Turkish elements in Russian, Latin in English, Hamitic in Keltic, & soforth; & omitting various Indian, Melanesian & other groups.

Scholars inform us that the major stages in man's efforts at communication are these: *animal vocalization* → *gesture communication* → *picture writing of paleolithic culture and neolithic culture* → *cuneiform inscriptions of Sumerians* → *Egyptian hieroglyphics* → *Indo-European family of languages* → *Greek and Roman numerals* → *Arabic mathematical symbolism* → *Western musical notation* → *post-Aristotelian symbolic logic* → *printed books and newspapers* → *current movie-radio- and telecast programs* → *radar and sonar techniques*. This panoramic survey of the evolution of symbolisms unfolds the long and sometimes tortuous road that man has traveled in the great human adventure, — and the end is not in sight. In the face of the multiplicity and diversity of symbolisms, is it any wonder that the inhabitants of the modern complex world often feel confused and disoriented?

II. Clogging the Channels of Communication

When a pupil asked Confucius what he would do first if he had absolute power, the Chinese philosopher replied, "I would reform language." Of course, as some unsympathetic outsider might observe, "Considering the fact that it requires thousands of ideographs to say what can be said, perhaps it ought to be reformed." But before one becomes snobbish about a language other than one's own, it should be remembered that the difficulties of communication are not peculiar to any one language. Let it be recalled, for example, that even when we speak what we think is the same language, we frequently don't seem to be using the same dictionaries. This point is illustrated (but not proved) by the comment concerning the inhabitants of Great Britain and the United States: "two peoples separated by a common language."

Indeed, in moments of despair one is inclined to look with favor on the thesis that the world is on the road to committing semantic suicide, — attaining a condition in which no one understands anyone. Professor Norbert Wiener, pioneer in the science of cybernetics, recently stated that "the community extends only so far as there extends an effectual transmission of information." This gives us one clue to the situation to which Kierkegaard referred as the "sickness of modern society." The failure of civilization, we find is then due not only to the breakdown of established symbolisms *within* ethnic groups, but is a result also of our inability to establish new bridges of symbolism to span the gaps *between* the disparate groups around the world.

To be sure, a common symbolism embodied in folkways, languages, rituals, the arts, and abstract science notations, is no absolute guarantee of understanding within and between groups. But since understanding extends no further than communication, communication is a precondition for understanding. In a word, a common symbolism is a necessary but not a sufficient condition for understanding and coöperation. It seems, therefore, that a universal symbolism must be produced before world understanding is possible.

Commenting on the sources and the consequences of the failures of communication in the United Nations, Stuart Chase points to the following factors as setting up roadblocks which obstruct the efforts at agreement: translation failure, cultural differences, lofty abstractions, diplomatic double-talk, and inside talk (clear to the delegates but misleading to the outside world). Of these sources of difficulty in communication, Mr. Chase regards cultural differences as the most serious.

It is true, of course, that one cannot climb out of his own culture. But allowing for personal differences that have their ethnic origins in regional environment, — the effects of environment turned into history, — it still remains true that if our social world is to survive, we must everlastingly strive for objectivity in truth-judgments and universality in value-judgments. Such a program should help provide the foundations for a civilization in which all men can be free from fear of mass destruction, mass unemployment, and mass starvation.

If one reflects on what has been taking place during the last century, one is overcome with a feeling of incongruity. The amazing thing about progress during this period is the rapid growth of the science of communication engineering as this is related to the development of electrical devices. But observe the curious paradox that has resulted: on the one hand, the electrical communication engineers have perfected radar to the point where it is possible to send messages to the moon, — only there is no one there to receive them. Here on the earth there are millions of people behind various kinds of 'curtains' ready to receive messages, — only we have no all-world messages to send them. Until our society can match the technologists, who have produced a mechanical integration of the world, with social inventors of cultural communication, we humans will continue to suffer from social frustrations. Until the techniques for mass communications are hooked up with a science of social cybernetics, still to be created, cultural anxieties will continue to plague us.

The tragedy is that in addition to the historical barriers which have come down to us from the traditional cultures, modern man has devised additional barriers to successful communication. These are: (1) political barriers to the free flow of information, especially to the dissemination of scientific knowledge which is curtailed for 'security' reasons; and (2) the increasing unintelligibility of each scientist to any scientists in other fields (not to mention the laymen outside all science fields), resulting from the race toward specialization in the various disciplines. That is to say, even when there is no secrecy barrier, there is technical jargon and code unintelligibility, so that a secret society of scientific esoterics is the end result.

One of the concomitants of over-specialization in education is the 'ethics of professionalism', — the doctrine that only the expert has the right to be heard on matters within the area of his specialty. Recalling the definition of an expert as "one who studies more and more about less and less until he knows everything about nothing," it becomes clear that on this principle the size of the area in which a person is permitted to speak is day by day becoming smaller. In this instance there is not an infringement upon freedom by way of state control: we have achieved a muteness by common consent.

Here, in brief, we have one of the crucial issues of our age: the failure to extract and communicate the implications of modern science and to formulate an all-world symbolism or semantography for the arts and for the primordial and universal experiences and insights of mankind, — a fundamental weakness in any democratic world wherein freedom to know and communicate the truth is the most fundamental of all human rights.

III. Symbolism for World Understanding

Up to this point we have been concerned with social diagnosis, — the search for the causes of our inability to achieve understanding and communication. Now let us consider some of the remedies for this weakness in communication.

The first observation to be made is that since the vocation of man is one that none of us can abdicate, and requires inter-communication for its fulfillment, it is necessary to revise the rule that only the expert has a right to be heard. Any device that keeps men on speaking terms deserves to be encouraged.

Another elementary observation is that if we are to have more complete understanding, the people involved in the communication process must have a common basis of experience, a common cultural frame of reference. That is, understanding the ideas and the experiences of other nations, religions, and classes, is not merely an intellectual process of linguistic intercourse: it is also a matter of cultivating feeling-attitudes based on sympathy. One must at least have a vicarious experience of 'love,' 'revenge,' 'mercy,' 'democracy,' 'sweetness,' 'sadism,' 'saintliness,' and the rest, in order to understand what it is that these words denote. Now it is doubtless true that some of the experiences designated by these terms, — for example, starvation, brutality, homosexuality, — are injurious to human beings, and one could at the most advocate a kind of imaginary sampling as a substitute for the original experience. Imaginative literature gives one a harmless familiarity with those 'deviate' experiences which sometimes isolate individuals from normal human relationships. Participation in 'group analysis' is another way to gain a sympathetic understanding of the experiences of others.

Examples of the lack of background experience necessary for understanding are found in such cases as the failure of the French delegates participating in the early years of the United Nations discussions to match in their native tongue the idea of a U. N. 'trusteeship'; not having experimented with this type of relationship in their colonial policies, they had no word for it and had to adopt the English term. In a similar manner, the Japanese people, prior to their defeat, had no notion of what 'democracy' meant to the Western nations. As Clyde Kluckhohn reported it, when our phrase, "life, liberty, and the pursuit of happiness," was translated into the Japanese language and then translated back into the English, the phrase came out as "the lustful pursuit of pleasure." The Japanese people at that time lacked the experiential background involved in the social processes which we associate with the word 'democracy.' In the same way, this word has necessarily meant something different to the German people, the Russians, and others whose histories are different from those of the Anglo-Saxons. This whole problem was pointed up by the investigation of *UNESCO* into the meaning of the term 'democracy,' and the ideological factors behind political tensions between nations. When the eighty-odd scholars around the world returned their definitions, it appeared that there were eighty-odd conceptions. As one commentator pointed out, the word 'democracy' is like a big tent in a high wind, — something hard to pin down. Another observer, trying to be cheerful, opined that this is not so bad when we consider that the word ambiguous is itself ambiguous!

To take note of these things is not to lay the groundwork for the attempt at a monotonous standardization of experience. The best solution is a middle-of-the-road policy: within a common framework of the psychological and social uniformities which are necessary if we are to have a world federation, each ethnic group should be free to enjoy its own customs, myths, traditions, and other types of symbolic manifestations. Regional groups should be permitted to act out that social heredity, — the mimesis of cultural symbolisms, — provided there is toleration of similar cultural 'deviations' from the norms of a world community on the part of other groups. Thus the world would in time become a self-integrating multiplicity of culture patterns.

Another suggestion that always comes to mind in connection with the efforts to promote world understanding is the proposal that we adopt an international language to serve as a universal medium for world communication. Of course there are those who will find this to be an inadequate solution. If we are to adopt an auxiliary language, they will argue, let us do a thorough job of it, — let it be in the spirit of Leibniz's *characteristica universalis*, that great forerunner of symbolic logic, semantography, and cybernetics.

For these ambitious reformers, the world of the future should possess a maximum of freedom from obsolete verbal habits. Mental shackles are forged by antiquated linguistic forms, and a higher mental-verbal world can come into being only with the emancipation from outmoded language patterns, such as the subject-predicate reasoning of the Indo-European family of languages. If, therefore, we are going to tinker with linguistic reforms, let us get down to fundamental problems. It has been calculated that there are about 3,000 languages in existence, over 2,000 of which lack a phonetic alphabet. Isn't it time to set up an international commission within *UNESCO* to study this problem? If and when a new language medium is produced and recommended for adoption on a world basis, the commission should also prepare a standardized set of connotations for these terms which now clog the communication lines with their semantic noise. But to make this statement is at once to point to the difficulty of the undertaking.

It is a curious fact that mathematical symbolism and musical scoring are the only approximations to an international 'language' (*Volupük*, *Esperanto*, *Ido*, *Interlingua*, and *Basic English* being quite restricted in their use), and this suggests that perhaps music and mathematics promise better than other media to satisfy the requirement of a world language. If music and mathematics could be integrated into a new art-form, — such a synthesis was foreshadowed in Hermann Hesse's novel, *Magister Ludi*, where the 'bead game' combined music and mathematics, — we might be on the right road. Perhaps we should also restudy the *Orbis Pictorum* of Comenius for further suggestions.

This is about as far as my own investigations had gone when, — to my surprise, — I received a communication from a student of these matters in Australia which conferred some confirmation on my own speculations. It turned out that Mr. C. K. Bliss of Sydney, Australia, had set out to realize the vision of the great mathematician, Leibniz, whose aim was the production of a symbolism, — a *characteristica universalis*, — that would provide a universal system of communication. Bliss now believes that he has achieved just that, the production of a simple picto-ideography, — *one writing for one world*. This new language has been praised by Bertrand Russell, and this suggests that we do well to study Mr. Bliss's creation, SEMANTOGRAPHY (see Diagram V, page 78).

The inventor of Semantography was long fascinated by picture writing. Following a study of ideographs of the Chinese, the Babylonians, the Egyptians, he reached back to the cave paintings of the earlier Aurignacians, always seeking the unitary elements of symbolism. By analyzing languages and separating out the units of meaning, Bliss arrived at the conclusion that he could produce a simple system, so that with an adjusted typewriter (or by hand) it is now possible to write a letter so that anyone who knows the symbols can comprehend the contents of the message.

It is my opinion that Semantography has rich possibilities. Among its advantages is the fact that Semantography offers a kind of literacy for millions of persons who cannot otherwise communicate with each other. Peasants in all countries could readily master *Bliss's Primer for Children*. Since primitive peoples are not able to adopt improvements in agriculture, hygiene, and the like, without some kind of literacy, Bliss's Semantography provides a potent aid to the "Technical

SEMANTOGRAPHY

is an AUXILIARY simple Picto-Ideography for interlinguistic Communication between Scientists, Technicians, Businessmen, and People who don't understand each other's Language.

EXAMPLES FROM "SEMANTOGRAPHY" by C. K. BLISS

100 Symbol Elements to overcome Babel in Reading, Writing and Thought

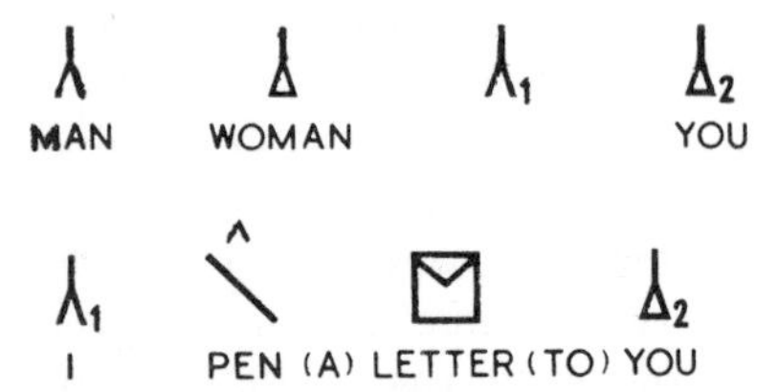

The A-ction indicator over the PEN (inclined writing position) means TO PEN.

MATERIAL THING — PHYSICAL ACTION — HUMAN EVALUATION

These are the 3 main symbols of the "grammar" of Semantography, dividing all words as referring to MATTER (square indicates structure), ENERGY (A-ctus, Action) and MIND (V-alere, Valuation).

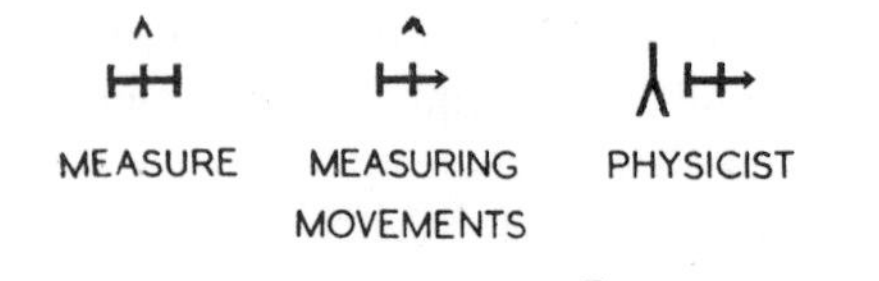

GRAVITATION, PRESSURE — MIXTURE — GAS

Gas is unpicturable, but in a liquid it forms bubbles, which go up.

The outline of a retort is an age-old symbol for Chemistry. ANALYSIS is "analysed" as (1) Chemical (2) Division of (3) Matter.

ILEUM — COLON

MEDICINE — DOCTOR — INTUSSUSCEPTION

A simplified Rod of Aesculapius for Medicine, in which Latin words can be used with the symbols.

EMOTION ID — REASON EGO — CONSCIENCE SUPER-EGO

The Heart is a conventional old symbol. The superimposed Mind signifies, according to Freud, the Mind of the Father, Mother and People in Authority. According to Jung it is the Mind of God.

CREATOR — NATURE — SCIENCE — SCIENTIST

Symbols for Believers and Unbelievers — in accordance with Greek Philosophy — the rational Mind contemplating Nature, its Harmony signified by geometrical configurations.

Here is an Example how the Logic and Semantics of Semantography works.

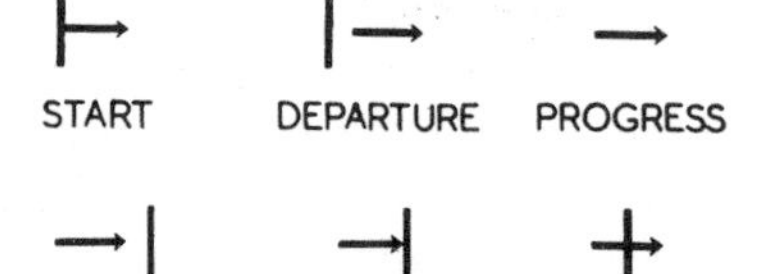

These Symbols can be used for Rail, Road, Ship and Air Communication. They show 2 Symbol Elements, (1) the ARROW indicating that something is moving, and (2) the LINE OF REFERENCE, indicating the space-time co-ordinate. Example:

START: Professor Reiser introduces Semantography to the AAAS, or YOU, wherever you may be, start reading this Leaflet.

PROGRESS: Your mind is contemplating this new Aspect of Science.

ARRIVAL: What Conclusions are you arriving at? Where is this going to stop? In a dustbin? On a dusty shelf? What will it mean to the Inventor? Dust to Dust?

DIAGRAM V

Assistance Program" of the United Nations. In a word, Semantography should prove useful within the realm of generally accepted relations and therefore can be made the basis for communication on the level of the common needs of peoples of diverse cultures. But such a system is of diminishing value in dealing with conceptual formulations high in the ladder of abstractions. Here mathematics and symbolic logic will continue to be of superlative value. Examples of the beauty of symbolic logic are presented in Chapter V.

It must be emphasized that the use of a unified symbolism would not automatically produce world understanding. What else, then, is required if the world is to achieve understanding? To answer that question we must penetrate to further depths.

IV. Symbolism for Science Communication

The problem of communicating the results of research in science to those who aspire to understand science is in part a problem of creating an improved symbolism. The enormous increase in knowledge about nature, man, and society, will continue to plague us, and nothing should be done to place a moratorium on progress in science as the enrichment of factual data. What can be done in addition lies in the direction of organizing and interpreting the factual information.

The simplification of the formal organization of science can proceed in two related directions. In the first place, if we had a unitary symbolism for the logical structure of science, — the same logical structure for every science, — this unitary symbolism would facilitate the processes of comprehension as investigators passed from one science to another. The beginning steps toward the formal systematization of bodies of knowledge into a common logical structure are familiar to students of the logic of science. My own efforts at formulating the *Logical Structure of Science* are schematized in Diagram VI (p. 80).

One motive behind the effort at setting up a unitary structure for science is the hope that as a student who has mastered physics (for example, *Relativity Theory*, which is $\Phi_1 D$), passes on to the study of psychology (*Freudian Psychoanalysis*, which is $\Phi_2 D$), he can more easily recognize the similarities of formal structure, even while the specific assumptions and conclusions are different, because he will have a feeling of familiarity as he passes into an otherwise strange territory. Moreover, the student should be able to transpose methods and conceptual devices for interrelating facts, laws, and theories within the disparate fields of thought.

DIAGRAM VI

THE LOGICAL STRUCTURE OF SCIENCE

TERMS 1. ...... 2. ...... 3.	(1) *Terms* (defined and undefined) are symbols which represent the *concepts* we use in our thinking.
POSTULATES 1. ...... 2. ...... 3.	(2) *Postulates* are the rules which tell us what operations are permissible.
THEOREMS 1. ...... 2. ...... 3.	(3) *Theorems* are the implications deduced from a set of postulates.

THE NATURE OF SYSTEMS

(1) Our base consists of ' classes ' of things, and a class consists of those individuals which satisfy a *propositional function.* Our *concepts* are thus propositional functions with one variable, ϕ_1 (*a*).

(2) Postulates are propositional functions with two variables, [i.e., ϕ (a, b)], which state the relations between (or operations upon) terms (or concepts). It is on this level that serial order appears. Serial order, like mathematics in general, is based on such logical relations as, ' is greater than,' etc. Relations are classes of couples which behave like classes. Thus the logic of relations is derived from propositional functions of two or more variables. In the *Principia Mathematica* mathematics is derived from the logic of relations and thus leans heavily upon propositional functions of two variables.

(3) A doctrinal function consists of all those theorems which validate a set of postulates. Thus any *theory* of science is a doctrinal function. It consists of the body of theorems deduced from a given postulate set.

In diagrammatic form this appears as follows :

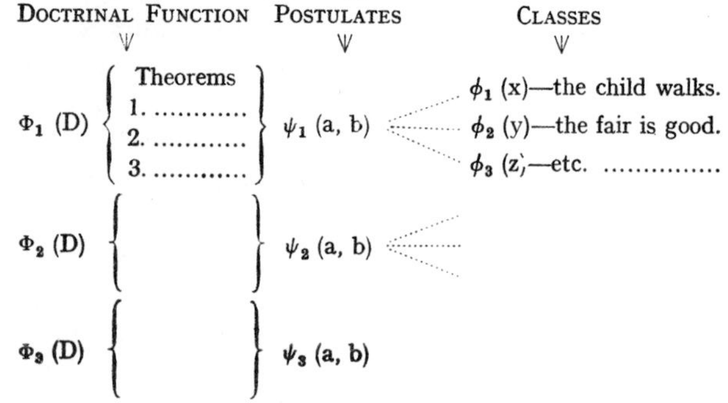

Another way to put this is to point out that a unified symbolism for all natural sciences makes it possible to find analogies (or homomorphic images) between the various areas of scientific data, so that the systematization of science is really a matter of filling the structural details into the broader transposable forms of common isomorphic patterns. Among such universal features of nature, man, and society, capable of uniform conceptual representation, are the following: *whole-part relations; polarity*, which has physical, biological, and social exemplifications; *forms or patterns of symmetry*, again on all levels; and so forth. Proposals looking toward the application of the notions of 'metabolic gradients,' 'organizers,' 'potentials,' 'dominance and subordination,' the principle of 'least action,' 'dimensional analysis,' and the like, to fields other than those for which they were first intended are examples of this movement toward the organization of knowledge through a unified symbolism for all the sciences.

One of the most interesting experiments along this line is the attempt to adapt the *regular solids* of Plato to the natural kingdoms and to the visual arts. Illustration of the Platonic solids, — first studied by the Pythagoreans and developed into a cosmology in Plato's *Timaeus*, — are presented in Diagram VII (p. 82). Johannes Kepler, discoverer of the three laws of planetary motion, employed these solids to explain the orbits of the planets around the sun, as Diagram VIII indicates (p. 83). In this manner, as Kepler believed, he confirmed the Pythagorean doctrine of the 'music of the spheres.' In this fundamental study, *The Regular Solids*, Professor H. M. S. Coxeter points out that three of the Platonic solids are found in crystals, while the two remaining solids "need the spark of life for their occurrence," appearing as they do in sea animals. It is most instructive to observe that this architectonic is not confined in its application to the non-human universe, for in the field of art Salvador Dali returns to the symbolism of the Platonic solids in his design, the 'Cross of Peace.'

When it comes to science communication, one must always consider the pedagogical soundness of the proposal for a symbolism. A 'natural' symbolism for the student of science should be based on an innate psychological disposition to respond, if such there be. The return to the Pythagorean-Platonic explanation of nature through the regular solids of Plato and Euclid may turn out to be 'psychologically sound' in the sense referred to, *provided Jung's conception of archetypes as potentialities of ideas is correct.* If one could begin with mathematical

DIAGRAM VII

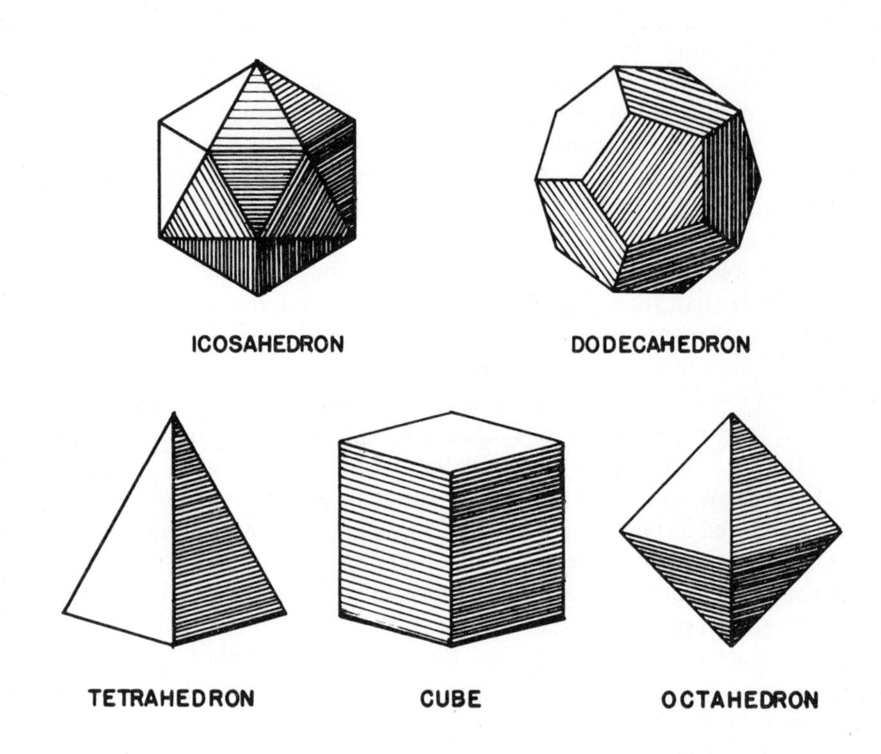

THE FIVE REGULAR (PLATONIC) SOLIDS

DIAGRAM VIII

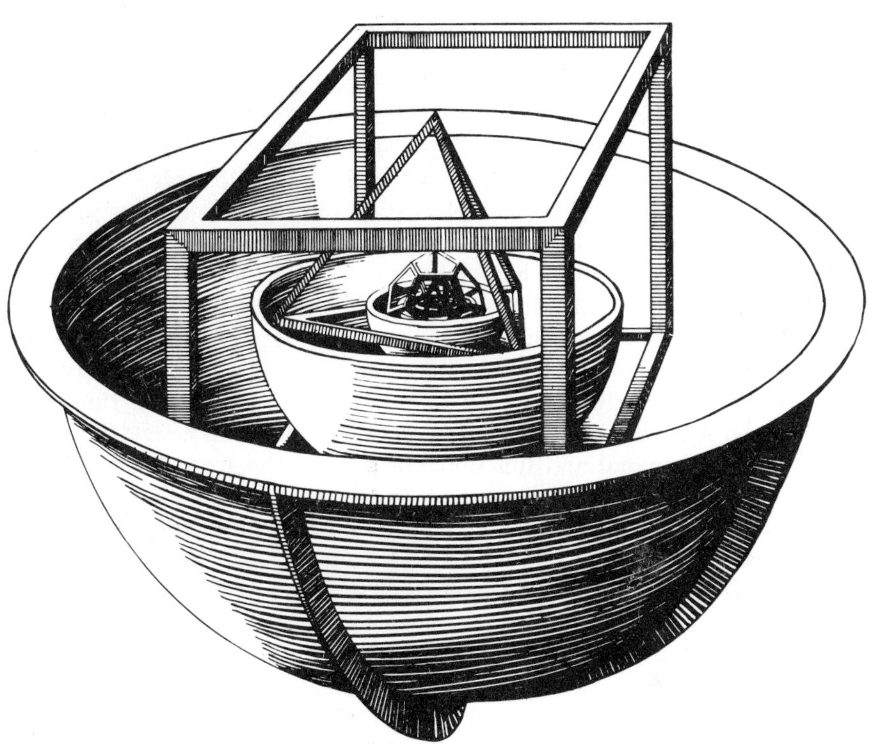

FROM KEPLER'S MYSTERIUM COSMOGRAPHICUM (TÜBINGEN 1596) ILLUSTRATING SUPPOSED RELATIONSHIPS BETWEEN THE FIVE PLATONIC BODIES AND THE NUMBER AND DISTANCES OF THE PLANETS THE CONCENTRIC FIGURES ARE INSCRIBED WITHIN EACH OTHER THUS:

OUTERMOST SPHERE OF SATURN	SPHERE OF EARTH
CUBE	20-SIDED REGULAR BODY
SPHERE OF JUPITER	SPHERE OF VENUS
4-SIDED REGULAR PYRAMID	8-SIDED REGULAR BODY
SPHERE OF MARS	SPHERE OF MERCURY
12-SIDED REGULAR BODY	INNERMOST CENTRAL BODY OF THE SUN

archetypes, — squares, triangles, circles, spirals, and three dimensional solids composed of them, — as the formal patterns of thought and reality, one might proceed upward from physics to biology, psychology, and sociology, by way of a natural symbolism which would yield a unitary scheme for isomorphic structures on all levels.

When one examines the problem of symbolism in science from the broadest viewpoint, it is clear that an adequate symbolism must provide a place for three universal aspects of nature. An adequate symbolism for science must recognize the existence of (a) the dynamic, evolutionary, and functional processes; (b) the static and structural features of nature; and (c) the teleological or purposive aspects.

In connection with the first two aspects of natural processes, it may be pointed out that such characteristics as are illustrated by 'change,' 'growth,' 'function,' and the like, belong to (a) the temporal aspect; whereas characteristics displayed in 'morphology,' 'structure,' 'isomorphism,' 'taxonomy,' and the like, belong to (b) the spatial aspect of nature. Throughout the history of science, — since the time of Zeno and his 'paradoxes of motion', — there has been a tendency to reduce the temporal and functional aspects to the spatial and structural aspects, as this is illustrated by the Platonic-Jungian form of explanation in terms of eternal archetypes which provide the changeless patterns or *Ideas* behind all existence. Today the problem is further complicated by the requirement that we symbolize the third feature (c), which introduces the teleological aspect of nature.

In the present approach to this problem we have built upon the pervasive reality of the 'spiral action of time.' Here the progressive time-line is suggested by the arrow (see Diagram IX p. 85), which indicates the direction toward increasing complexity of structures and unity of functions in the ladder of emergent evolution. The higher levels are pyramided upon the earlier and simpler ones, but there is a similarity of structure designated as *homomorphic images* indicative of the fact that gestalt or wholistic properties can be transposed from level to level. The symbol for the square root of minus one, $\sqrt{-1}$, is adapted from the theory of *quaternions* and refers to 90° or right-angle rotations, that is, to the appearance of a novel emergent in a higher (orthogonal) dimension which thereby adds a new level of reality to the pre-existent universe. Thus, as I shall try to show, the *Cosmic Imagination* supplies the guiding fields for evolutionary advance, as is indicated in Diagram II (p. 35).

DIAGRAM IX

ISOMORPHIC RELATIONS BETWEEN LEVELS

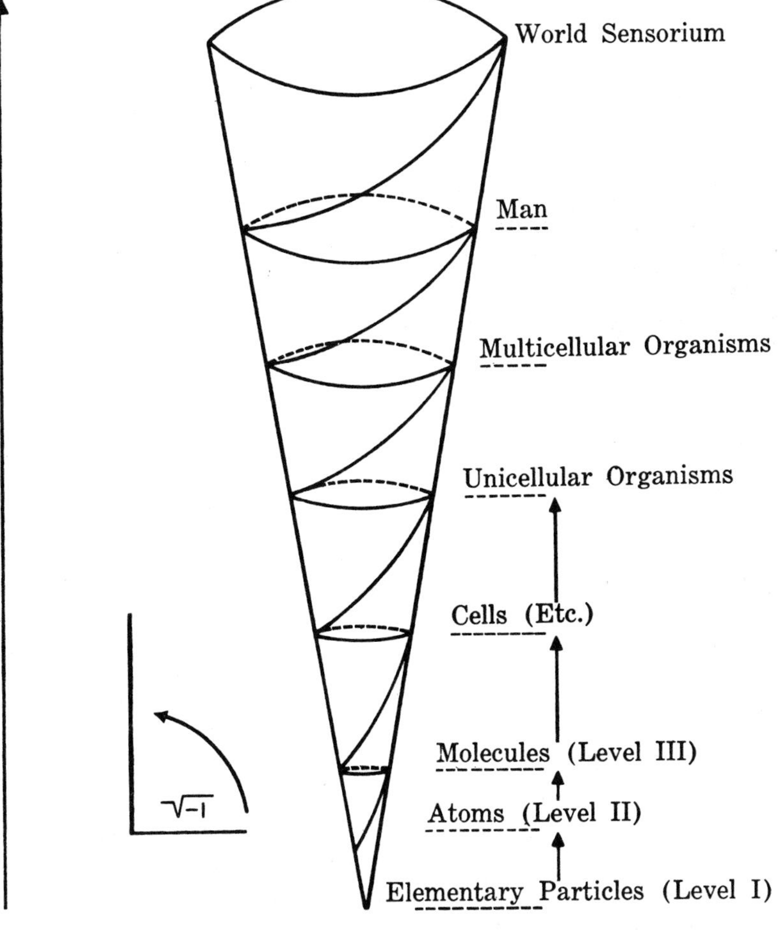

1. Spatio-temporal Correlations:
   (Serial Order; Whole-part relations; etc.)
2. Polarity:
   a) Atomic: north-south polarity
   b) Molecular: macroscopic spin-effects
   c) Cellular: dominance-subordination patterns
   d) World Sensorium: East-West synthesis
3. Gestalt Unity:
   (Functional integration of micro-rhythms emerge as macro-rhythms of $n + 1$ entities in the structural hierarchy of orthogonal dimensions)

In order to make the fullest use of a unitary symbolism for science it would be desirable that we shrink our knowledge, somewhat as skulls were shrunken by primitive tribes, so that modern knowledge could be put on a universal basis for transfer across the social whole. If it were possible to symbolize this 'reduced' knowledge and use the full play of international communication, perhaps through a planetary picture language such as Bliss presents, for radio and television sets, the heroic drama of mankind could be portrayed and thus lift up the lives of people everywhere by sheer evocation of spiritual powers from within. Thus history could be salvaged from the dark kingdom of insanity.

The need for the *condensation of knowledge* is pointed out by Dr. Vannevar Bush in his book, *Science, The Endless Frontier.* The physical problem of providing space for the books which store man's accumulating knowledge is reaching overwhelming proportions. The rate of growth of our 'mountains of knowledge' is creating a librarian's nightmare and a scholar's inferiority complex. Dr. Bush's proposal that the problem be solved by codifying our knowledge and the encoded material be put on micropunch cards is in keeping with the accelerating trend toward an *IBM* civilization dominated by electronic brains and *MANIAC* calculators.

There are some of us, however, who still cling to the notion of democracy as government by reasonable and informed citizens. Such persons do not wish to surrender the processes of discovering, interpreting, and preserving knowledge to a new secret society of electronic machines. The important thing that Dr. Bush calls attention to is the need for codifying our knowledge, *shrinking all knowledge for invariant transfer across the social whole,* as I have been stating it for many years. But the older problem of the humanization of knowledge is still with us, and this cannot be assigned to non-human machines. And that brings us back to the earlier theme of the place of art in life as a type of 'understanding.'

V. Man's Need for Symbolization

We have observed that the cure for Humanity's troubles is not to be found in trying to reverse the trend of history by returning to some mythical garden of Eden wherein languages could not confuse the human family. It is utterly impossible to stop the increasing rôle of symbolization in society. A return to 'primitivism' is out of the question, because there is in man a deep need for symbolic expression. It is not ordinarily realized that art, ritual, and even magic, represent excursions of the human spirit into the world of the symbolic, — yet such is the case. These facts have been portrayed by Dr. Susanne Langer in her valuable work, *Philosophy in a New Key*. Ernest Cassirer has also dealt at length with this theme in his studies of symbolism.

In her analysis Dr. Langer indicates how man's capacity for creating symbolic modes is responsible not only for myths, art, and metaphorical thinking, but for science also. Those who would solve such problems as the mystery of language, the source of myths, the origin of sacrament, and the meteoric rise of science, must perforce delve deeply into the central problems of symbolism. Whether he be mythical, mathematical, or practical, man is always the maker of symbols; inevitably, therefore, the problems of symbolism ramify in all directions, — into psychiatry, logic, religion, art, and phantasy. All the profoundest issues of our age are centering around the basic problems of *symbolism* and *meaning*.

The realization of the importance of the written and spoken word in human affairs is by no means recent, even though the science of semantics is of modern origin. The ancients no less than our contemporary students of language have recognized that the gift of articulate speech and the ability to communicate through symbols are a unique human endowment, peculiar to genus *Homo*. The 'Logos' doctrine of the Gospel of Saint John, and the declaration of Socrates that reasoning is the soul's conversation with itself, are ways in which the recognition of the power of language was manifested by the early students. Today our terminology is somewhat different; but the fundamental insight is the same. Now we say that 'thinking is subvocal speech'; that man lives in a 'semantic environment'; that human problems are 'neurolinguistic'; and so on. But in any case we are paying tribute to the fact that man, unlike the lower animals, is an inhabitant of two worlds. Beyond the world of things, man's second, and unique, world is his world of symbols, which serve as media of expression, sublimation, and communication.

It is because man is the creator of symbolic universes that he possesses the ability to rise above the limitations of time and place and give to 'airy nothings a local habitation and a name.' Man is the fabricator of culture because he can elaborate a world of imaginative constructions and then, sometimes, translate them into material forms. But man is also the destroyer of civilizations because, by the same arts of symbolism, he can arouse impulses of annihilation directed toward wrecking these symbolical embodiments of past cultures. And so today, for better or for worse, the art of influencing human opinions and actions through the use of symbols (flags, songs, signs, languages) is 'big business.' The very foundations of modern society rest on symbolic forms. 'Paper money' is a symbolic substitute for bullion, and this in turn is taken as a symbol of 'real wealth.' The signing of a contract, the writing of a poem, the setting down on paper and the subsequent playing of a symphony, — these are exercises in the expression and interpretation of symbols.

Newspapers, schools, radio stations, the cinema, and churches are among the social institutions which mold public opinion. Bombarded as we are by symbols, what chance is there to find out the 'truth' about anything? The gap which separates the domain of facts from its symbolic representation is sometimes so wide that it is frequently impossible to pass from what people say or picture to the original 'facts', — if indeed there are any. How can we penetrate the veil of symbols to the primary world of objects and events supposedly lying behind the world of symbols?

Here the science of semantics appears on the scene. promising a technique for straightening out the complicated relations that hold between facts and languages, symbols and objects. Doubtless the omnipresence of war propaganda in recent decades, the perfection of advertizing and public relations techniques, and the like, have stimulated the critical tendencies to make us more symbol-conscious and thus have also given a considerable impetus to semantics. Semantics, therefore, may be regarded as a phase of the modern developments in psychiatry and the mental health movement in so far as they aim at producing social sanity. As an example of words standing in need of semantic analysis, we may cite such terms as 'liberty,' 'rights,' 'toleration,' 'soul,' 'spirit,' 'aggression,' 'adequate defense,' and many others. It appears, therefore, that in semantics we have a possible antidote to the disease of symbolic phantasy. Invented largely by philosophers who had some interest in language, the new science of symbolism now threatens to destroy the house of cards called 'metaphysics' in which semantics was born and nurtured.

Once the study of man's symbolic activities was fully launched, many interesting problems were uncovered. It is not possible to explore all of them, but certainly some of the more significant of these problems will appear in the following list of questions.

VI. Problems Concerning Language, Communication, and Semantics

1. What is the symbolic mode of expression? What biological mutations were required to confer upon man the symbolic function?
2. Why don't subhuman animals, — such as anthropoid apes, — employ articulate speech?
3. What are the social conditions and geographical origins of human languages?
4. What are the important stages in the evolution of symbolisms from the crudest beginnings in primitive society to the latest and most refined forms?
5. How many functions are served by human languages, i.e., what several purposes does language serve?
6. How are words produced physiologically? How do children learn to talk?
7. Could man talk if he didn't have the capacity for ideas? Why do we forget some words and not others?
8. What does the anthropologist mean (Cf. Clyde Kluckhohn, *Mirror for Man*) when he says that a language is a philosophy?
9. Are there unconscious assumptions wrapped up in the structure of languages?
10. If, as Kluckhohn says, every language is a special way of looking at the world and interpreting experience, how is it possible for people with different languages to understand each other?
11. What is necessary to make world understanding possible? Would the adoption of a universal language automatically accomplish this?
12. What are the genetic relations of the world's families of languages?
13. Are all languages equally good for expressing the truths about the world in which we live? How can they be improved?
14. Is the Indo-European family of languages a completely reliable tool for human communication? Do the grammatical forms of this family (nouns, adjectives, verbs) correspond to the realities of the extra-linguistic world of events?
15. What are the various types of definition by means of which the meanings of symbols may be standardized for purposes of thought, expression, and communication?

We cannot here undertake to discuss all these problems. But it should be possible to throw some light on some questions. While it is difficult to give final solutions, there are speculations at hand, — a wealth of them, — and some of these hypotheses are probably headed in the right direction. With respect to the problem of the biological and social origins of language, we are still in the dark. But let us turn for a moment to the more basic question of the psycho-biological origin of the symbolic function.

VII. Why Does Man Use Symbols?

The problems of why man possesses the symbolic function can be discussed on two levels. On the neurological level we can ask the question, what happens in the brain when we create symbols? On the level of the psychology of conscious experience the corresponding problem is, what are the individual motivations and social functions of symbolic creations?

We have already discussed briefly the second phase of the situation as suggesting that 'fear of excommunication' is the personal motivation for creating a world of symbols which endures beyond the narrow limits of space and time of individual identity. In a way this explanation is a tautology: it presupposes what it attempts to explain. In such situations we may as well admit that we are face to face with an ultimate fact. In a sense, however, this 'explanation' is more satisfactory than Herbert Read's thesis in his *Icon and Idea*, that 'fear of the unknown' leads primitive man to geometric abstractions. It is not clear how this 'cosmic anxiety' could be responsible for neolithic man's addiction to symbolism; but on any theory there must have been magical elements present in primitive man's projection of existence beyond the hindering limitations of space and time.

The first phase of the problem, to a consideration of which we now turn, has hardly been recognized as a problem. My own theory on this matter will build upon some recent ideas concerning heredity as a kind of communication. This idea has been set forth by E. Taschdjian[2] and George Gamow[3]. In place of the notion of the gene as a 'particle,' Professor Taschdjian offers the concept of the *gene as a material symbol* which is copied by heredity. Briefly, the idea here is that gene multiplication is comparable to the duplication of a set of symbols, while the phenomenon of mutation is said to be akin to noise disturbance in the communication channel.

This is one of the suggestive analogies which the new science of cybernetics has made possible. By way of an extension of this line of thought, I shall propose that *the use of symbolism is natural in man because symbols are the means whereby functional aggregates (protein molecules), which are maps, express themselves as genes, which are territories, which in turn constitute the maps for the embryogenesis of organisms.* That is to say, there is symbolism on all levels of nature. This is only a special form of the projection of homomorphic images. This, ultimately, may result from the fact that the manifest universe is itself the visible symbol of the invisible archetypal field. Therefore, on a higher level of emergent evolution, the human nervous system gives rise to symbols because the brain is an elaboration of the nucleoproteins which the genes pass on in the enduring channel of cosmic imaging which becomes structuralized in the levels of emergence. I shall return to this line of thought at a later stage.

VIII. Man's Two Worlds

So much, for the moment, concerning the neurophysiology of symbolism. By virtue of the biological mutations in the brain and the speech mechanism which makes symbolism possible, man has become the creature who is able to live in two worlds: he inhabits a primary world of objects and a secondary world of symbols. Animals apparently live only in the first world; man has the added capacity of symbolic functioning, closely related to the human faculty of *abstraction*. Thus man enriches, and complicates, his life.

The primary world of objects is the world of external facts, and events, which man learns about and adjusts to through the use of his senses; the secondary world, comprising the knowledge which has been transmitted to us by word of mouth, through the press, radio, books, television, and the like, constitutes the uniquely human world. We humans begin where previous generations leave off, because we learn from the earlier generations who transmit their acquired knowledge to us through language. This is why man has acquired dominion over the earth.

Students are quite familiar with the non-causal connection between the secondary world of symbols and the primary world of facts; they therefore have no superstitions about the magical power of signs. The enlightened viewpoint is well stated by Humpty-Dumpty in Lewis Carroll's *Through the Looking Glass*, as follows:

> "When *I* use a word," Humpty-Dumpty said in a rather scornful tone, "it means just what I choose it to mean, — neither more nor less."
>
> "The question is," said Alice, "whether you *can* make words mean so many different things."
>
> "The question is," said Humpty-Dumpty, "which is to be the master, — that's all."

This realization of the arbitrary nature of words as symbols is foreign to primitive man. Primitive peoples treat word-structures as if they were the things themselves, not realizing that there is no necessary connection between the symbol and the thing symbolized (its 'referent'). As a consequence, throughout much of man's history there has been a deep-rooted tendency to suppose that because there is a word, there must be a reality that corresponds to it. This misconception results in the fallacy described as the reification of concepts or the hypostatization of forms of behavior, — thus 'consciousness,' 'insanity,' the 'group mind,' and the like, are hypostatized into 'entities.' Moreover, written or spoken words are, or should be, like *maps*: in order to be reliable, symbol structures must adequately represent the facts of the *territory* they represent. Obviously, many of our human problems arise from that condition in which individuals have false maps in their minds. Let us explore further the reasons for the discrepancies between maps and territories.

IX. Concepts by Postulation and by Inspection

We have seen that the uniquely human achievements involve the symbolic function and that man's world is a tenuous fabric woven from and by threads of communication. If it is true, as Norbert Wiener puts it, that the community extends only so far as there extends an effectual transmission of information, then it is obvious that the next step in human progress is dependent upon further extensions of present channels of communication and the creation of new channels.

We have noted that one source of confusion on the human level arises from the fact that language has different functions, and the mixing of these functions leads to misinterpretations. Santayana once stated that religion is poetry trying to become science. Presumably this means that religion serves primarily the aesthetic purposes in life, and goes wrong when it assumes that its affirmations are propositions which can be verified in the same sense in which the propositions of natural science can be confirmed.

In our own approach to the integration of knowledge we shall place the claims of poetry and religion, — but not the aesthetic and religious 'experiences', — outside the scope of science. In those areas wherein the expressive, the emotive, and the ceremonial uses of symbolism prevail, vagueness and lack of precision are legitimate: words like 'home,' 'mother,' 'sunset,' 'fatherland,' and the rest, are colored by emotional associations, they have no standardized connotations, and therefore are the proper vehicles of aesthetic experience. But for logical and scientific uses, more precision is desirable and therefore conventional connotations are required.

These remarks bring us face-to-face with one of the outstanding problems that arises from the study of language, namely, the relation between *connotation* and *denotation*, *intension and extension*. This problem comes about because, as previously noted, man lives in two worlds, — and is never completely at home in either one. The situation as we have it in mind has been portrayed by Ogden and Richards in their volume, *The Meaning of Meaning*. Here they give the triangle of reference, as follows:

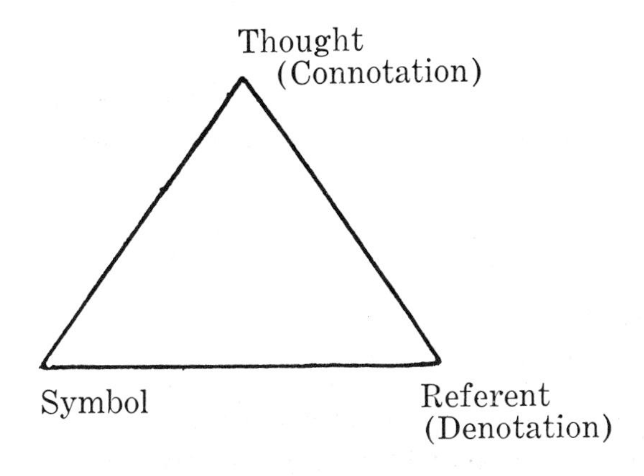

One important problem made evident by this triangle is this: *where is the starting point?* Where does one begin: with connotations of terms which somehow from the very outset have 'referents,' or with the denotation of symbols which somehow have 'meanings'? It is my opinion that this is an epistemological problem which cannot be solved in terms of a purely semantic analysis. My own answer will appear later as a part of a more inclusive philosophy.

Without introducing that philosophy now, an approach to the issue can be made by segregating the modes of human response under the two types of orientation:

INTENSIONAL ORIENTATIONS	Nominal or verbal definitions Connotations emphasized Non-empirical field, with no 'facts' Definition by postulation
EXTENSIONAL ORIENTATIONS	Real definitions employed Denotations emphasized Empirical science, based on 'facts' Definition by inspection (induction)

To simplify the language, let us say that at the extremes of human response there are two ways of forming our concepts: *concepts by postulation* or *pure intension*, as in mathematics, and *concepts by inspection*, or *pure extension*, as in physics. We shall not here adopt the philosophical theory which would add to the list what are called 'concepts by intuition,' though there is a sense in which 'intuition' appears in our philosophical theory, namely, as the equivalent of what gestalt theory calls *insight*.

The greatest difficulties we humans confront arise in those areas which may be called hybrid fields: politics, religion, economics, philosophy, and the like, are mixtures, each being a combination of a bit of science (empirical knowledge) plus a large amount of verbal magic, hoary tradition, and superstitition. How do you define 'spirit'? Or "God"? By postulation or by inspection? Did one ever 'inspect' God? How do you define 'democracy,' 'fascism,' 'communism,' and other terms used so loosely?

But even in the older natural sciences the going is not easy. Many of the concepts of physics are mixed (hybrid) concepts. To show that this is so, let us consider briefly the idea of 'time.' I begin by quoting from A. S. Eddington's book, *The Mathematical Theory of Relativity*, where the distinction between 'postulation' and 'inspection' is clearly recognized:

> "The pure mathematician deals with ideal quantities defined as having the properties which he deliberately assigns to them. But in an experimental science we have to discover properties, not to assign them; and physical qualities are defined primarily according to the way in which we recognize them when confronted by them in our observation of the world about us."

Now apply this abstract distinction to our example of the meaning of 'time.' Here I rely upon P. W. Bridgman's statement as given in his book, *The Logic of Modern Physics.* After quoting Newton's statement that "Absolute, True and Mathematical Time, of itself, and from its own nature flows equably and without regard to anything external, and by another name is called Duration," Professor Bridgman urges (p. 4) that "there is no assurance whatever that there exists in nature anything with properties like those assumed in the definition." In brief, even the great Newton failed to discern where definition by inspection left off and definition by postulation began.

Students of language inform us that an ideal language is one in which the structure of the language corresponds to the structure of the facts to be symbolized, — there should be a one-to-one correspondence between the *map* and the *territory*, a unique symbol for each individual fact. But is that practicable? For example, what is the physical fact that corresponds to the concept of negative number, irrational number, and the like? Or return to Newton's idea of an absolute time: when Einstein negated Newton's ideas, he in turn introduced a new 'absolute', — the *constancy of the velocity of light*, — but is this absoluteness an existentially observed *fact* or is it a *postulate* introduced into the system of relativity as a disguised definition?

In the present scheme we are committed to the view that every valid concept has some operational analogue in empirically observed reality, but to maintain this view it will be necessary to broaden considerably the meaning of the term 'physical universe' and include multi-dimensional manifolds. What the end-result of this mutual interaction of concepts by inspection and concepts by postulation is will appear in due time. It may be said at this point, however, that the view of the Logical Positivists that science can be built without non-empirical constructs is one we do not share. To state what sort of cosmology is presupposed by the enterprise of the special sciences is the job of those who believe in the possibility of the integration of all knowledge, — and this obligation will not be shirked. The later sections of the present chapter will begin to exhibit some of the consequences of this marriage of symbolism and nature; and at the same time these remarks will serve to introduce some of the epistemological problems we shall have to face in subsequent chapters. Meanwhile, before undertaking to deal with the metaphysical issues of semantics and epistemology, let us take time out to retrace the history of the study of symbolism and meaning.

X. The History of Semantics: Primitive Man's Views

One theory of the origin of the world's languages is that they are all derived from a parent stem, — an original language such as Adam might have spoken. Among those who held to this theory is William von Humboldt, who as a result of his studies came to the conclusion that all languages should be arranged according to a single line of development from the most primitive to the most advanced forms. Such a simple scheme of linguistic development is rejected by the vast majority of experts; but it is still true that diverse languages sometimes exhibit morphological similarities in syntax, and so forth. What we have today are families of languages which have common ancestries within these disparate families, but the 'missing links' which could relate these diverse families have not been found. Moreover, just because of the structural similarities in the various languages, it is possible to 'translate' the ideas or meanings of one language into another with some measure of success, never perfect. One scheme for representing the possible relations between the world's families of languages has already been provided (Diagram IV).

On the basis of his anthropological studies, Lucien Lévy-Bruhl arrived at the conclusion that primitive man is 'pre-logical,' in the sense that the so-called 'laws of thought' of later civilized humans simply do not apply to him. Primitive man's world view, permeated by 'mystical participation,' illustrates the system known to anthropologists as *animism*, wherein nature is believed to be alive (animated) because man projects his own vitality into the external world and interprets natural phenomena in 'anthropomorphic' terms. Following Korzybskian semantics, one would say that the primitive animistic system is based on 'false identifications', — i.e., the maxim that 'I am other things.' Here there are no sharp dichotomies between 'self' and the 'not-self,' because the classical laws of logic, the laws of *identity*, *non-contradiction*, and *excluded middle*, are not observed.

Lévy-Bruhl's thesis that the primitive mind is pre-logical has been contradicted by Professor F. S. C. Northrop and others.[4] As Northrop sees the situation, Lévy-Bruhl's theory has been rejected because it is attempting to judge primitives according to our own standards. According to this criticism, primitives are illogical by our concepts, but not by their own, and if we study such people sympathetically, from their own viewpoints, we find that what they do seems reasonable to them. My comment on this criticism is that Professor Northrop is confused on this point, — or else I do not understand Northrop. He is admitting that they are illogical *from our point of view*, i.e., they do not conform to Aristotle's laws of thought, — and that is exactly what Lévy-Bruhl is saying. Of course, if we give up our own standards of logic, what they do no longer seems 'illogical.'

In primitive man's world-view, — if one may term it that, — everything is 'living' and active, and his language is adapted to such a world. As Professor William Werkmeister points out in his book, *Philosophy of Science*, primitive man uses his own body as a reference system for spatial relations and numerical values, and then interprets the universe in terms of his own plane of coördinates and emotions. Metaphors, parables, and myths constitute the language of poets, prophets, and magicians; whereas mathematical equations and logical laws of thought become the tools of later Western science. We Western moderns rationalize and generalize by building up systems of classifications; but primitive man pictorializes and personalizes. It is no accident that Western culture had to wait upon the development of a monotheistic religion to replace earlier polytheism before scientific lawfulness and predictability could replace the capriciousness and uncertainty of spiritism.

'Word magic' is an inescapable part of primitivism. This semantic identification is based on the supposed unity of the symbol with the thing symbolized. For primitive people words are not arbitrary, as they are for Humpty-Dumpty. Words have power over objects, so that if you know the name of an object you have some control over it. Some names are sacred, and 'profanity' is the improper use of such words. 'Curses,' of course, also illustrate the power of words in producing effects. This superstitious attitude toward language is not confined to primitive cultures. We find the magical attitude illustrated in the Judaeo-Christian religious tradition. In *Genesis* it is stated: "And God *said*, 'Let there be light,' and there was light." And once the world and its contents were created by God, Adam begins his rule over living things *by giving them names*. Many other examples of the magical power of words could be lifted from the Scriptures.

XI. The Semantics of Greek Civilization

Early Greek philosophy shared some of the word magic of the primitive and the Hebrew-Christian linguistic superstitions. Even Plato's *Dialogues* reveal this naiveté, — the *Cratylus*, for example.

Certainly some of the pre-Platonic philosophers regarded words as revelations of the nature of things. This is true of Heraclitus, for example. As F. M. Cornford says of him in his work, *From Religion to Philosophy* (p. 45): "The Logos is revealed in speech. The structure of man's speech reflects the structure of the world; more, it is the embodiment or representation of it." This *Logos* doctrine, as already noted, reappears in the first five verses of the Gospel of Saint John: "In the beginning was the word . . . ," and so on.

It would indeed be surprising if the Greeks did not make some headway in the study of symbolic modes of expression. Aristotle, for example, investigated the various functions of language and laid the foundations for the science of deductive logic. But even Aristotle, — if one may believe Mauthner, — "was superstitiously devoted to words and made the extant forms of speech the objects of a superstitious cult, as though they were actual deities." This, perhaps, is an extreme judgment.

Aristotle, of course, is a controversial figure in the history of Western thought. Bertrand Russell represents one extreme, while medieval Scholasticism represents the opposite appraisal, — the apotheosis of Aristotelianism, one might say. Russell has on several occasions declared that he doubted whether anyone trained in the tradition of Aristotelian logic could ever free himself sufficiently to think clearly, — which means in terms of mathematical logic. In connection with this problem of the tyranny of traditional language and logic over human thought, Russell argues in *The Analysis of Mind* (p. 212) that many philosophers have erred in assuming that the structure of sentences corresponds to the structure of facts. He refers to the doctrine of A. H. Sayce, who maintained that all European philosophy since Aristotle had been dominated by the fact that these philosophers spoke Indo-European languages, and therefore supposed that the world, like the sentences they used, was dividable into subjects and predicates. This view would fit in nicely with the doctrine of Mauthner and Whorf that if Aristotle had spoken Chinese or Dacotan, he would have had to adopt an entirely different logic.

From this brief survey, we conclude that the full story of how the forms of Western thought and culture emerged as an embellishment on the grammatical forms of the Indo-European family of languages is still to be revealed, and the fulfillment of that undertaking will constitute one of the major projects in the history of human exploration.

XII. The Beginnings of Modern Semantics

How old is the science of semantics?

The publishers of a recent and popular book on semantics describe the volume as a layman's guidebook to the twentieth century's newest science. But those antiquarians who like to find the origins of all things 'modern' in the speculations of the ancients would doubtless propose that we may find the beginnings of semantics in the 'Socratic method' for discovering the meanings of words. Moreover, the pupil of Socrates, Plato, was something of a semanticist for in the *Theaetetus* it is pointed out that the meaning of a sentence is something more than the sum of the meanings of the words which make it up. Indeed, this doctrine might well be taken as the forerunner of the 'contextualist' theory of meaning and perhaps even an anticipation of the view of Ludwig Wittgenstein that only in the context of a sentence does a word have a meaning.

However that may be, it is certainly true that we do find among the early Greeks the beginnings of the emancipation of thought from language. The Sophists and the skeptics were no inveterate slaves to language, and it is difficult to find evidence of word magic in their doctrines, — such as they were.

Passing from the ancient philosophers to those closer to our times, one discovers that the next steps toward a science of semantics were taken by the *nominalists* of the middle ages. No longer interested in the 'ideal forms' and 'essences' of the Platonic and Aristotelian metaphysics, these pioneers in the rise of early modern science, — William of Occam and others, — tried to free themselves from subservience to language forms. Following close in time came Francis Bacon, that faithful personification of the modern scientific spirit. In his *Advancement of Learning* (1605) one finds a clear recognition of the 'distemper of learning' in which men study words and not matter. Bacon's statement that "men imagine that their minds have command of language; but it often happens that language bears rule over their minds," has a strikingly contemporary ring to it.

The next important figure in this developing study is John Locke, critic of authoritarianism and defender of political freedoms. Locke recognized the arbitrary relation between sounds (words) and ideas. He observed that "we should have a great many fewer disputes in the world, if words were taken for what they are, the signs of ideas only, and not for things themselves." So important was this subject to Locke that he devoted the entire Third Book of his *Essay Concerning Human Understanding* (1690) to the topic. This essay was of interest to Leibniz, whose work on a universal language marks a further step in the direction of a comprehensive science of communication through symbolism. We deal with Leibniz's views at more length in the following chapters. Among the others who also caught glimpses of the importance of these investigations were Thomas Hobbes, Taine, Whately, George and Mary Boole, Bentham, and Hans Vaihinger.

XIII. Twentieth Century Semantics

The first explicit use of the term semantics is to be found toward the close of the last century. In the year 1897 Michel Brèal published his *Essai de Semantique*, and in 1900 an English translation of this work appeared in London. Brèal's interest was not in the theory of meaning, but rather in linguistics and philology. As a matter of fact, in her article on Significs in the *Encyclopedia Britannica*, Lady Victoria Welby complains that Brèal nowhere gave a 'precise definition' of the term. Lady Welby therefore chose the term 'significs,' which she regarded as the science of meaning in all its phases, including that of logic.

Without intending to depreciate the importance of Lady Welby's investigations, it must be admitted that the initial discoverer of the subject of semantics is the American philosopher, Charles S. Peirce. The true stature of this soaring genius has been recognized only since Peirce's death, indeed within the last quarter century, during which period Peirce's previously unpublished manuscripts have been gathered together into his *Collected Works* (Harvard University Press).

In a paper published in 1868, Peirce declared[5] that "the man who makes researches into the reference of symbols to their objects will be forced to make original studies into all branches of the general theory of signs." This investigation Peirce termed *semeiotic*, from the Greek *seme*, meaning *sign*. As Peirce put it in his "Prologomena to an Apology for Pragmaticism," "By a *Seme* I should mean anything which serves for any purpose as a substitute for an object of which it is, in some sense, a representation or sign." It may be noted in passing that the entity for which the sign is a substitute is now termed the 'referent' of the sign.

Peirce's epistemological urge was directed toward the resolution of scientific problems, but his seminal ideas were soon to flower into the new system of thought known as 'pragmatism', — beyond doubt the most original contribution to philosophy that has come from the North American continent. In his famous paper on "How to Make Our Ideas Clear," published in 1878, Peirce enunciated the principle which James reinterpreted and generalized into a comprehensive theory of truth. According to Peirce, the meaning of a proposition is a "general description of all the experimental phenomena which the assertion of the proposition virtually predicts."

At this point it should be pointed out that Peirce anticipated the doctrine which P. W. Bridgman, in his treatise on *The Logic of Modern Physics*, terms the *operational theory of concepts*. This theory tells us that the meaning of a concept is synonymous with the set of operations associated with it. It also implies that any problem which demands for its solution an operation which cannot be performed is a meaningless problem. Taken over by the philosophical movement known as 'logical positivism', — to which we turn in a moment, — this doctrine has been converted into the Peirce-Wittgenstein principle that any unverifiable proposition is a meaningless proposition, and any unverifiable difference is no difference.

Before leaving this topic, it is pertinent to observe that Peirce later rejected the interpretation that James had placed upon his pragmatic principle. From Peirce's test of meaning, James concluded that if a belief, when tested by its consequences, results in any kind of satisfaction, that makes the belief 'true.' But whereas James included emotionally satisfying consequences, Peirce stressed that the inquiry which is suggested by the hypothesis ought to satisfy the intellectual demands of the scientific temper. If Peirce were to pass judgment on the matter today, one wonders whether he might not also repudiate the anti-metaphysical and anti-normative ramifications of Logical Positivism, which claims to have received some momentum from Peirce's semeiotics. But before considering that item, let us deal with the developments that came in between Peirce and the new positivism.

XIV. Ogden-Richards' Contributions and Korzybskian *G. S.*

As we have indicated, little was done with or about Peirce's researches in semeiotics. It was not until the close of World War I that a genuine interest in the problems of communication gave an added impetus to interest in symbolism and semantics.

Two events headed up this growth of interest in a science of semantics. In 1922 the important volume, *The Meaning of Meaning*, co-authored by two Englishmen, C. K. Ogden (inventor of *Basic English*) and I. A. Richards, was published. This work, which included an excellent historical survey of the field, helped enormously in focusing attention upon the problems. Here, among other things, Ogden and Richards brought out the importance of the distinction between the symbolic and the emotive uses of language, a distinction which the Logical Positivists have found useful in their work.

A second major event in creating interest in semantics was the publication of Alfred Korzybski's formulations, his two outstanding works being *The Manhood of Humanity*, first published in 1922, where the theory of man as the *time-binder* was first stated, and the monumental work, *Science and Sanity: An Introduction to Non-Aristotelian Systems and General Semantics*, which appeared in 1933. Count Korzybski, the Polish engineer who came to the United States after the termination of the first World War, invented the system known as *General Semantics*, which he presented in seminar courses until his death in 1950. Korzybski's seminars were first given in Chicago at the *Institute of General Semantics*, now located at Lakeville, Connecticut.

For Korzybski 'general semantics' is not a 'logic' or a 'psychology,' which are held to be 'elementalistic' subjects; general semantics is a psycho-logic of sanity. Here scientific methods, psychiatry, anthropology, mathematics, and a theory of evaluation all become part of the broad field of *G. S.*, the goal of which is the production of sane individuals living in a sane human environment. All languages, all media whereby man communicates knowledge, involves structural assumptions about the world, and only after a thorough study of fact-organism-language relations will it be possible to use language forms that are in keeping with the structure of the world of facts in which man lives.

Because of his prior familiarity with the work of the Polish logicians and semanticists in the European setting, Korzybski had a considerable advantage over the American students working in these fields. This is the case, for example, with the Korzybskian espousal of a 'multi-valued' orientation which was presented to replace the outmoded two-valued judgments of Aristotelian logic. It was only later that

American students like C. I. Lewis were able to take advantage of the non-Aristotelian logics which Lukasiewizc, Tarski, and other Europeans, had developed. True enough, to these contributions Korzybski added other and more original formulations, — such as *time-binding*, *multi-ordinality*, *non-elementalism*, the *structural differential*, and others, — all of them of such provocative nature that Korzybski's work will continue to influence semanticists for generations to come.

Indeed, the enthusiasm for the methods and results of Korzybski's General Semantics ran so high that Alfred Tarski[6] felt called upon to insist that semantics is not a panacea for all ills. In Tarski's words:

> "It is perhaps worth saying that semantics as it is conceived in this paper (and in former papers of the author) is a sober and modest discipline which has no pretensions of being a universal patent medicine for all the ills and diseases of mankind, whether imaginary or real. You will not find in semantics any remedy for decayed teeth or illusions of grandeur or class conflicts. Nor is semantics a device for establishing that everyone except the speaker and his friends is speaking nonsense."

This is a sober warning against the over-enthusiasm of some of the semanticists, — those who would make a 'cult' of the discipline. My own evaluation of the Korzybskian form of general semantics was presented on the occasion of the *Second American Congress on General Semantics*, and I shall not repeat what was stated there.[7]

For present purposes it is appropriate that we turn next to the 'Unity of Science' movement, wherein semantics once more appears as an essential ingredient.

XV. Semantics in the 'Unity of Science' Program

Among the American philosophers who have been influenced by Peirce's semeiotic is Professor Charles W. Morris, who shares responsibility for the consummation of the ambitious undertaking known as the *International Encyclopedia of Unified Science*, published by the University of Chicago Press. Professor Morris has set as his goal the fusion of the school of Logical Positivism, which originated in Europe, with the 'biological positivism' of the American pragmatists, and for this synthesis he proposes the name, Logical Empiricism. In his monograph, *Foundations of the Theory of Signs*, Morris recommends semeiotic as the instrument of all science, since every science makes use of and expresses its results in terms of symbols. Metascience, the science of sciences, must use semeiotic as an organ, so that the entire *Encyclopedia* is conceived to be nothing other than the language of science.

In developing a comprehensive theory of signs, Morris points out that semiosis has three aspects or dimensions, as follows: (1) the relations of sign vehicles to what is designated or denoted is called the *semantical dimension of semiosis*, and the study of this dimension *semantics:* (2) the relation of sign-vehicles to human interpreters is called the *pragmatical dimension of semiosis*, and the study of this dimension *pragmaticism:* (3) the remaining semiotically relevant relations of sign vehicles to other signs may be called the *syntactical dimension of semiosis*, and its study *syntactics*. As Morris says, "semeiotic, as the general science of signs, thus contains the subordinate science of syntactics, semantics, and pragmatics."[8] Unlike many of the Logical Positivists, Professor Morris is much interested in the aesthetic, ethical, and humanistic forms of activity. Here he comes closer to Dewey's attitudes than to the views of the 'orthodox' Positivists.

And now the time has come to deal with the new developments which we have on several occasions referred to, namely, Logical Positivism and the derivative schools of 'analysis', — by all odds the most impressive philosophical movements currently demanding our attention.

XVI. Semantics and Logical Positivism

Logical Positivism is fundamentally a philosophy of science. It has had its period of most rapid growth since the close of World War I, receiving its initial impetus from the group of investigators in Europe known as the Vienna Circle (*Wiener Kreis*).[9] Among the Continental thinkers associated with the early group, between the two World Wars, were Philipp Frank, Otto Neurath, Moritz Schlick, Hans Hahn, Richard von Mises, and Rudolf Carnap. More recently some of the Positivists have come to the United States where they continued their work and influence after being forced to discontinue them during the Hitler madness in German-dominated countries.

This group of philosophical iconoclasts has created a great stir in the intellectual world by pronouncing the traditional problems of philosophy to be 'pseudo-problems', — meaningless questions. In taking this stand the New Positivism ruthlessly steps on the feet of moralists, humanists, metaphysicians, idealists, and even the older positivism of Auguste Comte, by insisting that most of what occupies the attention of philosophers belongs not to philosophy but to the realms of poetry and wishful thinking.

As the name indicates, Logical Positivism is a fusion of the older positivistic tendencies of Auguste Comte and Ernst Mach with the logistics contributions of such men as Frege, Peano, Bertrand Russell, and Ludwig Wittgenstein. Like all positivism, the Vienna school started out as an anti-metaphysical movement. Persuasive statements of this approach are given in von Mises's book, *Positivism, A Study of Human Understanding* and Reichenbach's study, *The Rise of Scientific Philosophy.* More recently, however, Gustav Bergmann has published his volume, *The Metaphysics of Logical Positivism*, and the title is indicative of a 'deviationist' tendency within Positivism. By and large, however, Positivism foreswears any philosophy concerned with domains beyond human experience and it condemns those problems not amenable to the logico-empirical methods utilized so effectively by the sciences.

The new Logical Positivism differs from the older positivism of Comte in two ways: (1) it does not regard an interest in social reform as an essential part of the program of philosophy, and (2) it sets forth an original conception of the nature and the function of logic. With respect to metaphysics, the contention of Logical Positivism is that the controversies engaged in in that field are unnecessary, — and futile. They are superfluous because so-called metaphysical questions are spurious problems resulting from the uncritical use of language. The function of philosophy is not to 'solve' the alleged problems of God, Freedom, and immortality, mind versus matter, and the like, but to dissipate the pseudo-problems that have been built up around these terms. As one Positivist puts it, metaphysics is simply bad grammar, it is a result of the confusion of the 'formal' and the 'material' modes of speech, as Carnap stated the matter.

In passing we have referred briefly to the historical background of Positivism. The Central European brand of Positivism had its origins not only in a certain phase of Auguste Comte's philosophy, but also in the ideas of the Austrian physicist, Ernst Mach. Thus Vienna and Prague share honors as points of origin for Positivism in its creative period. To the early group belonged also the mathematician Hans Hahn, the political economist, Otto Neurath, the physicist, Philipp Frank, and others, who supplemented Mach's ideas with the philosophy of science expounded by Henri Poincaré — all these soon to be integrated into the more recent investigations in logic and mathematics. These converging lines of research took on a strong central tendency when Hahn (now deceased) called the attention of the Vienna group to the significance of the work of Wittgenstein, a former pupil of Bertrand Russell. Hahn also succeeded in securing the appointment of Moritz Schlick to the University of Vienna and induced Rudolf Carnap to join the group.

It is to these figures primarily that the 'circle' owed much of its later character, a character enhanced by the influence of the Berlin group organized around Hans Reichenbach. Later, — until his death in 1953, — Reichenbach taught at the University of California at Los Angeles. Thus the influence of Positivism has spread like wildfire. Subsequent years have witnessed a growing interest in this vigorous movement and many American teachers of philosophy, for example, Ernest Nagel (Columbia), W. V. Quine (Harvard), and others, have helped to extend the Positivist ideas and influence. Several Congresses for the 'Unity of Science', — a phrase coined by Neurath, — have been held, the first at Prague (1934), the second at Paris (1935), the third at Copenhagen (1936), the next at Cambridge in England (1938), then at Cambridge, Massachusetts (1939), and then at Chicago (1941). The great virtue as well as a possible source of disharmony of this 'school' has been and is that it has included among its members investigators who are outstanding thinkers in their own right. These scholars, with their individual slants on the problems of philosophy, have in recent years modified the views of the original circle, and it becomes increasingly difficult to give the presently 'correct' views of the Positivists on specific questions. My own summary therefore outlines the original common foundation upon which the various representatives of Positivism have built their philosophies.

XVII. Positivism versus Metaphysics

According to the Logical Positivists, the aim of philosophy should be the clarification of the meanings of the terms and propositions, — the purification of language and the elimination of meaningless assertions. In such a program the scope of philosophy is considerably altered. In many respects it becomes narrower; but in other respects its scope is increased.

As we have indicated, the narrowing aspect of Positivism consists in purging certain types of questions from the field of philosophy. The intention is not to liquidate them entirely, but simply cease to regard them as belonging to philosophy. Some of these questions are assigned to special sciences, but others are banished forever from the fields of knowledge. Among those that meet the first fate are psychological and ethical problems. Psychological and sociological investigations are necessary, but these are empirical and scientific investigations, and it is best to entrust them to trained experts. Those that meet the second fate are metaphysics and the normative sciences, and their banishment from the realm of knowledge has irritated many of the 'old line' philosophers.

The term 'metaphysics' has a rather narrow connotation in this controversy. By it is meant all propositions that claim to yield knowledge about something that is over or beyond experience. As Carnap says,[10] "We do not include in metaphysics those theories, — sometimes called metaphysical, — which purport to arrange the most general propositions of the various regions of scientific knowledge in a well ordered system." Thus Carnap would not necessarily object to the title of Professor Bergmann's book. Nevertheless, such attempts at "arranging knowledge into a well ordered system," Carnap would insist, belong to the enterprise of science, not philosophy. Whatever one may mention as a significant piece of intellectual labor that can be trusted to philosophers must be identical with what the Logical Positivists call 'logical analysis', — the only proper function of philosophy. Here, then, is the new 'Revolution in Philosophy,' to use the title of the recent book, edited by Gilbert Ryle (1956).

Before considering what is meant by 'logical analysis,' let us say something more about the rejection of metaphysics. The attitude of the Positivists was well expressed in Wittgenstein's affirmation that the assertions of the metaphysicians are not false but senseless. Metaphysical doctrines are generally of the sort to which it is not possible to apply clear-cut criteria for judging them as true or false. There are too many debates waged in which there is not adequate definition of what is being debated. A Logical Positivist sees no sense in taking sides in an argument in which the terms are not accurately defined, or, — what is worse, — are inherently indefinable.

When anyone asserts that "there is a God," that "Reality is mental," that "The external world exists," or even the dictum of nineteenth century Positivism that "Only what is given in experience is real," the Logical Positivist does not say to him that his assertion is false, but simply insists that the affirmer explain what he means by his statement. In terms of this approach, it appears that there are in the main two kinds of propositions: the first belong to the empirical sciences and point ultimately to something given by way of sensations; the second class of propositions betray themselves as meaningless because they really assert nothing, but at best express a sort of feeling for life. Such propositions may have emotional values, but they have no place in science or philosophy. Logical Positivists challenge anyone to show that what philosophers have to say about reality has any effect upon the studies of the special sciences. Metaphysical assertions are totally inconsequential with respect to verifiable knowledge.

Along with metaphysics, Logical Positivists cast out the 'normative sciences,' especially ethical judgments which purport to discriminate good and evil. Science is concerned with knowledge, not with values or preferences. It is a reliable guide when it comes to finding the means for realizing given ends, but science cannot determine what ends ought to be chosen. Science can study what particular people do in fact like and desire, but it cannot legislate what they ought to desire. One can be sure that any proposition that pretends to tell what *the* good is, what God's will is, and the like, is not a scientific statement. Neither is it a proper philosophical one. The only function philosophy can have in the realm of values is to insist upon a clear distinction between knowledge and preference in any given situation. Once a preference is really known, philosophy can indicate what actions it implies, but it cannot say whether it is good or bad. Like science, philosophy is relevant to the true and the false only, and not to the 'good' and 'bad.'

XVIII. Philosophy as Logical Analysis

After eliminating metaphysics, normative science, and all psychological and sociological considerations from philosophy, what do the Logical Positivists leave for the philosophers? The answer is that the function of philosophy is logical analysis. And what do they mean by logical analysis? By logical analysis is meant the analysis of languages. By language is meant any medium for communicating knowledge, any set of symbols and their 'syntax' or rules of combinations of symbols. Every method for trying to make anything more intelligible requires a different language. Thus physics and psychology have their own languages, as do Germany and China.

The investigations of the operations of thinking as they actually occur is not the task of logic but of psychology, say the Positivists. Nor is it the task of logic to determine the 'correct' ways of thinking. Learning to think correctly is as much by way of the special sciences as by way of logic. The business of geology is to learn to think correctly about rocks, that of astronomy how to think correctly about stars, and so on. All the sciences must employ languages, possibly parts of the same language, so that, in effect, the competent scientist is one who can handle scientific language successfully.

In a sense every science is a logical analysis, but logic is the logical analysis of logical analysis. Logic as such is concerned with the internal structure of language, whereas science must relate formal structures to empirical facts. Logic cannot decree what the facts should be, — to discover what the facts are is the business of empirical investigations, — but logic can point out where the difficulties encountered in any investigation may be due to an improper use of language and the principles of symbolism.

Logic, accordingly, is concerned with the internal structure of language and not with experience. Logic cannot be contradicted by empirical data because it says nothing about them. By adopting this position the Logical Positivists avoided the difficulties encountered by the nineteenth century empiricists in their futile efforts at accounting for logic and mathematics on an empirical basis. This difference constitutes one of the major distinctions between the older and the present schools of positivism.

Logic is analytic and not synthetic. This means that it is limited to tautologies, and that it contributes nothing to knowledge, aside from indicating the formal relations between propositions. The principles of logic are simply rules for tautological transformations, rules for repeating in whole or in part what has been said in another form. Given a proposition, there are ways of transforming it into others, and if the transformation is legitimate there will be no alteration of the meaning content. Logic as purely tautological has no more effect on the alteration of the meaning of a proposition being transformed than does the shuffling of a deck of cards, — marks on paper are merely rearranged. Logic does not change meanings; it merely elucidates them.

On this theory, logic as such cannot be 'inductive.' New knowledge can be gained only empirically. In the last analysis, the propositions of factual science must be recognized as expressing only probabilities. They do not yield absolute certainties; only tautologies can do that. The empirical sciences are essentially the application of symbol-patterns to the representation of facts. But symbols themselves can be manipulated and set up into systems without applying any concrete interpretations to them, apart from the fact that different symbols must be distinguishable and recognizable as such. When empirical meanings are given to symbols, the system suffers with respect to certainty.

In summary: the positivistic attitude with respect to the relation between science and philosophy is simply that there is no need for duplication of functions. It is the business of the special sciences to cope with particular problems. The business of philosophy is to resolve pseudo-problems. This it can do by means of logical analysis, which amounts to no more than determining proper forms for adequate language systems and pointing out exactly where a given symbolism violates the syntactical order of the language being used. In view of the present confused state of affairs, the Logical Positivists believe that the job assigned to philosophy is an important one. If it went about this task seriously, which means piecemeal resolution of pseudo-problems, philosophy would someday make itself superfluous. As the Positivists put it, in such a time no more books on philosophy would be written, but all science books would be written philosophically.

This ambitious program would indeed be impressive, were it not that such high-level figures as Peirce, Whitehead, and Russell, who did so much to lay the foundations for a Logical Empiricism, do not share this optimism. Aside from that, we shall find other reasons for a measure of caution toward the program of positivism. These difficulties will be considered at later points. Meantime, let us consider Russell's contributions in this field.

XIX. Russell's Semantics and Epistemology

We come now to the greatest of the contemporary semanticists, — though Russell seldom uses the term. Bertrand Russell, whose theory of 'logical types' and other contributions to mathematical logic may constitute the most important intellectual discoveries in the first half of the twentieth century, is among the world's top flight thinkers in his chosen field.

Starting out as a mathematician, Russell turned to philosophy for an answer to the question: *is mathematics true?* The attempt to answer this question resulted in the greatest work in modern logic and mathematics, the *Principia Mathematica*, written by Whitehead and Russell. Some writers, — Morris R. Cohen, for example, — have surmised that Russell was ruined so far as penetrating work in philosophy is concerned, when, at the outbreak of the first world war, Russell's pacifism led him to oppose the position of the British Government in declaring war on Germany. This, it is argued, stirred Russell's emotions to such an extent that he never after was able to free himself from involvements in unpopular social causes. That this judgment is wrong is amply demonstrated by Russell's recent books, such as *Human Knowledge, Its Scope and Limits*, and here his astute intellect returns to tackle again the recondite problems which concerned him as a young man.

Over the decades Russell has been devoted to exploring the foundations of our knowledge. In one of his volumes, *An Inquiry Into Meaning and Truth* (1940), Russell attempts to construct a bridge between logic and psychology. Here, approaching the problem from the standpoint of language, he tries to show how the most refined intellectual processes have developed from pre-linguistic sources such as are illustrated in animal behavior. In carrying forward this enterprise, Russell first deals with 'meaning' in relation to words, and then passes on to a consideration of the relation of experience to the sentences that partially describe it, all of this culminating in an analysis of the empirical foundations of knowledge. Thus he covers much of the ground surveyed by the Logical Positivists, but from a somewhat different point of view and with rather different results as an outcome.

Like the Positivists, Russell's studies have been concerned with an investigation of the structure of the external world and the structure of symbolism, with a view to determining whether the use of language makes it possible to arrive at inferences about nature. Russell finds that many inferences that are drawn in traditional philosophies are based on crude objectifications of linguistic artefacts, and this is responsible for much bad philosophy. None the less, because there is something in common between the logical structure of language and the ontological structure of the world, the language which philosophers employ can make contributions to our knowledge of nature. This is an important conclusion, but to reach it Russell has had to travel a long and difficult road.

If we may summarize Russell's undertaking concisely, we may say that his aim is to arrange the propositions which constitute our knowledge in a hierarchy of such a sort that the later propositions are accepted because of their logical relation to those which come before them. The procedure is pretty much as follows.

XX. Russell's Hierarchy of Languages

Language is a system of conventional signs called symbols. These signs may be coördinated according to rules, and since the process can be repeated, we can introduce signs referring to signs, and so on. Thus we develop levels of languages. The ordinary base language, referring directly to objects of experience, may be called the *object language;* while the language of a higher level may be called the *metalanguage.* In the object language we speak about whatever we speak about, and in the metalanguage we speak about the object language itself. In this manner it is possible to build a hierarchy of languages by employing signs which refer to signs, and so on. In this scheme the language which is termed the object language by Russell is analogous to what the Logical Positivists mean by the *protocol language.*

From this it is clear that modern logic is rich in its inner content. Like the modern chemist, who works with atoms and molecules to build immensely complicated compounds, the modern symbolic logician also has his *atomic propositions*, *molecular propositions*, and more intricate organizations. Aristotle dealt with *subjects* and *predicates;* Boole dealt with *classes;* Peirce dealt with *relations;* and the *Principia Mathematica* of Russell and Whitehead dealt with *propositions;* now modern symbolic logic or mathematical logic deals with all of them.

Working with these classes, propositions, properties, and relations, we discover that in our hierarchy of symbol-structures we can have classes of individuals and classes of classes; propositions about individuals and about propositions; properties of individuals and properties of properties . . . and so on. But the important thing in building up a hierarchy of statements is to remember the *range of significance* that holds for any such type of statement or symbol-structure: *a statement about any type of symbol-structure is of a higher type than the symbol-structure that defines that type.* Here is the lesson that Russell's theory of types has to teach us, and learning that lesson, we now see how to avoid the 'paradoxes' which result from mixing the types of statements. When a person says, "I am a liar," he must, — if he is talking sense, — be prepared to say what type of liar he is, i.e., whether of the first type or a higher type, which means, whether the proposition he asserts applies to everything else he says except the proposition . . . and so on.

The discovery of the theory of types was first announced by Russell in 1903. The paradox familiar to Frege, — which he tried to solve, but could not, — of the "class of those classes which are not members of themselves" was solved when Russell pointed out that only an individual can be an element of a class of the first level, and only a class of the nth level can be an element of a class of the $n + 1$ level; and this applies to properties as well.

Although Russell's theory of types has been of considerable value in understanding the nature of symbol-structures, it, in turn, has led to new problems. To escape these new difficulties, Russell introduced what is known as the *axiom of reducibility,* which declares that to every function in a hierarchy of types there exist equivalent predicative functions; or in simpler terms, to any characteristic of a higher order there are equivalent characteristics of a lower order. But the validity of this principle is still in question. It appears, therefore, that while the 'theory of types' and the supplementary 'axiom of reducibility' were supposed to provide an escape from the fallacy of 'illegitimate totalities' and the paradoxes arising from the unrestricted use of 'all,' modern logic still faces difficulties and has not reached the end of the trail.

The previously-mentioned process of designating signs of signs leads to some interesting results. One of the major achievements of modern symbolic logic appears in the light it throws on the traditional problem of the proof of the consistency of a set of statements (postulates). As we shall see in Chapter VI, Kurt Gödel indicates why it is impossible to give the proof of consistency within the language to which the consistency test is applied. The proof of 'consistency' must always be in the higher metalanguage to which reference has already been made. Suppose it were possible to give the proof of consistency, not in the metalanguage, but in the object language itself: then we would have both the consistency of the language and the validity of the proof, and this would constitute a circular situation, as Hans Reichenbach points out in his volume, *Elements of Symbolic Logic.*

It is now generally admitted that one result of Gödel's theorem is to show that the problem of finding a general method of proving consistency is insoluble. *Every system of logic requires a wider system within which its formulas may be demonstrated.* This means, among other things, that every system of logic is incomplete. Or in terms closer to what we have already stated, the formal operations with the symbols of the object language are made possible through material thinking in the metalanguage.[11]

This theory of the levels of language is most important. But it is interesting to note that various interpretations of the situation are possible. According to Alonzo Church,[12] this notion of levels means that no system of logic can embrace all forms of reasoning that are correct. Our own interpretation emphasizes another point. If it is true, as I shall try to show in Chapter VI, that Kurt Gödel's theorem proves that every system needs a wider system to justify it, and if it is also true that logic, mathematics, and even ordinary language, can in fact tell us something about reality, then we may conclude with Dr. L. O. Kattsoff[13] that there can never be a complete and final theory of reality, free from all possible presuppositions, though we may put our confidence in an evolutionary scheme, a dialectical interpretation of reality. With Kattsoff's conclusion we concur, and upon its assumed validity we shall continue our own enterprise of building a modern temple of knowledge.

XXI. Metalinguistics and the Structure of Facts

In the present chapter we have dealt with the problem of symbolism. We have reviewed the history of semantic analysis and examined the more important theories in the field. The most important conclusion we have arrived at relates to the question of whether anything about the nature of the world can be inferred from the manipulations of symbols. In this matter we have favored Russell's view that such conclusions can be drawn, provided relevant conditions are satisfied.

It has appeared that while Russell has much in common with the views of the Positivists, — for example, he has contempt for the vague generalities of the grandiose systems of philosophy and a suspicion of any effort at a value-system based on a metaphysics — nevertheless, he disagrees with the Positivists on at least one important point, namely, he must reject the nihilistic attack of the Positivists on metaphysics as complete foolishness. Unlike the Positivists, who excoriate metaphysics, Russell believes that with sufficient care the properties of language may provide a guide to the analysis of the structure of the world. Russell holds that the structure of non-verbal facts is not wholly knowable, and the inferences which the structure of language does permit us to make about the actual world in space and time are fewer in number than was assumed to be the case in traditional philosophy; nevertheless, after a life-time of study, Lord Russell arrives at the innocent-appearing but philosophically significant conclusion that a complete metaphysical skepticism is not possible.

This conclusion is completely consonant with our own viewpoint. It provides ample justification for our enterprise of the 'integration of knowledge' as a form of inductive metaphysics. To state the kind of systematic philosophy which emerges as the outcome of scientific knowledge is the job of those who believe in the possibility of such unification of knowledge. In our own scheme we aver that every valid concept has a physical exemplification in reality, but in order to maintain this view it is necessary, — as indicated, — to enlarge the connotation of the term 'physical' and make sufficient provision for the higher components of a multi-dimensional cosmos. The additional dimensions are manifestations of the evolutionary attainment of emergent simplicities, representing the orthogonal time-axes of historically new syntheses. This theory, if adequate to the requirements, will provide the *theory of coherence* which Alfred Korzybski hoped would someday be produced by the students of General Semantics.[14]

In the present world-view it appears that the foregoing novel macroscopic wholes, — the 'emergent simplicities', — are pyramided upon the foundations of structures already laid down. The 'new,' however, if it is to endure, must be congruent with the 'old,' in the sense of exhibiting gestalt patterns of isomorphism between the higher and the lower levels. Given the fundamental archetypal forms of the physical world at the lowest level, — hydrogen atoms being the first integrated manifestations in the world of matter, — nature progressively builds level upon level, from *atoms* → *molecules* → *crystals* → *viruses* → *genes* → *unicellular organisms* → *multicellular organisms* → *man*. Here, for the moment, nature pauses to gather new energies for the next advance. What the next emergent simplicity is likely to be is a matter for investigation. There is no reason, however, why we should not seek to envisage the outlines of the coming world organism and perhaps in the process help to bring it into being. But more of that as the argument progresses.

XXII. Frames of Reference and the Sociology of Knowledge

In recent years there has been much discussion concerning the 'sociology of knowledge.' In the present viewpoint ample provision is made for the cultural background of knowledge. In following through on the social basis of the forms of thought we have concluded (see Diagram X p. 117) that it is possible to isolate three levels of mental-social evolution, as follows: (1) the primitive or pre-Aristotelian level; (2) the Aristotelian level of classical science and philosophy; and (3) the coming non-Aristotelian mentality or mode of orientation. As we have explained this in previous studies, — *The Promise of Scientific Humanism*, for example, — the first level is the one-valued semantics of primitive mentality; the second is the two-valued semantics of Aristotelian logic and metaphysics, with self-identity of subjects (substances) and mutual exclusion of the plurality of substances; the third and coming level of non-Aristotelian orientation seeks to escape from slavery to staticity by functionalizing the notion of substance, thus overcoming the dualisms inherent in the traditional way of thinking, as Dr. Mario Lins has also noted.[15]

It is true that Aristotle repudiated the atomism of Democritus. Nevertheless, he borrowed something from the elementalistic viewpoint, as did the other Greeks, including the philosophers and scientists who succeeded Aristotle in time. All were guilty of what is now (following Whitehead) termed the fallacy of *simple location*. In our own language, the idea that all natural objects have intrinsic and changeless 'essences' is described as the fallacy of the absolute individuality of substance, the subject of predication. It is in this sense that traditional thinking was *elementalistic:* both atomism and Aristotelian logic attribute to objects immutable characteristics which fix their positions in nature in such a manner that natural objects do not enter into the functional dynamics of existential situations.

DIAGRAM X

LEVELS OF HUMAN ORIENTATION

PERIOD	CHARACTERISTICS
I. PRE-ARISTOTELIAN OR PRIMITIVE ORIENTATION (Began perhaps 500,000 years ago and terminated with early civilization of 5,000 years ago.)	One-valued semantics. Pre-logical period. Emotional elements predominate. Sub-vocal (gesture) communication. Old brain activity (thalamic). Assumption is: "Everything is everything else." Poor differentiations. "Mystical participation." No "laws of thought;" no categories, such as "space," "time," "matter" and "causality." No fallacy of elementalism. Group consciousness strong — no individualism (or "egoism").
II. ARISTOTELIAN ORIENTATION (This is the semantics of Western European and American culture, about 3,000 years and still used.)	Two-valued semantics. Period of restricted identification. Emphasizes "reason" and excludes "emotion" from science. New-brain activity. Highly verbal and cortical. Abstract symbolism enters. "Law of identity" appears. Scientific categories, such as "space," "time," "matter," "causality" are developed. Fallacy of elementalism appears. Science becomes A-E-N. Axiom is: "This is this, that is that, this is not that." Social individualism (egoism) appears.
III. NON-ARISTOTELIAN ORIENTATION (For a coming, or new civilization — yet to appear.)	Multi-valued semantics. No fallacy of identification. Results in a psycho-logic, a fusion of "reason" and "emotion." Cooperation between cortex and thalamus ("head and heart"). We recover some of primitive man's sense of the "unity of nature." Coordination and synthesis of knowledge. Fallacy of elementalism is overcome. No splitting verbally of things that are not split factually. Space-time universe. Science is A-E-N. Social egoism is subordinated. No racial-religious identifications. A new, Scientific Humanism appears.

Now, however, as we move into the coming level of understanding, we are progressively emancipating ourselves from the ancient and obsolete ways of thinking. To achieve freedom from elementalism we are refashioning our logico-conceptual tools. Given the new, *dimensional theory of thought-systems*, it is possible to set up isomorphisms (homomorphic images) between constructs and existential situations. The emancipation of thought-systems from bondage to traditional forms is still incomplete. Modern science, philosophy, and religion even now are hampered by the hang-over from obsolete conceptual forms reflected in substantialistic modes of reasoning in all areas. The logic of staticism, based on thought-forms of immutable being, cannot provide the conceptual schemes for imaging empirical reality in its hierarchical organizations.

The present powerful drive toward establishing functional interrelations between various dimensions of reality now makes it possible to overcome the profound cleavages and fragmentations in nature, man, and society, which resulted when things were treated as members of classes sharing common 'essences', and variabilities and processal instabilities were considered to be mere 'accidents' or 'deviations.'

It is not enough, however, to substitute the dynamic for the static: we must relativize both the structural and the functional, the material and the energic. This is accomplished by developing a more general conceptual scheme which does not completely repudiate the Aristotelian absolutes, but includes the Aristotelian principles within a wider logic in which the static is made dynamic and the dynamic is such within a relational whole. That is to say, the dynamic in turn is invariant within its own inclusive relational whole, with reciprocal dependencies between the parts and the whole on all levels and between levels in an emerging hierarchy.

As our argument proceeds, we are attempting to show that in spite of the differentiations of structure in existential domains, we discover also that there is between levels of reality a similarity of relation-structure which makes possible transposability of gestalt or wholistic properties. Superposed on various special frames of reference there are general laws which, because of their functional transposability, are invariant whatever the frame of reference. This invariance is extracted from the existential conditions of the situational fields through the formalization of their typical recurrences (to employ Dr. Lins's rephrasing of my argument). The general laws (archetypal invariances) that derive from the recurring patterns presuppose that certain factors remain constant or stable. This stability of factors within a field of relatedness is itself relative to the frame of reference within which we are operating. For example, if for a field (K_1) we require that certain factors (a_1, b_1, c_1 . . .) should remain constant so that we may discover a typical recurrence (R_1), then in another field of a more inclusive organization (K_2) of which the recurrence of (R_1) is a particular case, the more general factors (a_2, b_2, c_2 . . .) must remain constant, if we are to discern a more inclusive typical recurrence (R_2). Thus there are degrees of invariance within our formalizations, depending on whether we are dealing with frames of reference that are more general or less.

If it should happen (as it does in emergence) that there are two situational fields (K_1) and (K_2) which are internally differentiated, each one having a structure of its own with relations exhibiting gestalt patterns dependent upon internal coherence, they may be integrated into another structural field of a higher order of organization (K_3), with its own behavioral unity and transposability, and the higher integration will possess a more general structure within an appropriate frame of reference. But in the forward motion of the evolutionary sequence there is a unidirectionality that is no longer relative, — and this is a point that has been overlooked by many students. In this new way of thinking *the static is made dynamic and the dynamic is made static*, but each is what it is within a level of relatedness. It only needs to be remembered that the static or the dynamic is observed to be such on an n-level of organization, while the other is on an $n + 1$ or $n - 1$ level, depending on whether, e.g., one is considering an atom as a constituent of a molecule or as a synthesis of electrons and nucleons.

The same principle holds with respect to social integrations. The relativist denies the possibility of super-individual standards. For him social norms ('values') are functions of perspectives or frames of reference, and he fails to see the transposable relational similarities (functional invariances) that transcend the special frames of reference. Thus the transposable values of a given social order are like *polarity*, *dominance-subordination*, *entropy-information*, and other gestalt patterns. The relativity of frames of reference does not exclude the possibility of higher and more inclusive organizations, provided nature succeeds in creating them. If man can fabricate the simplicity of a world society with its higher transposable properties, he will escape the relativism of the merely perspectivist approach. This is certainly one of the more fruitful insights of a scientific humanism. But strange to say, few students have recognized the value of this viewpoint. Among those who have commented favorably on this approach is Dr. Albert Einstein.

This sociology of knowledge has implications for epistemology, as we have noted; but it also has consequences in terms of a cosmological model, — a theory of reality, — still to be established. As we shall see in the following chapters, we live in a multi-dimensional universe which has its being within a Cosmic Field that exercises an overlordship through guiding influences. This is a universe that is alive, throbbing, growing in the manifest features, permeated by imagination as a morphogenetic force that guides the evolving structures of the visible world. Such is the model of reality that emerges, — a model that is built upon what is termed the dimensional nature of thought-systems.

FOOTNOTES CHAPTER III

[1]See the volume, *Psychology and Alchemy,* by C. G. Jung, *Collected Works,* Vol. 12, Bollingen Series, 1953.

[2]Cf. "Heredity as Communication," by E. Taschdjian, *Scientia,* Febuary, 1955 (Vol. 112).

[3]Cf. "Information Transfer in the Living Cell," by George Gamow, *Scientific American,* Vol. 193, 1955 (October).

[4]Cf. "Toward Valid Integrative Concepts," *Main Currents in Modern Thought,* Spring, 1949, 7-11.

[5]Cf. *Proceedings, American Academy of Arts and Sciences,* Boston 1868, Vol. III, p. 295.

[6]See Tarski's article, "The Semantic Conception of Truth," in *Readings in Philosophical Analysis,* edited by Herbert Feigl and Wilfred Sellars, 1949, p. 56.

[7]See my address, "Historical-Cultural Significance of the Non-Aristotelian Movement," published in the *Papers* of the Congress, 1943.

[8]Quoted from "Esthetics and the Theory of Signs," by Charles W. Morris, *Journal of Unified Science* (Erkenntniss), The Hague, 1939, Vol. VIII, pp. 131-150.

[9]For a survey of the historical background of Positivism see *Modern Science and Its Philosophy,* by Philipp Frank (1949), Introduction; see also A. J. Ayer's article in *The Revolution in Philosophy,* London, 1956 (Introduction by Gilbert Ryle).

[10]Cf. *Psyche* (London), Vol. XIV, 1934, p. 102.

[11]We have here employed the language of Hans Reichenbach as set forth in his *Elements of Symbolic Logic,* 1947, p. 166.

[12]See the discussion on this point in Alonzo Church's volume, *Mathematical Logic,* p. 111.

[13]Cf. *A Philosophy of Mathematics,* p. 198.

[14]The need for such a "theory of coherence" is pointed out in my review of Dr. Anatol Rapoport's fascinating volume, *Operational Philosophy: Integrating Knowledge and Action,* in the *General Semantics Bulletin,* Winter-Spring, 1954, pp. 88 ff.

[15]These ideas have been developed and expounded by Dr. Mario Lins in a series of articles. "The Social Frames of Reference," presented at the International Institute of Sociology, meeting in France, September, 1954, and "Perspectives for the Logico-Conceptual Integration of Science," given at the International Congress for the Philosophy of Science meeting in Switzerland, August, 1954, are both valuable.

4

THE EPISTEMOLOGICAL FOUNDATIONS OF SCIENCE

"You may not divide the seamless coat of learning."
— Alfred North Whitehead

"When the law of humanity is completed, it is the law of the universe."
— Zen Buddhism

I. How Knowledge Grows

In the preceding chapter we began our study of the foundations of knowledge by considering the rôle of language in human culture. Before the turn of the century that would not have appeared to constitute a proper way to make a beginning. Now we have a different view; we know better. Only after we have discovered the sources of our language-logic preconceptions and have achieved a measure of freedom from provincialisms can we hope to attain an equal measure of objectivity in our views.

Knowledge is a social product, the result of interpersonal communications based on the use of common representations of facts. While symbolism serves as the vehicle for transmitting cultural achievements it exerts a formative influence in molding the thought-patterns of new generations. Precisely because symbolism expresses a philosophy and thus helps to fashion thought, its rôle needs conscious recognition: we are free only in so far as we know what mechanisms are operative on our thought processes.

To be sure, there is a limit to the value of the study of language for purposes of epistemology. Perhaps a law of diminishing returns is followed. Somewhere in the scrutiny of the rôle of language we must call a halt. Any sort of enterprise involving the use of tools presupposes some confidence in the tools we already possess. The situation here is circular: we improve our tools as we use them, discover their limitations, and invent better instruments. In such a situation we cannot suppose that at any given time we have attained perfection. We do the best we can in formulating a theory of knowledge, gradually improving our knowledge of the knowledge process.

II. What Is Given in Experience?

The problem of knowledge is extraordinarily difficult. Everyone seems to agree that we must begin the search for knowledge with what is given, where 'given' is what is present to the knower with a minimum of interpretation added. Quite probably there is no such thing as a 'presuppositionless' philosophy. One must begin with what comes as close as possible to a primitive datum. But what is it that we can use as the initially given? The sense-data empiricists, the adherents of Husserl's phenomenology, the idealists, those who believe in 'essences,' and others, have different starting points. Little wonder that the problem of knowledge bristles with difficulties.

In my own approach to the problems of knowledge, I follow the path of gestalt theory. This was first outlined in an American journal three decades ago , where von Ehrenfels' classical criteria for *gestaltsqualitäten* were discussed and illustrated. More recently a definition of 'emergent wholistic properties' was presented by C. Hempel and P. Oppenheim.[1] This definition, stated in terms of the non-deducibility of the properties of the whole from the properties of the parts, recognizes the nature of emergent gestalt properties, though it adds little to our understanding of the existential nature of the phenomenon.

From the phenomenological point of view immediate experience is characterized by the perception of organized wholes or gestalten — e.g., a *figure* on a *ground*. Even for the child, experience does not start with a "booming, buzzing, confusion," as William James puts it, but with the perception of meaningful patterns, such as a 'friendly' face. Aside from external stimuli, there are also inner organic sensations, which come by way of proprioceptors. As the human organism matures, these stimuli which originate outside and inside the organism are progressively differentiated and integrated into more articulate patterns, and enriched with attached meanings that are related to the individual's experiences (ontogeny). Perhaps behind all experience on the human level there is also a racial memory (phylogeny), as Carl Jung's theory of the 'collective unconscious' supposes. This, of course, is a moot point. [2] But it is not controversial that the cultural milieu has an influence on our perceptions,— the results of the 'Transactional Psychology' of Hadley Cantril and his coworkers at Princeton University definitely confirm the importance of cultural background in perceptual experience.

But it would be a mistake to describe man's primordial experiences in terms peculiar to any given culture, even when such experiences are colored by cultural residues. It is doubtful whether there is anything like a uniquely 'religious' or 'mystical' experience, just as it is doubtful whether we should categorize an experience as 'poetic,' or 'scientific,' or 'philosophical.' The deeply moving experiences of 'poets,' 'saints,' and 'ethical geniuses,' are no more 'religious' than 'philosophical,'— except that in one case the emotional components may predominate over the cognitive elements, and so on. We fit our experiences into categories according to the social structure of a culture, and this has much to do with the degree of specialization in any given civilization. This conclusion has some bearing on the so-called conflicts between art, science, and religion. These are partly class conflicts.

III. The Problems of Perception

"Out of the imperfections of his senses man has built himself a raft of thought to venture into the seas of the unknown,"— thus did one scientist summarize the basis of human knowledge. But the senses are notoriously unreliable, — how then is knowledge possible? In order to appreciate the difficulties of the problems of sensory experience, let us consider the matter.

All perceptual patterns are complexes of sensory qualities arranged according to the forms of space and time. So far as the external physical manifold is concerned, which supposedly is the source or the 'cause' of our perceptions, we may begin with what A. N. Whitehead termed the "ether of events," conceived as a four-dimensional volume from which 'space' and 'time' are obtained by a process of abstraction.

When sensory qualities are organized according to the forms of perceptual experience, the mode of organization involves a space-pattern and a time-parameter. From this point the higher mental processes of conception may take over; for example, symbolic processes, which involve higher levels of abstraction, can then transpose the spatial characteristics of the objects of perception into temporal syntheses having only conceptual existence. The transposability of patterns having temporal organizations into spatial patterns has its cause in gestalt perception, and this provides a basis for what is termed the 'intuitive' aspects of experience.[3] The physiological basis for this will be worked out in terms of cybernetics theory.

With these general considerations in mind, let us turn to a specific form of perception, — that of visual experience. Here we face all the problems of knowledge on the perceptual level.

The usual diagram employed to represent the facts of visual perception is given in Diagram XI (p. 127.) If we generalize the principles involved, we arrive at the figure given in Diagram XII To many theorists this looks like good 'psychology' and 'information theory.' But what is left out in the schematisms is what the older investigators termed the influence of 'mental set' or 'apperceptive synthesis', — which predetermines what it is that we shall be interested in and respond to. Not only does the psychological interest control what one selects, but, — as noted above, — even the cultural environment has an important influence on what one sees and how he sees it. The case of vision is peculiarly significant, since man's explanatory concepts, his very thinking processes, are closely integrated with his visual experience. It will therefore repay us to gather together and study the relevant facts and reflect upon the meaning of vision for scientific synthesis.

IV. Vision and Reality

Light brings us news of the universe, as Sir William Bragg once put it. But man is not merely the passive recipient of 'news', — he goes in search of it. In getting the news, vision is man's main avenue of approach. As the principal organ of distance reception, sight is a kind of anticipative touch whereby we find our way around. Students of evolution are well aware of the manner in which the development of vision has kept pace with the progressive elaborations of man's higher psychic functions.

The eye sees by responding to visible radiation, — or the light reflected by illuminated bodies. The universe of radiation is rich in frequencies. Out of a total of over sixty octaves of vibration frequencies, the eye responds to but one octave, that lying between

DIAGRAM XI

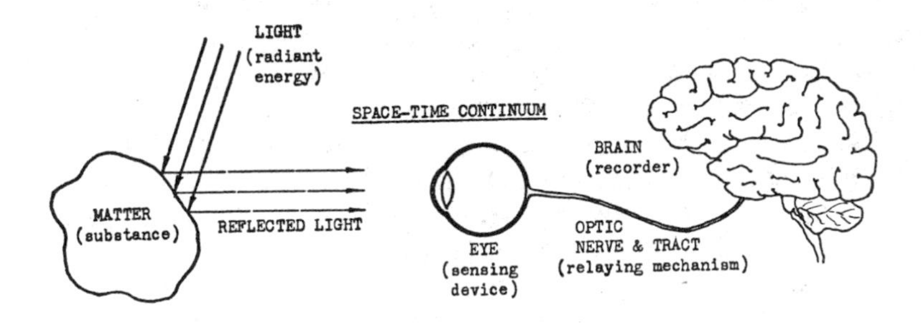

THE EYE-BRAIN APPARATUS

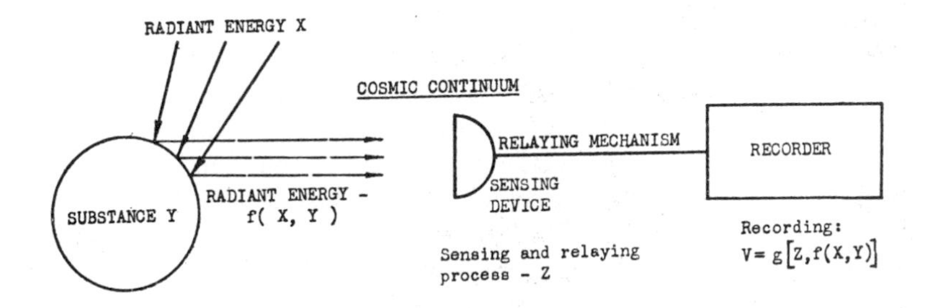

DIAGRAM XII

400 and 800 millionths of a millimeter in wave length. Why this narrow span of vision? It is a curious fact that ultraviolet rays, which are physiologically most active, are invisible to the human eye,

though some animals appear to respond in this region of the spectrum. Likewise, at the opposite end of the visible spectrum, the infra-red or heat rays are invisible to the human eye.

When we consider that the electromagnetic spectrum extends from the long radio waves with wave lengths of hundreds of meters to the very short gamma rays produced by radioactive materials, we note that the human eye responds to but a small portion of the total spectrum. This, no doubt, is the result of an evolutionary adaptation of man's sensory equipment to the environment, for the one octave of visibility coincides with the 'optical window' in the earth's atmosphere which allows this radiation to reach the earth's surface. Fortunately, the transparency of the earth's atmosphere is such that there is another 'window,' the radio window, considerably wider than the optical window, which permits a range of radio waves to come into and to leave the earth's surface, — a fact most important for the purposes of astronomy in gaining knowledge of the wider universe of stars, planets, nebulae, and beyond.

If, now, one compares the spectrum of radiation which reaches the earth from outer space with the visibility curve of the light-adapted eye, — as given, for example, in my book, *Philosophy and the Concepts of Modern Science,* — one cannot but observe the coincidence of the two curves. Is this coincidence fortuitous? One expert on vision, Sir J. H. Parsons,[4] has put forth the idea that the human eye has evolved so that it can make the best use of the energy of sunlight. This, he argued, was evidenced by the fact that the brightest part of the visible spectrum coincides with the curve of radiant energy. But in opposition to this suggestion, other investigators have pointed out that if another variable (frequency) is substituted for wave-length, the brightest part of the spectrum is changed so that the highest peak of the new curve lies outside the limits of the visible spectrum. These students have concluded that the coincidence of the two curves, the curve of the sun's radiation and the visibility curve of the human eye, is fortuitous, i.e., a result of the method of plotting variables in relation to each other. In attempting to arrive at a synthesis of these seemingly opposing views, I then pointed out[5] that on either alternative we can still agree that *vision is now so constituted as to bring out as clearly as possible the outlines of bodies.* This means that the extension of visionin to the shorter (ultraviolet) or longer wave-lengths (infra-red) would be attended by a loss of sharpness of visual images.

It is for this reason that my note to *Nature* asserted the thesis that *the evolution of vision has proceeded in such a direction as to sharpen the meniscus between matter and the field.* This is the evolutionary background for the dichotomy of matter ('particles') and 'empty space.' In this sense vision 'falsifies' physical reality. In order to solve the wave-particle, or field-matter, dualism, we shall have to undo the course of evolution, i.e., counteract the intellectual consequences of visual experience and restore to nature the unity which vision and intellection have bifurcated. Thus, we recover the invisible world of field forces as the complementary component of the manifest world of particles.

When we recall that embryologically the eye is a direct outgrowth of the brain, we begin to realize that Bergson is correct when he suggests that the geometrizing intellect atomizes bodies for purposes of action upon the physical world of matter. But where Bergson goes astray is in his conclusion that the intellect is an unreliable tool in philosophy and must be replaced by intuition, if metaphysics is to grasp the true nature of time and life. For us, the synthetic aspect of experience will be taken care of by *insights*, intellectual syntheses, which are a part of the total process of comprehension. Here Bergson might have learned from gestalt theory.

Given a perception of an external object or event, the task of the scientist is to investigate the physiological basis of the ensuing conscious state. In our own approach to this problem we follow the principles of isomorphism, to be explained at later points. Pursuing further the chain of causal connections, the scientist will also infer the structure of events in the physical world which presumably was responsible for the perception. On the basis of a realistic philosophy, science postulates the existence of an external world independent of the percipient, even though one can not point to anything which *is* independent of the knower. Scientists never interpret the 'egocentric predicament' as a justification for solipsism, the idea that I alone exist.

V. Empirical and Theoretical Components

Every scientist agrees that in the enterprise of science two sorts of entities are called for: (a) perceptual or observational data, and (b) theoretical principles or constructs. One problem is how these two components are related, and what the proper balance is. The movement toward empiricism is strong in the philosophy of science, and such statements as the following are generally accepted:

(1) "No problem is genuine unless the statement of it contains data by the scrutiny and interpretation of which a solution to the problem can be obtained."[6]

(2) "No question of law can be said to have meaning unless it forms part of an image of nature which can be used as a criterion for the adequacy of a set of observations."[7]

These two quotations recognize that natural science data (unlike the purely formal sciences such as logic) must be verifiable by appeal to a series of observations of facts.

The main trouble, — or a considerable part of it, — comes from the fact that it is difficult to formulate an absolute distinction between the empirical statements of science and the theoretical constructs which are not directly connected with perception. For as Henri Poincaré noted in his volume, *Science and Hypothesis*, we can transform some of the theoretical components into empirical statements and some of the empirical content into theoretical constructs. As an illustration of this process of transforming discoveries into definitions, Poincaré cites the case of the principle of the 'conservation of energy.' This empirical law is really a definition in disguise, he tells us, for 'energy' is defined as that which is conserved. Unfortunately, the viewpoint of *conventionalism*, as it is termed, does not explain *why anything is conserved*, nor does the 'law' have any sort of content.

In this matter one might distinguish three possible points of view: (1) pure rationalism of the sort that Plato, Descartes, and Eddington might adopt; (2) pure empiricism such as the phenomenalism of Karl Pearson and the physicalism that the Logical Positivists approximate; and, (3) a dialectical viewpoint which is a compromise of (1) and (2), containing elements of both. The weakness of pure rationalism is illustrated by Eddington's statement in his book, *Relativity Theory of Protons and Electrons* (1936, p. 327) that, "Unless the structure of the nucleus has a surprise in store for us [it did!] . . . there is nothing in the whole system of laws of physics that cannot be deduced unambiguously from epistemological considerations." The weakness of the superb theoretical structure that Eddington managed to create, — reminiscent of the *Summa Theologica* of Thomas Aquinas, — is that the universe contained 'surprises' which Eddington did not anticipate.

The only way to avoid the mistakes of an exclusively Aristotelian deductive science (thinking here of the opponents of Galileo) is to refer to facts, as the starting point in an investigation and as 'markers' in the forward progress toward the construction of a coherent *doctrinal system,* — a body of propositions which organizes the widest range of facts in terms of a minimum set of principles. The dialectical approach holds that we can move toward the construction of such a system through the back and forth interplay between facts and theories and from theories to new facts and laws. This is a kind of circular reaction-arc relation, but whether this will turn out to be a positive or negative feed-back circuit is too early in the game to state. But for all his empiricism, the scientist is always forced to invent 'mental models' of the external realities, which 'constructs' purport to explain *why* we have such and such percepts of the outer world.

VI. Explanation and Mental Models

In his book, *A Short History of Science and Scientific Thought,* Professor F. Sherwood Taylor presents two schemes for the pattern of scientific inquiry, the first scheme being as follows:

Observation → Laws → Mental Model → Mathematical Theory Prediction of New Knowledge

This pattern is described as the 'older series.' The new sequence is then outlined as follows:

Observation → Laws → Mathematical Theory → Prediction of New Knowledge

Comparison of the two sequences reveals that 'mental models' are omitted in the second pattern, the reason given being that since we can no longer visualize the mechanisms, especially in atomic processes, there is no point in trying to set up such models.

It seems to me that the 'old' scheme has merit. The difficulty with 'mental models' which employ visual imagery results from the fact that we have not enlarged our notion of an 'image.' If we expand our repertoire of conceptual models and make use of the new mathematical operations of topology and isomorphism, it is possible to salvage the device of mental models. Visual representations of *complex number* quaternions as instances of topology, and of geometrical isomorphisms, are given in Figures *A* and *B*, respectively, of Diagram XIII (page 133). *Quaternions*, for example, as *rotations* (*tensors*) in the domain of complex numbers, have their analogues in lower level *vectors*. That is, a tensor is a vector that has been operated on in such a manner that both its direction and magnitude have been changed; as one might say, a tensor is a second degree operator, — an operator on an operator. In the theory of quaternions we deal with operators on a higher level where the products do not commute, that is, multiplying p and q is not equivalent to multiplying q and p. Much of this development was inspired by the pioneering work of Sir William R. Hamilton, whose contributions will be utilized in later chapters.[8]

Hamilton's discoveries were astonishingly fruitful. In the first place, we have here the beginnings of non-commutative algebras, the most recent of which is the non-commutative algebra of the theory of *matrices*, as employed, for example, in quantum mechanics where the 'spin matrices' of Pauli and Dirac represent rotations or angular momenta; and secondly, the conception of *action* is perfected so that in relativity theory it can be assimilated to quaternions to represent rotations in a four-dimensional space. Thus, much of modern physical theory is made possible by Hamiltonian dynamics.

Since the time of Immanuel Kant it has generally been supposed that progress in science is commensurate with the ability to translate the data of science into mathematical form. This, at any rate, was the view until recent times. But with the development of topology as a qualitative geometry of spatial relations quite free of quantification, new types of mathematical 'models' have become possible. For example, Kurt Lewin's topological psychology, with its concept of 'life space' functioning as a part of the *field-theory* approach, is indicative of novel possibilities. In my own scheme, I shall combine *quaternions* (*counterclockwise rotations*, as the dynamic aspect of Figure *A*) and *topology* (the static aspect of Figure *B*) to give us a 'mental model' of the isomorphic relation between three-dimensional brain events and the higher-dimensional projective geometry of consciousness. Here the isomorphism appears as the one-to-one correspondence between the emergent or $n + 1$ dimension of experience and the shadowgraph performance studied, for example, by the electroencephalograms that record the brain waves.

As indicated, the subjects of topology and isomorphism will come up repeatedly. But at this point it is sufficient to note that the entire

DIAGRAM XIII

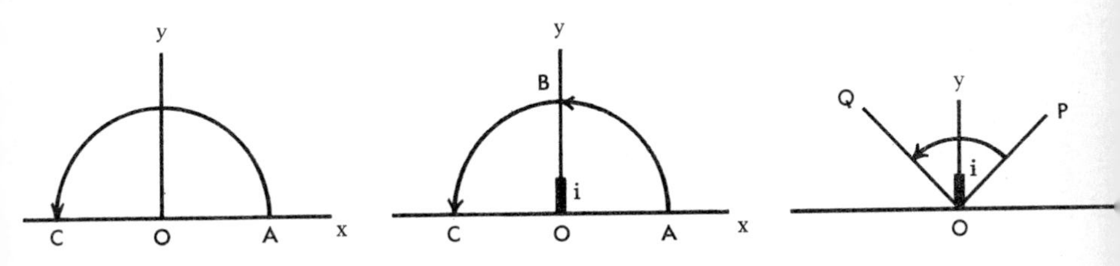

COMPLEX NUMBER, made up of a real number and an imaginary one, the square root of —1, is used to describe the length and direction of a line segment. When complex numbers are added, subtracted or multiplied, the process is equivalent to a geometrical operation, *e.g.*, rotation. In the diagram to the left the line segment OA, representing the number +4, is multiplied by —1, which changes it to the line segment OC, or —4. Thus multiplication by —1 is equivalent to rotation through 180 degrees. In the middle diagram multiplication by—1 is done in two steps, i.e., multiplication by $\sqrt{-1}$ and by $\sqrt{-1}$ again. (The square root of —1 is usually written *i*.) Consequently multiplication by *i* can be considered rotation through 90 degrees. This leads to the idea of measuring imaginary distances on the y axis, as is indicated by making *i* the "unit vector" on that axis. The diagram at the right demonstrates that multiplication by *i* has the effect of a 90-degree rotation even if the starting point is not the x axis. The line segment from point O $(x = 0,\ y = 0)$ to point P $(x = 4,\ y = 3)$ is represented in complex-number notation as $4 + 3i$. Multiplying this number by i gives $4i + 3i^2$, or $3 - 4i$. The latter number represents the line segment OQ $(x = -3,\ y = 4)$, or a 90-degree rotation of the line OP.

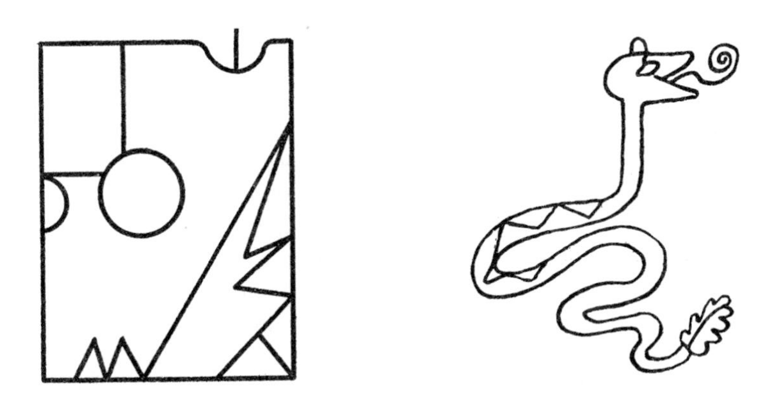

IDENTICAL FORMS in the topological sense have a quite different appearance. Both design and drawing have 11 polygons, 33 edges and 25 corners.

subject of mathematical models is becoming crucial for science.[9] However, the statement that modern science has no need for 'mental models' is correct only if one employs a very narrow notion of a 'model.' It is true, of course, that we still need to show how the theory of quaternions (as dealing with four-dimensional rotations) can be treated as an example of 'isomorphism.' Perhaps the term 'homomorphism' is better suited to the analogies we have in mind. But before turning to such recondite matters, we need to come to terms with the givenness of immediate experience, which is what all philosophy must start with.

VII. Intuitionism and Experience

What we start with as 'given' are spatial and temporal patterns with qualitative attributes. For example, the pattern could be a visual perception of a flat or two-dimensional surface (since the perception of *depth* or a third dimension is an acquired or learned response), or/and a temporal pattern, or at least an experience of time-passage. In this sense, we subscribe to a form of 'intuitionism,' — but it is not the doctrine of 'innate ideas' that John Locke was concerned to refute. Our intuitionism is comparable to that of the Dutch mathematician, L. E. J. Brouwer, to be dealt with at more length in later chapters. Because of the dangers of possible misinterpretation, I shall use the term *insight* rather than the multi-connotational word *intuition* as a name for this primordial element in experience.

In Brouwer's intuitionism what is given is the experience of time, and this (for him) seems not to involve any spatial attribute. It seems desirable to correct this by adding that (for us) the manifold of psychical experience is a space-time unity, no less so than in the case of the physical continuum. In this respect, my own view comes close to that of Dr. S. Alexander. A prevailing theory of time is that it is a one-dimensional order of change, i.e., the 'time-line' is an irreversible continuum embodying the traits of *succession* and *unidirectionality*, — the *transitivity* of *before* and *after*. Moreover, in this (prevailing) view, the three dimensions of space are held to be independent. But in Alexander's view, as set forth in his work, *Space, Time and Deity*, the three features of time and the three dimensions of space are not unrelated. According to this view, space without time could not have even one dimension, not to mention the other two.

In the development of his view, Alexander rather convincingly shows that if succession in time is to be irreversible, we need more than one dimension of space; on the other hand, points in space are ordered in virtue of their time-character. In brief, the reason space has three dimensions is that time is successive, irreversible, and uniform in direction; while spatial order arises out of the temporal nature of positions in space. Space to be space, must be temporal. I do not see that this contradicts Brouwer's notion of the primacy of time in living experience and subsequent thought-systems. Whether the space-time continuum can have no more than four coördinates (dimensions) remains to be determined, but I do not see how or why my theory of 'emergent dimensionality' is invalidated by the foregoing decision.

As far as I am aware, no one has attempted to interpret Brouwer's intuitionism in terms of a dialectic. This is one of the goals of the present undertaking. As part of our analysis of the experience of time-flow, we find a dualism of the *here* and the *not-here*, the *now* and the *not-now*, with a power of rising above the antithesis in a higher moment of becoming. This is the basic prototype for the power of the mathematical continuum and the nisus of emergent evolution. Thus, 'physical reality,' like the mind which is its organismic core, has the potentiality of transcending the 'thesis' and the 'antithesis' in a higher unity.

On the level of logic an exemplification of this dialectic was provided by George Boole in his formula for resolving conflict-patterns by rising above the opposition to a higher viewpoint. The formula, $x + (non\text{-}x) = 1$, means that a problem-situation, representing an antithesis between two apparently exclusive viewpoints, can be transcended by enlarging one's vision so as to include the seemingly incompatible elements, x and *non-x*, in 1 or *unity*. This is acccomplished by stepping up to the next higher level from which the antithetical elements, a *class* and its *complement*, can be viewed as a whole. In this manner, for example, it appears that the oppositions of the *here* and the *not-here*, the *now* and the *not-now*, are unified in a wholeness which is a time-spanning synthesis. The therapeutic value of this approach to human problems is that from the higher vantage-point the conflict loses its features of an irreconcilable opposition and some of the rivalry-tension is resolved because one sees the relativity of the theses in the light of their inclusion within a wholistic synthesis.

VIII. Fundamental Concepts of Epistemology

Given the phenomena of human experience, the perceptual data of science, these must be interpreted, — fitted into a system within which orderly relations obtain. Thus, as a body of laws and theories, science is a product of conceptual abstraction. Psychologically a concept is a unified group of percepts which isolates the invariant properties of the individuals composing the class, individuals that belong together because of the possession of significant common properties. Logically the definitions of the terms we use to denote the individuals referred to give the *intension* of the concepts; while the entities thus designated constitute the *extension* of the term (or its antecedent concept). This much we noted in the previous chapter.

But, one may ask, what is the utility of concepts for the enterprise of science? In our own monism of action the concept of anything is the law of its behavior, and such concepts, properly integrated into a system (*Doctrinal Function*) are necessary if we are to 'understand' the world in which we live. Concepts tell us how things will invariably behave under specified conditions; they enable us to predict what will happen. We will see later that there are difficult problems that arise in connection with the uses of *classes* of entities. These have to do with what are called the 'paradoxes' of the theory of aggregates, i.e., collections of entities. The theory of 'collections,' first formulated by George Cantor, was taken over by Bertrand Russell and generalized so that, as indicated previously, there could be classes of individuals, classes of classes of individuals, classes of classes of classes, and so on. This then led to the paradoxes of the theory of aggregates. For example, the concept of 'man' is not a man, yet the concept of concept is a concept. But is the concept of the concept which does not include itself (i.e., a collection of the collections which does not include itself) a concept which includes itself? The solution of this abstruse problem (for Russell) was found through the development of the *theory of types*, which stipulates that the elements of a class must always be assigned to their own level of denotation. The discussion of this matter will be postponed until the next chapter. Suffice it to say here that there is no need for a logical nihilism: there are no insoluble paradoxes of logic, and any confusion created by thinking can be resolved by further thinking. Having stated this belief, as an article of faith in the philosophy of science, let us return to our more immediate task.

In the present theory of knowledge it is necessary to employ an assortment of concepts, symbolized by appropriate terms, and now it is pertinent to state these concepts and give their definitions. The terms, and their definitions, are as follows:

FACT: anything that exists. To 'exist' means to be in space and time, — to be somewhere-somewhen.

PERCEPT: the recognition by an organism of the existence of a fact. There are two kinds of perception: the recognition of the existence of objective facts and subjective facts, that is, facts referred to the world outside the skin and inside the organism.

IDEA (CONCEPT): an idea is an intellectual image or representation expressing the invariant elements of an object (or class of objects) obtained through the unification of a group of percepts. The percepts may be of outer entities or facts (tables, horses, etc.) or of inner objects (tooth aches, purposes, images, etc.). Accordingly, we can frame concepts of external things or of subjective entities, like *id*, *ego*, etc.

PROPOSITION: an expressed judgment; a statement about a percept or idea. Propositions may refer to subjective facts or to objective facts.

BELIEF: the acceptance of a judgment (or proposition) as true; the attitude of assent toward some judgment about a fact, or supposed fact, whether subjective or objective. Of course, subjective facts are pretty much what they are experienced to be, though here, too, one's interpretation may be wrong, — as in the interpretation of one's motives for conduct.

TRUTH: the correspondence of beliefs (accepted propositions) with facts. One may have true beliefs about objective facts or subjective facts. Truth is a property of propositions. The facts are neither true nor false, — they just are.

FALSITY: the non-correspondence of beliefs with facts. As Bertrand Russell says, facts are what make propositions true or false. But I see no reason why we should not utilize a multi-valent logic in situations where 'true' and 'false' are inadequate (this to be discussed later).

KNOWLEDGE: the sum-total of true beliefs (confirmed propositions). It is possible that a person thinks he has knowledge of a subject when in fact he does not. The 'knowledge' of one age may be the 'superstition' of another era.

THINKING: the manipulation of ideas for the purpose of gaining the knowledge necessary to solving human problems.

It will be observed that on this theory we have two worlds: there are the two types of facts, two kinds of observation, and two kinds of knowledge, as follows:

Two Kinds of Facts	1. *Subjective Facts: these exist in the space and time of our inner world.* 2. *Objective Facts: these exist in the space and time of the external or 'physical' world.*
Two Kinds of Observation	1. *Introspection via interoceptors.* 2. *Extrospection via exteroceptors.*
Two Kinds of Knowledge	1. *Self-knowledge: the kind of knowledge introverts possess (e.g., Oriental Mystics).* 2. *Knowledge of external World: extroverts and western objective science.*

Before we are through, it will appear that the above dualisms do not create a rift in nature, — the dualism is a relative one, analogous to the 'dualism' in physics of matter and energy, and is resolved in a 'monism of action.'

For purposes of illustration, let us apply the above definitions to the problem of the status of 'illusions' in our world. Suppose a person who is suffering from hallucinations were to say, "I see pink elephants." Is the proposition true? Does he 'see' them? The answer depends on the interpretation of the statement. If one means (a) that 'there are pink elephants in the external world of objective facts,' then the proposition is false, — no one 'sees' hallucinatory objects in that sense. But if one means (b) that 'there are images of pink elephants in my consciousness' (i.e., in the internal world of subjective facts), then the proposition is true. It is a fact that the victim of the hallucination thinks he sees objectively real pink elephants. But he is wrong in his interpretation, if he supposes that there is an objective reality corresponding to and causing his image in consciousness.

American psychology of recent decades (Behaviorism) is to be criticized for ignoring the rich inner world of consciousness. Logical Positivism also suffers from the same prejudice in favor of 'physicalism' when it disregards subjective experience, introspective methods and data.

Fortunately, psychoanalysis, psychosomatic medicine, and gestalt theory have helped to correct the one-sidedness of the so-called 'objective' approach. Current psychological science now relegates Behaviorism to its proper place, — physiological psychology. The materials for a genuine science of human nature must include contributions from the arts, literature, the humanities, and the like. As we view the situation, the major problems of modern culture are these: (1) How to achieve a balanced personality which unites subjective knowledge and aspirations and knowledge gained from the objective sciences of nature; (2) how to formulate a theory which adequately represents the relations between the space-time manifold of physics and the space-time continuum of mental life; and (3) how to harmonize and integrate the findings of oriental mysticism and the findings of Western objective science and technology. In the present work an attempt is made to come to grips with these issues.

From the discussions in previous chapters, the reader is aware of the fact that in the present enterprise we are not only concerned with discovering how past philosophies have molded present habits of thought through the grammatical and syntactic structures imbedded in traditional systems of symbols: we are also interested in recreating present and future conceptions of the world by a creative semantics, — new media of communication, — helping to proliferate a new planetary civilization. Here the science of cybernetics will prove of utmost service.

IX. Cybernetics and Gestalt Theory

One virtue of the present approach is that it enables us to establish contact with the science of cybernetics, a discipline which, in considerable measure, is a study of isomorphism and gestalt properties.[10] Cybernetics is useful in providing us with the isomorphic bridges which span the chasms separating the various natural sciences (from physics → biology → psychology), thus giving greater universality to basic archetypal forms. Nevertheless, something is still missing in cybernetics. The gestalt theory of form visualization as cybernetics interprets it, — that is, as *scanning via the alpha rhythm of the cortex,* — remains to be completed. There must be some integrative action present which makes possible the perception of wholeness and the recognition of this wholeness in relation to memory processes. For example, a machine possesses 'rote' memory in its magnetic tapes or on the image-face of its cathode-ray tubes, but the machine is unable to step from this type of discrimination to the recognition of meaningfulness, i.e., *it is unable to generalize in cases where an element of induction comes in.*

As part of our general philosophy, it is our thesis that by some process, which is illustrated on a lower level in the compounding of rotations of the microscopic constituents (e.g., atomic polarities) to produce macroscopic or overall rotations (e.g., molecular polarities), nature moves in a helical pattern in time, so that spiral forms get ingrained at many levels (spiral nebulae, periodic table, earth's course as dragged through space by the sun, spiral forms of plants and animals, and so on). Later it will be proposed that this is all a part of a galactic rotation in which a Cosmic Field plays an important part in transmitting spin (angular momentum) to matter.

The significance of this in and for a pantheistic cosmology still remains to be outlined. But given a pantheistic cosmology, one finds this has implications for epistemology. We cannot do everything at once, but it is pertinent to point out that in this pantheism of a Cosmic Guiding Field we are committed to the theory of the internality of relations. This raises some problems as well as solves some problems. Is it true (for example) that in the *Unmanifest Universe* (see Diagram III) time does not count, so that while this universe (like the Absolute of Hegel and Bradley) contains histories, it has no history of its own? This question will be answered subsequently. Meantime, it suffices to note here that the theory of the internality of relations, — that all relations modify their relata, or at least the relata are what they are because of the more inclusive fields of organization in which they exist, — implies the following propositions:

1) No thing in nature, taken in complete isolation, is real.
2) No proposition, taken in complete isolation, is true, — or even meaningful.
3) Since every culture is selective and partial, the whole truth (a complete and final philosophy) can be attained only through a combined synthesis of all phases of knowledge and all aspects of reality.

X. The Dialectical Synthesis in History

The student of the history of thought will recognize the influence of Hegelian ideas in the foregoing propositions. This is a correct diagnosis in the sense that 'archetypal synthesis' requires some sort of dialectical process to overcome the incompleteness of thought and things. In our own mapping of the evolutionary course of the human mind, we, like Hegel and Comte, rely upon a three-level schematism. Our outline of the three levels of mental-social evolution is presented in Diagram X (page 117).

The tremendous undertaking of providing the higher synthesis of Level III, the level of a non-Aristotelian culture, is already upon us. It will require time and much skill to consummate the reforms, and many a lusty battle will be fought before the outcome is known.[11] In the present effort at advancing the program, I am building on the archetypal forms which physics has discovered in, and mathematics lifted from, the structure of reality. This archetypal basis of knowledge is visualized in Diagram XIV (page 142). From the natural base of physical reality we ascend the ladder of emergent evolution, using the isomorphic rungs of reality as they are pyramided in an hierarchy of levels, culminating in the mind of man, — with its capacity for grasping the universal scheme of things, — because our mental operations epitomize the action patterns of that universe. Thus, as will appear in due time, there is a celestial cybernetics as well as a cybernetics of reverberating circuits in the human thinker.

It hardly needs to be pointed out that the introduction of the problems of cosmogony and cosmology, — problems of the origin, evolution, and structure of the universe, — interpose issues that are incredibly difficult, and yet, if our theory of archetypal synthesis has any validity, it must throw some light on these profound mysteries. In any case, they are too fascinating to be ignored, as recent discussions indicate.[12] The following remarks, therefore, merely prepare the way for a fuller discussion of the matter.

XI. Emergent Evolution and the Creation of Matter

There are two principal theories of the origin of the elements scattered in varying degrees of abundance throughout the cosmos. The first theory (a) is connected with the 'explosion' cosmology of Le-

DIAGRAM XIV

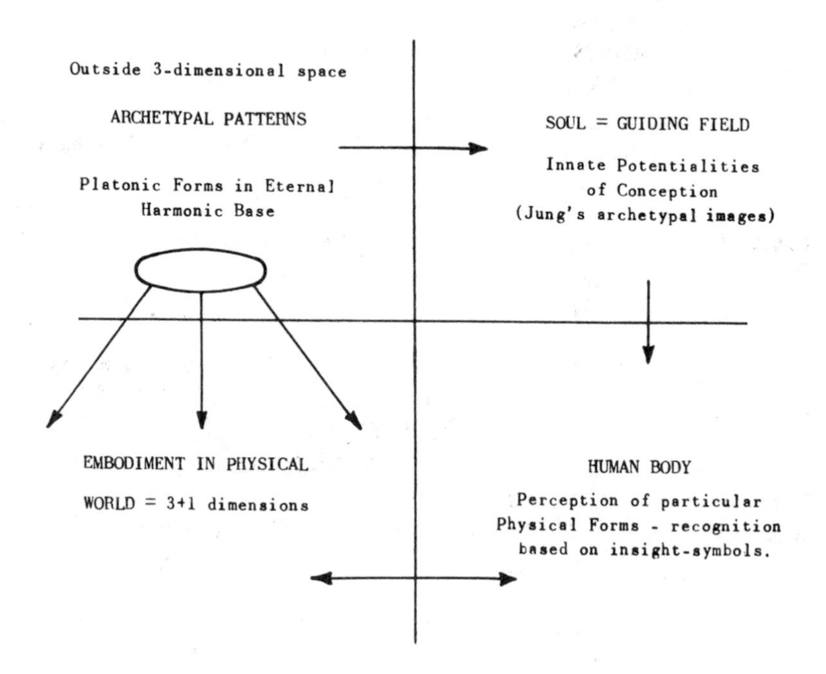

THE ARCHETYPAL BASIS OF KNOWLEDGE

maître and Gamow, and the second theory (b) is a part of the steady-state universe of Fred Hoyle. Each of these is associated with its own theory of the evolution of the universe.

The first theory (a) assumes that the universe began as a single primordial hyper-nucleus (the *sun-atom* of Lemaître and the *ylem*-pulp of Gamow) which subsequently exploded into space. The neutron density (in Gamow's version of creation) is asserted to be high enough for successive neutron captures by protons to create the nuclear species in their present abundance and distribution. The second theory (b) has several forms, the best known being that of Fred Hoyle. This theory postulates the continuous creation of matter (hydrogen atoms) at a rate sufficient to replenish the matter which, once created, rushes off into the infinite depths of space to disappear over the horizon of visibility. If, in the steady-state or equilibrium theory, matter is continually being created, there must be a mechanism for building up the heavy elements. According to Hoyle, this is provided by the supernova explosions which scatter the heavy elements into space, after they have been created from hydrogen by great increase in density and rapid collapse of the star.

The present *cyclic-creative* cosmology is a form of the steady-state universe. But it does not necessarily assume that exceedingly high temperatures are required for the creation of matter, as Lemaître and Gamow assume for all elements and as Hoyle assumes for the heavy elements. Very high energies (billions of electron volts) concentrated in very small areas *are* required. But is temperature the only source of such energy? Isn't there any other way to get particles into existence? Is it possible that the problem of the creation of matter is artificial, arising from the fact that the amount of energy that is *equivalent* to matter is very large, as illustrated by the fact that when you 'destroy' matter (in an atomic bomb, for example) you get such terrific energy displays?

This 'equivalence' is a ratio or proportion. But if we remember that the Cosmic Field (or sub-ether) has an infinite energy potential, it appears easy for the 'Cosmic Imagination' to make matter. Perhaps all the Cosmic Lens needs to do is twist a wave into a circle or a filament into a knot.

The problem here is not merely physical, but logical, — or both, — since what is involved is a solution of the wave-particle dualism. In my own cosmology the use of a non-Aristotelian logic is introduced as a means of solving this dilemma. This means of escape has also appealed to several other theorists.[13] In the classical two-valued logic the statement that light is both corpuscular and undulatory involves a contradiction, for the two classes of behavior denoted by 'particles' and 'waves' are mutually exclusive. The difficulties involved in the attempt to combine the two sets of phenomena in the compound entity 'wavicle' (Eddington's term) can be avoided if we substitute a weaker logic which forbids the reasoning that leads to the contradiction. Then the wave- and particle-descriptions have the logical value of 'possible,' and both may be applied to the same subject in a non-contradictory way.

In my own solution, I do not reject the foregoing approach. But it seems to me that if the metalogician is to be helpful to the physicist, a more general philosophy of physics must be integrated into the logical analysis. In my handling of the problem an effort is made to formulate a theory of how discrete particles emerge from the energy continuum or Cosmic Field. This, it seems to me, calls for a conception such as that proposed by Sir J. J. Thomson, or the alternate form developed by Louis de Broglie. In the 'weakened' logic, particles and waves are on an equal footing and neither has any logical priority over the other. But in the present conception the particles emerge from the field, and this concretization is an example of the emergent dimension orthogonal to the antecedent ground conditions.

Without going into details at this point (since it will be discussed later), we may indicate that, on our view, the ocean of electrical energy (Cosmic Field) is focalized by the Cosmic Lens and the 'form waves' thus individuated constitute the Platonic archetypes of physical realities as they emerge in the manifest world. Thus hydrogen atoms, the 'mother stuff of galaxies,' are created, — not *ex nihilo*, however, but out of the field-plenum, subsequently to evolve into the heavier elements of the universe.

In order to solve the problem of the persistence of elementary particles in time it is necessary to return to some form of the idea of 'constituent waves' of a sub-ether, these waves entering into the composition of 'group waves' in such a fashion that the nodes of overlapping are responsible for the creation of particles. This distinction between 'constituent waves' and 'group waves' will be dealt with later. In the meantime, it is sufficient to note here that, for us, the particles that persist in time are true 'emergents', — unitary modes of behavior of subconstituents ('microrhythms') which are organized into a macroscopic swirl or spiraloid along an orthogonal time-axis. These swirls have the property of spin as a macroscopic effect. As we have already pointed out, this phenomenon of spin is an important component of our theory of nature; but when applied to the course of emergent evolution this spin takes on the aspect of a spiral, the helix which is curved in a higher dimension than two-dimensional rotation or angular motion, thus creating the orthogonal or emergent time-axis of our cosmology.

The great importance of spirals in nature has long been recognized by the naturalist. The following quotation illustrates the ecstasy that suffuses the modern Pythagorean when he surveys the harmonies of nature. As an example of the high enthusiasm which the mathematician may experience as he contemplates the artistic aspects of mathematical forms, and dealing specifically with the equation whose curve represents the logarithmic spiral, Dr. Robert E. Moritz has this to say:

"This equation discloses at a glance the spiral character of the curve; a closer examination reveals all other visual properties: the curve crosses each radius vector at the same angle; its pole is an asymptotic point; the curve no matter how magnified reproduces itself; any radius vector is a mean proportional between any two others making equal angles with it; lengths of arcs of the curve measured from its pole are proportional to the radii drawn from the end points, etc. These properties, however dimly perceived by the eye, endow the curve with pleasurable aspects. But the equation reveals also other properties which the eye not even suspects, such as: its evolute, and its pedal with respect to the pole, and its caustic both of reflection and refraction from the rays emanating from a luminous point at the pole, are all spirals exactly equal to the original spiral. The overwhelming spiritual satisfaction aroused by these visible and invisible properties entitles the logarithmic curve to a place among the most beautiful curves known to art or to science. As to sheer abstract beauty the logarithmic spiral may well be considered to stand unsurpassed among the objects of human imagination."[14]

An illustration from the visual arts (See Frontispiece) will help the reader 'see' the beauty of the logarithmic spiral, concerning which Dr. Moritz rhapsodizes. But where do his remarks leave the philosopher, whose concern is with the more fundamental question of the relation of mathematics to nature? As we proceed, we hope to throw more light on this problem of epistemology.

The unfortunate thing is that while spiral forms do introduce the dynamic into nature (at least where 'growth' is concerned), spatial representations of the time component do not do justice to the experience of duration, as Bergson pointed out. The forward motion of time is irreversible, and in Diagram X this is represented by arrows which symbolize the spiral action of time.

These excursions into the field of cosmology which appear in the are necessary journeys. In a pantheistic scheme the cosmic basis of knowledge is important, as the following observations on information and entropy will help to demonstrate.

XII. Information, Entropy, and Cosmology

In the present volume we are, among other things, dealing with the isomorphism between the physical gestalt and the associated conscious configuration. In the language of semantics, this is the *map-territory* relation. The *territory* is the *prototype*, and the *map* is the *homomorphic image* of its prototype. The physiological image (map) resulting from its external physical prototype (territory) in turn becomes the prototype for the conscious image. This approximate one-to-one functional correspondence is an example of the transmission of information. Now the *entropy* principle as employed in cybernetics tells us that no 'image' can contain as much information as its 'prototype.' But on the conscious level of *meanings*, past experience in the way of interpretation seems to add information and thus transcends the entropy principle.

There is nothing here which violates our thesis that the time-sense, the unidirectionality of experienced time, is related to the irreversibility of the second law of thermodynamics when applied to living organisms.[15] In mechanical systems we deal with behavior that is relatively independent of the previous history of the system. Here there is little memory of the past or anticipation of the future. But in mental life meaning as time-synthesis adds to the information involved in perception. How is this possible? To answer this, it is necessary to say more about *entropy*, especially as it is related to 'information theory.'

Students in the field of information theory and cybernetics are perfecting what may be termed the entropy theory of communication. This synthesis of two supposedly disparate fields constitutes an integration of ideas which rivals Einstein's unified field theory in boldness, and it is not surprising that investigators are pushing these ideas with considerable enthusiasm. Previously entropy has been (and still is) a fundamental concept of thermodynamics, referring to the fact that energy runs 'down hill' or degenerates into heat which radiates off into space and becomes progressively unavailable for useful work. By treating entropy as the 'logarithm of the probability' present work may seem superfluous, but this is not the case. These of a state, Boltzmann was able to show that the increase of entropy is a law of large numbers which expresses, for complex statistical ensembles, the chance of the most probable state being realized.

The next step in this unfolding story came with the suggestion that the second law of thermodynamics is applicable to the processes of communication no less than to observations on the statistical behavior of molecules in a gas. In both cases we are dealing with the probabilities of statistical mechanics. Thus the quantity which in communication engineering is called 'information' has the same form as negative entropy in thermodynamics, — that is, entropy with the algebraic sign reversed, hence the possibility of relating these two fields. The idea is that since entropy is a measure of the disorderly tendency, and since information is a measure of order, we should designate information as the logarithm of the reciprocal of the probability, which is *negentropy*, as L. Brillouin termed it. Here, then, we have another possible example of *isomorphism*, which makes it possible to transpose theorems from the domain of thermodynamics to the field of information theory. As an illustration of this, we have the statement of Dr. Warren McCulloch that, "The second law of thermodynamics, which insures an increase of entropy, means that information can never increase as it passes through a computing machine."

Much of the credit for this synthesis must go to Dr. Norbert Wiener, Claude Shannon, and R. V. Hartley, who applied physical principles to the problems of communication engineering. These fascinating developments acquired a more authentic character when Erwin Schrödinger added his voice to those who were calling attention to the intimate relation between negative entropy and life processes. In his little classic, *What Is Life?*, Schrödinger suggested that "life feeds on negative entropy." This raises philosophical problems of much interest, to which we shall return at a later stage.

In our own scheme the irreversibility of experienced time has long been tied in with the increase of entropy. Also, in this view, the second law of thermodynamics has been interpreted as expressing the fact of interaction between 'particles' on any given level which thereby 'communicate' with each other. This situation, wherein the environment gains energy at the expense of the potential energy stored up in the constituents of each system, involves a transfer of 'information.' This 'signal' transfer becomes 'meaningful' when, on the human level, 'symbols' are employed. Thus we can agree with Warren

McCulloch when he states that sensation is entropic coupling between us and the physical world, and interchange of ideas is entropic coupling among humans. In our approach, however, we give a peculiar interpretation to the concept of 'negentropy.' This designates the anti-chance factor, an accumulation of microscopic spin effects to create a macroscopic rhythm of behavior which is the new level of emergence. Thus communication by the interactions of parts of an emergent whole does not produce 'disorder' in any absolute sense, — it is the tendency to bring about another kind of order, once the new level has been attained. Information transmission on the physical level is indicative of the trend of statistical fluctuations of a local ensemble to produce a more inclusive system with a transposable public time and a macroscopic spread of gestalt or social properties.

The entropy-information isomorphism is of interest to us as students of philosophy because it has two possible fields of application. As we have indicated, in the field of psychology the use of electronic calculators is supposed to illustrate the application of the concepts of thermodynamics. Partly for reasons already given, but more especially because of considerations to be presented in the following chapter, we cannot go all the way with this 'physicalist' interpretation of the thinking process. Machines cannot substitute for this phase of human thinking and choosing because of the creative nature of inductive thinking. This fact is admitted, — begrudgingly, it almost appears, — by some of the cyberneticists. Professor Warren McCulloch,[16] for example, has calculated that it would take as much electric power as could be generated by Niagara Falls to construct a machine with a brain, and all the cataract's water to cool the brain's electronic tubes, — and then the monster would only have as much 'intelligence' as an earthworm!

On the other hand, and more recently, Dr. W. Ross Ashby,[17] an English scientist, claims that it is possible to build a machine more intelligent than its builder, — that if, for example, the physical power of radio waves can be amplified, it is possible to do the same for intellectual power. Since the complex issues of man's human-social problems require for their solution an I. Q. far beyond man's present intellectual powers, and since geniuses like Immanuel Kant and Albert Einstein appear only once in a century, we must resort to 'power amplifiers' for our calculating machines and let them solve our problems. This is indeed a bold claim, the validity of which we shall test in the next chapter. Here we shall see that while electronic calculators are better than humans at deductive logic and formalized mathematics, the computers lack the creative capacities required by the inductive procedures whereby we gain new knowledge. Creativity is the prerogative of the Cosmic Imagination and man, — in so far as man is god-like.

Accordingly, the spirit in the machine, — in man and in the cosmos, — transcends the second law of thermodynamics, even while it uses its unidirectionality as a base upon which are pyramided the levels of emergent evolution which rise in a hierarchy of isomorphic structures. This fact has some bearing on recent developments in inductive logic, and I pause long enough to make a point.

In a stimulating article, Dr. Jerome Rothstein[18] traces the analogies between information and entropy and indicates how measurement can be regarded as a type of observation in which the information represents the statistical expression of the second law of thermodynamics. By replacing 'information' by 'observation,' it is possible to regard 'negentropy' as a theory of observation. From this it is clear that, — given the correctness of this line of thought, — it is only a matter of time before we have electronic computers which will perform inductive inferences for us which will yield the 'laws of nature' that hitherto have been the product of the creative originality of the great geniuses of science. Indeed, efforts are already being made to bring Rudolf Carnap's theory of induction within the scope of the 'thinking machines' of cybernetics.

My own view of this matter, stated above and reiterated later, is that even if Carnap's theory of induction provides an adequate basis for inductive generalizations *on any given level of nature*, it is inadequate as a philosophy of science because it does not recognize the fact of emergent evolution, the transordinal laws whereby nature rises to new levels of behavior. I shall return to this problem in a later chapter.

Having glanced at the psychological applications of the entropy-information synthesis, let us turn for a moment to the wider universe of the cosmologist and study some applications of this synthesis. In a recent article, Dr. Norbert Wiener[19] points out that when information is transmitted from one system to another by light, the employment of light for purposes of communication entails a certain degradation of energy. This means, according to Dr. Wiener, that light loses its ability to convey information about the system which emits it, so that Maxwell's 'sorting demon', — which is hypothetically able to reverse the degradation of energy, — is incapable of reversing the tendency toward entropy increase because the 'demon' eventually runs out of the information necessary to reverse the trend toward disorder. Another implication of this line of thought is that the universe must eventually run down, because perpetual motion is impossible in a universe in which the second law of thermodynamics is operative.

In commenting on Dr. Wiener's reasoning, I pointed out that this conclusion appears to be correct for closed (finite) systems, since, as Wiener notes, light quanta can be received only by apparatus with which they collide, and this interaction affects both the matter collided with and the light itself.[20] The average result, as Wiener notes, is to lower the frequency of light and its ability to carry information. But it must not be forgotten that this tendency toward the degradation of energy has been shown to hold only in closed systems. The extrapolation of the entropy principle to an infinite and eternal cosmos may well be illegitimate. Surely in the boundless space of an infinite universe an overall equilibrium between the Cosmic Field and matter is required, if we are to understand why the universe has not run down long ago to the dead level of heat-death ("wärmetod").

In our cosmology the Cosmic Lens maintains a macroscopic steady-state. In order to do this it must 'know' the conditions prevailing in 'all' local systems. This means that there can be no time-lag in the transmission of information. But the principle of relativity teaches us that there *is* such a time-lag, since effects are delayed relative to their causes by an amount corresponding to the finite velocity of light. In our cosmology we escape this difficulty by pointing out that in the theory of relativity we are dealing with the transmission of causal influences on the level of electromagnetic and gravitational fields, *while for us the medium for the transmission of information about the state of the universe is a super-dispersive field, a sub-ether for wave mechanics, wherein energy can be transmitted at any velocity.* In this 'celestial cybernetics' there is no time-lag, just as there is no overall increase of entropy, and this relates to the cosmic causality which sustains the manifest world.

It is not possible at this point to enunciate all features of this conception. These will appear in due time. But it is obvious that in our cosmology there is something like Maxwell's sorting demon at work: this is the *Cosmic Imagination*, which introduces the anti-chance component in nature. The universe as a whole does not run down because it is supermechanical in the same manner in which imagination makes the human brain supermechanical. The spirit in the machine, — in man and in the cosmos, — transcends the second law of thermodynamics, even while it uses its unidirectionality as a base upon which new levels of emergence can be pyramided. The fact of emergence requires the trans-ordinal laws which designate the transition from level to level. As we shall see later, probability is discontinuous in the saltatory aspects of nature, and that is why entropy is characterized by non-additivity.

XIII. The Temporal and the Eternal in Creativity

In some respects the 'Unmanifest Universe' of archetypal forms resembles the *Sensorium Dei* of Sir Isaac Newton's philosophy of nature. Perhaps there is also a similarity to the *noumenal* world of Immanuel Kant. But most of all, I think, the Cosmic Field is analogous to the *Absolute* of Josiah Royce. Whatever the final judgment about Royce's philosophy may be, one must admire the resolute way in which he attacked the problem of the relation between the temporal and the eternal, the finite and the infinite in time.

For Royce the 'actual infinite' is not an end-term in the ordinal process which generates cardinality, — it is the '*nth*ness' which is the invariant character present in all stages of the process of self-representation. This makes possible Royce's notion of the Absolute as the experiencer of all possible experiences and the fulfiller of all finite ideas and volitions. I would not be willing to transfer all these attributes to the Unmanifest Universe; but I would be willing to build upon the notion of the dynamic infinite as Royce conceived it, i.e., in a manner which resembles Brouwer's infinite as this will be presented in a later chapter. In terms of this approach, it would be possible to say that the Unmanifest Universe ('Absolute'?) is not exhausted by serial enumeration. Paradoxically, as it may seem, the Unmanifest Cosmic Field is aware of its own infinity while yet incarnating through points of entry into the manifest physical world by way of elementary particles, — such as electrons, protons, and other pair-production particles, — which arise everywhere and are present in all finite universes through an unending series of self-representations. Here we get the first glimpse of the inseparable manner in which *zero* and *infinity* are tied together in a mathematical complementarity.

One of the great difficulties confronting the physicist in the development of a field theory of matter is the problem of infinite energies: why do the energy interactions of the physical world come in finite packages, according to quantum relations? Theoretically, the energies which well up in the physical world are infinite; but in actual fact they emerge in finite quanta. The corresponding philosophical problem is this: what is the principle of limitation (or negation) which imposes a restrictive structure upon a realm of infinite potentiality? One might say that *in the beginning was limitation.* This is what gives form to the formless, finite structure to infinite potentiality. For a pantheist, the immanence of the infinite everywhere and all the time is evidence of the omnipresence of a Cosmic Imagination in every created being. It is for this reason that one may affirm that pantheism provides a firm foundation for ethics: the fact of an immanent infinite enables us to say that man (the god-like quality in man) is potentially the whole cosmos. Man is in and of the universe, but he can be out of it too, — as the spectator of all time and all existence, to quote Plato.

XIV. The Postulates of Unified Symbolism

1) The physical world is constituted of two kinds of waves: group or form waves and constituent or guiding waves. The constituent waves are the guiding fields which subsist in a sub-ether, a super-dispersive field-plenum in which the waves may travel with a velocity faster than light. Thus the Cosmic Field is the continuum of the Unmanifest world of potentialities from whose bosom materiality emerges.
2) The form or group waves which arise at nodal points of reinforcement represent the archetypal patterns as they are expressed in the elementary particles of the manifest world.
3) The invisible-unmanifest field and the visible-manifest world of materiality sustain each other through a relation of cosmic complementarity.

4) There is a cyclic conversion of matter into field energy and of field energy into matter transpiring endlessly in time and at appropriate points in space.
5) The function of light is to reveal physical reality. The velocity of light is so adjusted that there will be a veil of separation between the two worlds, the unmanifest and the manifest worlds. Vision has so evolved as to sharpen the meniscus between the two domains of reality.
6) The time-lag in the physical world is a manifestation of the inverse relation between group waves and constituent waves. The product of the two velocities is a constant of nature.
7) This inertia of physical reality represents the resistance to transformation which matter offers to energy. The record of this time-lapse is imbedded in the structure of the logarithmic spirals which preserve the history of creativity in the manifest world.
8) The fact that light represents a mean or proportionality between the manifest and unmanifest worlds is what makes it possible for the eye-brain mechanism of the organism to look out upon the world which the Cosmic Imagination has created.
9) Symbolism on all levels is the evidence of the reality of the Cosmic Imagination. The Supreme Imagination creates the physical world by envisioning it: hydrogen atoms are the thoughts of the Cosmic Imagination. The process by means of which man sees the universe is the reverse of the process whereby the universes are created. The world is created through lenses and is seen through lenses.
10) The Cosmic Imagination knows what is going on everywhere all the time because It makes (creates) these goings on *via* the constituent waves whereby the archetypal forms or images of the sub-ether express themselves in matter.
11) The dualism of consciousness and the electrochemical processes in the nervous system is a special case of the (relative) dualism in physics of fields of energy and matter. Energy fields are the soul of matter.
12) Bergson is correct when he tells us that the eye was evolved to enable the organism to see, and Goethe is correct when he reports in his *Farbenlehre* that the eye was formed in

order that the light from within could meet the light from without.

13) As part of the process of creating matter, the Cosmic Imagination thus makes it possible for the creatures It has created to communicate with each other *via* the finite velocity of light.

14) More effective communication among humans *via* electrical systems will require a planetary semantography, a symbolism with gestalt properties transposable across the social whole.

15) As we shall see later, the doctrine of a panpsychistic electromagnetic society is based on a homomorphism: just as communication among the individual cells (and cell-groups) in the brain provides the cortico-thalamic basis of consciousness, so the individual persons constituting the planetary brain will be able to function as cells in the world consciousness, the field-plenum of social wholeness.

16) The flickering and fitful phenomena of parapsychology (*Psi* phenomena such as *ESP* and *Pk*) are premonitory indications of a coming and more stable unity of individual consciousnesses in an all-embracing world sensorium. This last 'postulate' is highly speculative and may well turn out to be unjustifiable. We shall return to the problem in a later chapter.

FOOTNOTES CHAPTER IV

[1]See my article, "Gestalt Psychology and the Philosophy of Nature," *Philosophical Review*, Vol. 39, 1930, 556-572.

Cf. "Studies in the Logic of Explanation," *Philosophy of Science*, Vol. 15, 1948, 135-175.

[2]The cumulative documentation of instinct in species has been further established by study of migratory birds, E. G. F. Sauer reports on "Celestial Navigation by the Birds," See *Scientific American* (August 1958, pp. 42-47).

[3]On this matter see the article, "The Rôle of Gestalt Perception in Animal and Human Behavior," by K. Z. Lorenz, *Aspects of Form*, edited by L. L. Whyte, pp. 157-158.

[4]Cf. "Light and Sight," *Nature*, 1928, p. 94.

[5]See my letter in *Nature* on "Vision and Reality," Vol. 121, 1928, p. 575.

[6]Cf. "Reality, Science, and Metaphysics," by C. J. Ducasse, *Synthese*, Vol. VIII (1950-51), p. 11.

[7]Cf. *Theory of Experimental Inference*, by C. West Churchman, 1948, p. 183.

[8]Cf. "William Rowan Hamilton," by Sir Edmund Whittaker, *Scientific American*, Vol. 190, 1954 (May), 82-87.

[9]Cf. "The Validity of Unique Mathematical Models in Science," by Eugen Altschul and Erwin Biser, *Philosophy of Science*, Vol. 15, 1948, 11-24; and "Mathematical Models in Biological Theory," by J. A. Rafferty, *American Scientist*, Vol. 38, 1950, 549-567.

[10]The literature in the field of Cybernetics is large. Readers will find eight pages of references in F. L. Stumper's "A Bibliography of Information Theory," *M.I.T. Report*, Feb. 2, 1953.

[11]Some indication of the nature and the strength of resistance to non-Aristotelian developments is indicated by the quality of the articles dealing with this topic. A bibliography of the writings in this area was given in my book, *The Promise of Scientific Humanism* (1940, p. 79), now out of print. A more recent listing of articles in the field of many-valued logics, frequently termed non-Aristotelian logics, appears in the volume on *Many-Valued Logics*, written by J. Barkley Rosser and Atwell R. Turquette, appearing in the series, *Studies In Logic*, published by the North-Holland Publishing Company, Amsterdam, 1952.

So far as I can discover, the first person to use the term 'non-Aristotelian logic' was Professor H. B. Smith (now deceased), who regarded Boole's logic as a non-Aristotelian logic because Boole introduced the symbols for *zero* and *one* into logic, the former (*zero*) being a concept which the Greeks did not possess. These technical problems are currently discussed in the issues of the *Journal of Symbolic Logic*.

[12]The philosophical aspects of this problem are discussed in the following articles: "Some Highlights of Modern Cosmology and Cosmogony," by Adolf Grünbaum, *Review of Metaphysics*, Vol. 5, 1952, 481-498; "Creation and the 'New' Cosmology," by Milton K. Munitz, *British Journal for the Philosophy of Science*, Vol. V, 1954, 32-46; "Science and Modern Cosmology," by Herbert Dingle, *Science*, Vol. 120, 1954, 513-521.

[13]For a discussion of this problem in terms of a multi-valent logic see the article, "The Relativity of Logic," by Louis Rougier, *Philosophy and Phenomenological Research*, Vol. 11, 1941, 138-158.

[14]See his brochure, "On the Beauty of Geometrical Forms," *Scripta Mathematica*, p. 19.

[15]See my article, "Probability, Natural Law, and Emergence," *Journal of Philosophy*, Vol. 23, 1926, 421-434, for the first statement of this thesis.

[16]Cf. "On Digital Computers Called Brains," by Warren S. McCulloch and John Pfeiffer, *Scientific Monthly*, Vol. LXIX, 1949, p. 370.

[17]Cf. "Design for an Intelligence Amplifier," by W. Ross Ashby, in *Automata Studies*, 1956, edited by Claude E. Shannon and John McCarthy.

[18]Cf. "Information, Measurement, and Quantum Mechanics," by Jerome Rothstein, *Science*, Vol. 114, 1951, 171-175.

[19]Cf. "Cybernetics," by Norbert Wiener, *Scientia*, 1952, IX, 234-236.

[20]See my article, "The Field Theory of Matter in a Pantheistic Cosmology," *Scientia*, 1954, Vol. 89, Nos. 7, 8.

5

THE LOGICAL FOUNDATIONS OF SCIENCE

"Man is but a reed — the weakest thing in nature — but he is a reed that thinks. It is not necessary that the whole universe should arm itself to crush him. A vapor, a drop of water, is enough to kill him. But if the universe should crush him, man would still be nobler than that which slays him, for he knows that he dies; but of the advantages which it has over him the universe knows nothing. Our dignity consists wholly in thought."

— Blaise Pascal

I. The Historical Background of Logic

Thinking or reasoning is one of the most universal types of human activity. The reasoning process includes both logic and the scientific method. The former, logic, is frequently associated with the 'deductive' phases of reasoning, while the scientific method, is usually related to the 'inductive' phases of inquiry. However, we shall view both logic and the scientific method as parts of one comprehensive discipline, namely, the methodology of science, the fundamental modes of procedure whereby the fields of knowledge are enlarged and integrated.

Until recently there was a pronounced tendency to regard logic as a complete and perfect science in itself. Until newer developments appeared on the scene, logic had a fixed and stable character, — largely due to the impressive authority of the Aristotelian tradition in logic. That is, the solidified character of the science of reasoning resulted from the fact that logicians and others accepted the historical development of the subject up to the twentieth century as a definitive statement of the nature of reasoning in its two phases of deductive and inductive inference. This dualism may be summarized as follows:

THE DUALISM IN LOGIC

Deductive	Inductive
Pure	Applied
Formal	Empirical
Consistency	Truth
Necessary	Probable
Aristotelian	Francis Bacon and John Stuart Mill
'from general to particular'	'from particular cases to general laws'

The development of the above dichotomies in the field of logic gave logicians the problem of harmonizing the two types of inference.

Preceding generations tended to regard logic as a closed field, due in no small measure to the influence of the Aristotelian tradition in logic. Aristotle, perfected deductive logic, — later termed *formal logic*, — which was primarily concerned with the *validity* or *consistency* between conclusions with their premises. Although Aristotle recognized a type of 'induction' in reasoning, it was so close to an intuitive classification into *genera*, or types according to essences, that his 'inductive' procedure was closely related to deductive reasoning.

Aristotle's type of reasoning was highly prized by the medieval Scholastics. The logic of Thomas Aquinas, the greatest of the Scholastic thinkers, was patterned after that of the 'master.' The belief existed that all knowledge is already known in the form of generalizations, having been given to man in the revealed truths of the Scriptures and the secular learning of the great Stagirite. Therefore, there is no need for observation and experiment. As a result, inductive logic and experimental science were practically unknown in the Middle Ages: all that was thought possible was to deduce the consequences of truths already known through revelation, authority, and intuition. To be sure, there were dissenters from the official position, — such men as Roger Bacon, Duns Scotus, William of Occam, and others, — but for the most part, Scholastic thinking adhered to the Aristotle-Aquinas stereotype in form and content.

With the advent of the Renaissance, there flourished a renewed interest in nature and in man's achievements. Men like Galileo, Vesalius, Giordano Bruno, Francis Bacon, personalized the new spirit of inquiry and exploration into the widening frontiers of the unknown. Thus came in to being what Francis Bacon called the 'new instrument' of reasoning (*Novum Organum*), which employed the logic of experiment and generalization from factual observations to establish true propositions or 'laws of nature.'

Here, then, we have the background for the two types of reasoning, neither of which is complete in itself, and both apparently necessary to each other. Nevertheless, an unsatisfactory dichotomy existed between formal logic and empirical logic which created a problem of knowledge that has sorely troubled epistemologists. Some theorists, such as Descartes and other Continental thinkers, attempted to reduce all reasoning to the deductive form, from principles or axioms that are intuitively known; while others, for example the British empiricists, sought to subordinate the deductive processes to inductive procedures. In this respect, Francis Bacon, John Locke, J. S. Mill, and David Hume, share a common heritage and purpose.

Within recent decades, criticism of the traditional and superficially convenient dualism has grown in strength. This dissatisfaction comes from various motivations, one of the more important of which is the pragmatic or instrumentalist motivation as exemplified by John Dewey's definitive work, *Logic; The Theory of Inquiry*. Here, in criticizing the inherent dualism of the traditional approach, Dewey builds upon the foundations laid in his earlier work, *How We Think*.

The present volume does not accept any absolute distinction between logic and scientific method, between formal reasoning and empirical investigations. Mathematical logic (deductive reasoning) and the scientific method are regarded as two phases of one broad enterprise, namely, the methodology of science, which is concerned with the fundamental modes of procedure whereby the fields of knowledge are enlarged and integrated.

In the steps for overcoming the dualism in logic we cannot ignore the valuable contributions of John Dewey. Indeed, in dealing with scientific methodology as a totality, there is nothing to surpass John Dewey's outline of a complete act of thought, which contains the pattern of the *hypothetico-deductive* methodology. The steps in this pattern are as follows:

1. *Origin of the problem.* A 'problem' results from the observa-

tion of a fact or a situation which arouses our curiosity. What is it? How shall I respond to this situation?

2. *Clarification of the difficulty.* Before one proceeds to explain a situation, or solve a problem, one must know what it is that he is 'up against.' Just what are the essential facts in the case? Why is this a problem for me?

3. *Rise of suggestions.* Here one looks back into one's previous experience for suggestions, for hypotheses, to be used as tentative solutions to the difficulty. This is the stage of inductive reasoning, in the sense that a tentative explanation ties the facts together into a unity. Reasoning by analogy ('insight') is the usual form that this type of thinking utilizes.

4. *Deductive elaboration of hypotheses.* Here one works out mentally the consequences (implications) of the tentatively accepted hypotheses. These suggestions are treated as premises from which one reasons to consequences (conclusions). If my hypothesis is true, what further implications can I deduce from it?

5. *Verification of the hypothesis.* Here one looks for the facts whose existence has been inferred from the suggestion one is testing. Most experiments in science are guided: observations are made to confirm the alternative hypotheses, and if the predicted facts are found, this adds plausibility to the selected hypothesis. In some cases an hypothesis may be regarded as 'verified,' and so acquire the status of a 'law.' But 'laws' should be regarded as generalizations which ordinarily possess a high degree of probability. The techniques of 'verification' are complex, involving the idea of *system.*

A full discussion of these steps is given in elementary textbooks of logic. I shall take this knowledge for granted, at least until we reach Chapter IX, where the problems of inductive logic are considered.

II. The Influence of Mathematics on Logic

The science of logic has had a new birth within the last century. Much of the vitality exhibited by this renascence comes from its contact with modern mathematics. Another life-giving impulse had its origin in the discovery that the principles along which reasoning proceeds have not all been discovered and formulated in traditional logic. The search for new principles of thinking and the development of what are called non-Aristotelian logics has stimulated investigations in recent years.

One of the key figures in the early development of modern logic is the German philosopher, Gottfried Leibniz. It was Leibniz (1646–

1716), once described as "the greatest logician between Aristotle and Bertrand Russell," who first outlined the program which is now termed *symbolic logic*. His contributions are scattered through many manuscripts, some of which are still unpublished. Along with Newton, he is credited with discovering the infinitesimal calculus. The importance of his contributions warrant a glance at Leibniz's theories.

Leibniz believed that all ideas were combinations of a small number of elementary ideas. If each of these is symbolized by a character (or 'ideograph,' such as appears in the Chinese alphabet), which would be the same throughout the world, we could construct a language or universal alphabet of human thought. This universal language (or *characteristica universalis*) for the expression of ideas was to be supplemented by a calculus of reasoning (or *calculus ratiocinator*) which would exhibit the universal relations among such concepts or ideas. By making the various possible combinations according to the rules of construction, Leibniz believed that we could anticipate all possible knowledge.

Speaking of this universal abstract language, Leibniz says[1]:

> "Telescopes and microscopes have not been so useful to the eye as this instrument would be in adding to the capacity of thought . . . If we had it, we should be able to reason in metaphysics and morals in much the same manner as geometry and analysis . . . If controversies were to arise, there would be no more need of disputation between two philosophers than between two accountants. For it would suffice to take their pencils in their hands, to sit down to their slates, and say to each other (with a friend as witness, if they like), 'Let us calculate'."

This concept of a universal science of reasoning has in a measure been achieved. However, subsequent developments have failed to confirm other points in Leibniz's great vision. In general, it may be said that later developments have confirmed the idea of a 'characteristica universalis,' and have refuted the possibility of a 'calculus ratiocinator.' Here is why that is so.

The fundamental weakness of Leibniz's position seems to lie in a 'mechanical' conception of the nature of thought and reality, i.e., that the more complex aggregates of thoughts and things are a result of a compounding or additive mixture of simple parts. Today we know a great deal more about the non-summative properties of physical, biological, and mental syntheses, — such non-additive properties as gestalt theory and emergent evolution theory have stressed, — and we realize that in 'chemical mixtures,' as opposed to 'mechanical mixtures,' novel properties may emerge which make the new whole something more than (or different from) the sum of the properties of the parts.

These discoveries of the reality of 'creative synthesis' in all fields have nullified the feasibility of Leibniz's program for anticipating all future possible forms of thought through a compounding of elementary ideas. The same difficulty frustrates the prediction of the 'infinite calculator' of Laplace, and will continue to plague those modern disciples of Leibniz and Laplace who, like Norbert Wiener, envisage the possibility of electronic machines which will duplicate and even supersede the human brain. It is no accident that Dr. Wiener recognizes Leibniz as a forerunner of 'cybernetics.'

However, it must still be conceded that Leibniz did anticipate one development which promises to stand the test of time. His idea of a universal language for science is realized to some extent; modern symbolic logic is a kind of 'characteristica universalis', — or will become so, when men have mastered the ideas and the symbolism of this superb tool of scientific method. The steps in this remarkable development may be pictured in the following diagram, with the key figures arranged as follows:

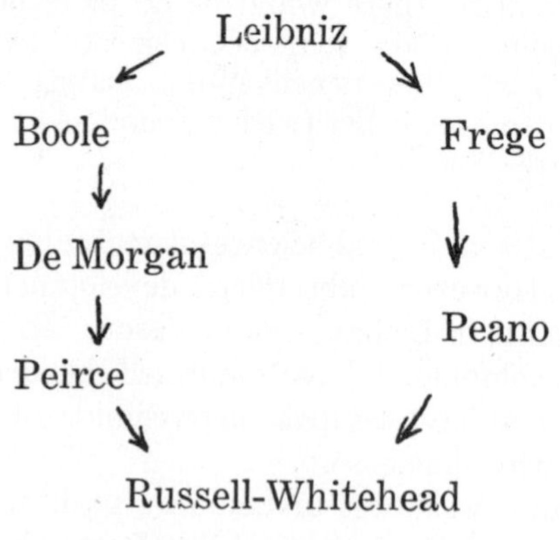

The names in the left-hand column represent the developers of logical theory, while the column on the right names the key figures in mathematical developments. These two streams converge and meet in the Russell-Whitehead synthesis, two men who collaborated in writing *Principia Mathematica*. This chapter shall be concerned primarily with modern logical developments, and in the following chapter the mathematical evolution will come under scrutiny. We begin with a general survey of what is called 'symbolic logic.'

III. The Nature of Modern Symbolic Logic

The term *symbolic logic*[2] is synonymous with the term *mathematical logic*. What mathematical logic is will appear in a moment, but one error we must avoid at the outset is that of supposing that symbolic logic is traditional Aristotelian logic expressed in some sort of symbolism. Undoubtedly, modern symbolic logic is an historical outgrowth of the Aristotelian formulation, but it has gone beyond it in many ways. As a matter of fact, the use of an elementary symbolism has characterized traditional logic from its earliest infancy; for instance, in the use of letters, to symbolize the terms of propositions and syllogisms. Therefore, the increased use of symbolic devices is not the main feature which differentiates traditional and modern symbolic logic. The character of logic itself has been modified by the increased use of symbolism, so that Aristotelian logic was transformed into mathematical logic by the very process of applying symbolism to the traditional forms. Thus new validating forms of inference have arisen.

It is difficult to exaggerate the benefits of an increased use of an adequate symbolism. The benefits to be derived from this process number at least four. In the first place, symbolism is desirable because of the economy of mental effort which it provides. An excellent illustration of this is found in mathematics. As Lewis and Langford point out, operations which any fourth grade child can accomplish in modern notation taxed the best minds of the age of Pericles, because the Greeks had no symbol for zero and used the letters of the alphabet for other numbers. A second illustration of this is offered by L. S. Stebbing when she observes that while Newton and Leibniz both invented the differential calculus, Leibniz's notation was much superior to that of Newton, and those who used Newton's symbolism were much hampered by Newton's notation. For this reason, during the next century no important mathematical discovery was made by an Englishman, while on the Continent, where Leibniz's notation was employed, rapid progress was made.

A second value of symbolism is that *it makes possible more complicated forms of reasoning.* Thus modern symbolic logic makes evident the fact that the syllogism, which historically has been stressed almost to the exclusion of all other forms of deductive inference, is really only one small hill in a vast mountain range of deductive inference. Aristotle considered only a few 'validating forms' for inference, mainly the principle of the syllogism $[(A < B) \cdot (B < C) < (A < C)]$, whereas we know now that this is only a special case selected from a much larger number of validating forms. The study of these extra-syllogistic forms of inference, begun by Leibniz, now reveals the fact that such asyllogistic forms are to be derived from the logic of transitive, asymmetrical relations. Let us therefore say a bit more about the logic of relations.

In Aristotelian logic a proposition consists of two terms related by some form of the verb 'to be.' Accordingly, 'Cain killed Abel,' was interpreted as, 'Cain was the killer of Abel.' The logic of relations, due largely to Charles Peirce, added other relations to the Aristotelian relation of class inclusion, designated by 'to be,' and for this reason symbolic logic achieves greater generality than the older logic.

Relations are now analyzed as to whether they are *symmetric* or *asymmetric*, *transitive* or *intransitive*, *correlated* or not. There are other forms of relations; but these are among the better known. The following indicates the utility of relational logic:

[If aRb, then bRa] may always be true, may never be true, or may be true or false depending on a and b. If R is a relation such that bRa, then R is a symmetric relation. If bRa is always false, R is an asymmetric relation. If the last possibility holds, R is a non-symmetric relation. *Equality* is a symmetric relation, *greater than* is asymmetric; and *lover of* is non-symmetric.

If aRb and bRc, then the relation of a to c indicates whether R is transitive or not. If aRc holds, R is a transitive relation. If aRc is always false, R is an intransitive relation. *Greater than* is transitive; *father of* is intransitive; and *friend of* is non-transitive.

Correlation deals with the question of how many terms the relation relates. Relations can be *one-one* (or *isomorphic*), *one-many*, *many-one*, or *many-many* (the last three being *homomorphic*). Thus, if A is the husband of B, then the relation is *one-one* (in a monogamous society), since for any given A there can be only one B, and for any given B there can be but one A. However, if aRb, and for a given a there can be more than one b, but for a given b there can be only one a, then R is one-many. An example is *father of*. If aRb, and for a given a there can be only one b, but for a given b there can be more than one a, then R is many-one. An example is *son of*. The meaning of *many-many* should be obvious, an example being *fellow-student of*.

Although some of the rules of the new logic seem unfamiliar, their great merit is that they thus make it possible to arrive at more complicated inferences by the proper manipulation of the symbolic machinery. Moreover, through the use of such operations it appeared possible for Peano to 'reduce' mathematics to arithmetic. Since 'reduction' is transitive, Bertrand Russell concluded that if it were possible to reduce Peano's postulates to logic, *all mathematics would be reducible to logic.* Whether this program has been successfully carried through we shall decide in the following chapter.

A third value of symbolism in logic is that *it has exhibited the fact that Aristotelian logic assigned an undue importance to the supposedly self-evident 'laws of thought'*, — especially when they are interpreted as 'laws of reality' as well as 'laws of thought.' This double duty is brought out in the following table:

	As a Law of Reality	*As a Law of Thought*
Law of Identity	1. Whatever is, is. 2. A thing is what it is.	1. A word means what it means. 2. The meaning of a term must remain constant in any discourse.
Law of Contradiction	1. A thing is not what it is not. 2. Whatever does not exist is non-existent.	1. A word does not mean what it does not mean. 2. Two negatives make an affirmative.
Law of Excluded Middle	1. A thing either exists or it does not exist. 2. An existent thing has a certain property or it does not have it. 3. A thing cannot have contradictory properties.	1. A proposition is either true or false. 2. Two contradictory propositions cannot both be true. 3. A class (or term) is either included in another class, or it is not.

Modern symbolic logic, on the other hand, informs us that these three traditional 'laws' have no privileged position in our thinking. The recognition of this principle implies that modern symbolic logic now holds that the three Aristotelian laws (the *law of identity*, the *law of non-contradiction*, and the *law of excluded middle*), *are neither more nor less important* than the other principles which are employed to validate the inferences of any given deductive system. A more radical statement of the new outlook would be to say that modern mathematical logic teaches us that *there are no laws of thought*, in the sense that there are laws of physics. If we combine the views expressed by Hilbert and Wittgenstein, we come out with this thesis: *deductive system* (*including pure logic and mathematics*) *is the manipulation of meaningless* (*though recognizable*) *symbols, according to arbitrarily selected rules of operation, the inferences deduced being simply strings of tautologies which unravel the logical possibilities wrapped up in any such selected set of postulates* (*or rules of operation*).

As a special consequence of this third value it may be noted that symbolic logic indicates that Aristotelian logic is an illustration of what is termed a two-valued logic: *truth* and *falsity* (non-truth) are the two truth values of propositions. The fact that propositions are either true or false (non-true) results from the acceptance of the law of excluded middle. However, modern research has uncovered the possibility of logic of more than two values. Lewis, for example, has developed a four-valued logic in his system of 'strict implication.' According to Lewis' theory, there is no reason why we can't have an n-valued logic, translated into probabilities, with many alternatives, — although in such cases there is an analogue to the old law of excluded middle: an $n + 1$ law of exclusion, as it may be termed.

The fourth value of symbolism is that *it reveals form*. The use of a proper symbolism may show (*a*) that apparently similar logical forms (relation-structures) are actually dissimilar, and (*b*) that forms which appear to be dissimilar are really similar. In connection with (*a*) we may note that the Aristotelian tradition treats certain forms as identical which modern symbolic logic regards as essentially unlike. Thus in Aristotelian logic the verb 'to be' expresses the relation between the subject and the predicate (S *is* P) of a proposition. This same form was used to cover both the identity-relation ($S = P$; Socrates is the wisest man of Athens) and the relation of class inclusion ($S < P$; all men are vertebrates). These, and other, uses of the verb *to be* are now clearly distinguished. In this connection, one recalls the statement of Bertrand Russell, in his *Introduction to Mathematical Philosophy* (p. 172), that the use of 'is' to express both predication and identity 'is a disgrace to the human race.' Aside from this over-simplification, traditional logic was forced to emasculate compound propositions (expressing conjunctions and disjunctions) in order to fit them into the subject-predicate Aristotelian logic of classes.

With respect to (*b*), symbolic logic shows that relation-structures which appear to have little in common may possess the same *logical form*. It is a simple fact of experience that if we see certain formal similarities on a printed page, as made evident by the proper symbolism, we can recognize intellectually the underlying equivalence of meaning, or relation, or inference. Thus the generalization from the *propositional functions* of Bertrand Russell to the higher level *doctrinal functions* of C. J. Keyser, or the *system functions* of H. M. Sheffer, is made more obvious by the formal similarity. Adopting the language of gestalt psychology, we may say that the *logical gestalt* is an outgrowth of the *visual gestalt*, or pattern of symbols, — as is shown in Diagram VII (p. 82). When we recall that mathematics has been defined as the science of form, the importance of this is clear.

The last value of the new symbolic logic is that it has made possible a genuine insight into the nature of mathematical reasoning and a better understanding of the relation of mathematics to logic. In the process of accomplishing this, the recent developments also promise a resolution of the paradoxes, such as are dealt with in Russell's theory of types, and other paradoxes which are peculiar to mathematics, — such as occur in the theory of *aggregates*. We have already made reference to the first type of paradox. The second type of paradox will appear in the following chapter.

IV. Logic and Mathematics

The view that logic and mathematics are not separate domains, but that symbolic logic supplies the premises for mathematics, is expounded at length in *Principia Mathematica*. Here Professors Whitehead and Russell attempt to show that logic consists of those undefined ideas and premises from which mathematical concepts (such as number) and mathematical inferences are deduced. Russell's definition of mathematics fits in with this approach. In his book, *Principles of Mathematics* (p. 3) he informs us that, "Pure mathematics is the class of all propositions of the form 'p implies q', where p and q are propositions containing one or more variables, the same in the two propositions, and neither p nor q contains any constants except logical constants." Having convinced himself that this derivation has been successfully accomplished, Russell triumphantly announced: "the fact that all mathematics is symbolic logic is one of the greatest discoveries of our age."

In the foregoing use of terms, a *constant* is a symbol that expresses form, — thus the symbol $\supset$ expresses the relation of 'implies' or 'entails'; whereas a *variable* is a symbol that represents the elements of a class. There is thus an analogy between the 'variables' of logic and of mathematics. A variable in mathematics is a symbol which may take on a number of values, while yet certain truths are characteristic of it; and in logic a concept covers the instances exemplified by the concept.

DIAGRAM XV DOTOLOGY

• • • • • ● . . . "things"
a *b* *c* *d* *e* *f* . . . "symbols"

		Propositions		Propositional function
Atomic Propositions	(1)	*a* is small (subject-predicate)	$\phi_1 a$	ϕx
	(2)	*b* is to the left of *c* (relational)	bL_1c	xRy
	(3)	*b* is a dot (class-membership)	$b \epsilon \alpha_1$	$x \epsilon \alpha$
	(4)	There are dots (existence)	$\exists ! \alpha_1$	$\exists ! \alpha$
	(5)	Some dots are large	$(\exists x) \cdot \phi_2 x$	$(\exists x) \cdot \phi x$
	(6)	All dots are black	$(x) \cdot \phi_3 x$	$(x) \cdot \phi x$
	(7)	*d* is large and *a* is small	$\phi_2 d \cdot \phi_1 a$	$p \cdot q$
	(8)	*f* is large or *a* is small	$\phi_2 f \vee \phi_1 a$	$p \vee q$
	(9)	*c* is not both to the left of *b* and bigger than *b*	$\sim (cLb \cdot cBb)$	$\sim p \cdot q$
	(10)	If a dot is to the right of another dot, it is larger than it.	$(x) \cdot x\, Ry \supset x\, By$	$p \supset p$

In order to exhibit the power and beauty of symbolic logic, and also give an example of some of the foregoing formulations, Diagram XV on *DOTOLOGY* is presented. There the various possible propositions about 'dots' arranged in serial order are stated. On Diagram XVI the fundamental principles of logic, such as the 'law of identity' and others, are presented, — but stated in modern notation.

In the preceding sections we have dealt with some of the more specialized developments in recent logical advances. Now we turn for a moment to something more 'philosophical', — the problem of the meaning of *implication*. Again and again one hears the statement that this or that is an 'implication' of something else. What does this mean? And what is the 'necessity' which is said to inhere in such 'implications'? This we now consider.

V. The Meaning of Implication

In formal logic 'necessity' arises from the fact that the symbols on the left side of an equation occur on the right side. Necessary implication, therefore, really seems to be a case of partial identity, since complete 'identity' would not represent an implication. For example:

x is red {*implies*} *x is colored*

This is a necessary inference. The 'necessity' in the implication simply expresses the acceptance of a meaning. This, of course, is one form of the *tautologous theory of inference:* that is, all logical necessity is explicative of some agreed-upon meaning or set of alternatives. In pure reasoning (intensional use of symbols) the definitions are not themselves true or false. No empirical reality can ever upset such definitions or inferences, because they have no empirical content. This distinction between the *intensional* and the *extensional* uses of language has already been established in the previous chapter.

The same remarks apply to formal systems. For example, Euclidian geometry is neither true nor false: it should be internally consistent, and it may apply here and there in nature (be a good 'fit,' as Euclidian geometry is applicable in surveying small areas on the earth); but there is no one, god-given, absolute geometry. Formal structures are analytic of a set of meanings accepted at the outset. Every 'logical law' is therefore relative to accepted meanings. 'Two plus two equals four,' is true in certain accepted meanings of the terms that are being

DIAGRAM XVI

THE FORMAL PRINCIPLES OF REASONING

Principle of —	Classes	Propositions	Meaningless Symbols
1. Identity:	$a < a$	$p \supset p$	$\Delta < \Delta$
2. Contradiction:	$aa' < 0$	$p \supset \sim(\sim p)$	$\Delta\Delta' < 0$
3. Excluded Middle:	$a + a' < 1$	$p \supset \sim p \lor p$	$\Delta < \Delta \lor \Delta'$
4. Commutation:	$\begin{cases} ab < ba \\ a + b < b + a \end{cases}$	$\begin{cases} p \cdot q \supset q \cdot p \\ p \lor q \supset q \lor p \end{cases}$	$\begin{cases} \Delta \Box < \Box \Delta \\ \Delta \lor \Box < \Box \lor \Delta \end{cases}$
5. Association:	$\begin{cases} (ab)c < a(bc) \\ (a + b) + c < a + (b + c) \end{cases}$	$\begin{cases} (pq)r \supset p(qr) \\ (p \lor q) \lor r \supset p \lor (q \lor r) \end{cases}$	$\begin{cases} (\Delta \Box) \odot < \Delta (\Box \odot) \\ (\Delta \lor \Box) \lor \odot < \Delta \lor (\Box \lor \odot) \end{cases}$
6. Distribution:	$\begin{cases} (a + b)c = ac + bc \\ ab + c = (a + c)(b + c) \end{cases}$	$\begin{cases} (p \lor q)r \supset pr \lor qr \\ pq \lor r \supset (p \lor r)(q \lor r) \end{cases}$	$\begin{cases} (\Delta \lor \Box)\odot = \Delta \odot \lor \Box \odot \\ \Delta \Box \lor \odot = (\Delta \lor \odot)(\Box \lor \odot) \end{cases}$
7. Tautology:	$aa = a$	$p \lor p \supset p$	$\Delta\Delta = \Delta$
8. Absorption:	$\begin{cases} a + ab = a \\ a(a + b) = a \end{cases}$	$\begin{cases} p \lor pq \supset p \\ p(p \lor q) \supset p \end{cases}$	$\begin{cases} \Delta \lor \Delta \Box = \Delta \\ \Delta(\Delta \lor \Box) = \Delta \end{cases}$
9. Simplification:	$\begin{cases} ab < a \\ a < a + b \end{cases}$	$\begin{cases} pq \supset p \\ p \supset p \lor q \end{cases}$	$\begin{cases} \Delta \Box < \Delta \\ \Delta < \Delta \lor \Box \end{cases}$
10. Composition:	$\begin{cases} (a < b) \cdot (c < d) = (ac < bd) \\ [(a < b) \cdot (c < d)] = [(a + c) < (b + d)] \end{cases}$	$\begin{cases} (p \supset q)(r \supset s) \supset (pr \supset qs) \\ [(p \supset q)(r \supset s)] \supset [(p \lor r) \supset (q \lor s)] \end{cases}$	$\begin{cases} (\Delta < \Box)(\odot < \mathbb{C}) = (\Delta \odot < \Box \mathbb{C}) \\ [(\Delta < \Box)(\odot < \mathbb{C})] = [(\Delta \lor \odot) < (\Box \lor \mathbb{C})] \end{cases}$
11. Syllogism:	$(a < b) \cdot (b < c) < (a < c)$	$(p \supset q)(q \supset r) \supset (p \supset r)$	$(\Delta < \Box)(\Box < \odot) < (\Delta < \odot)$

employed. The same holds true for the 'law of excluded middle.' An Aristotelian logic is one in which, as this principle of *tertium non datur* states, a proposition is either true or false. But, as we have seen, it is possible to devise a modal logic with three values (or *n*-values). In such a case, propositions that are 'true' in Aristotelian logic may no longer hold in the multi-valued logic. Of course, once one has committed himself to a meaning for a symbol, this same symbol should continue to have the same meaning (in the same universe of discourse), and that is all the 'law of identity' tells us. But, as we have elsewhere indicated, this 'law' would more appropriately be termed the *principle of symbolic univalence*, — a single value for one symbol.

The program of *logistics*, largely associated with Bertrand Russell, is, in Russell's own words (*Introduction to Mathematical Philosophy*, 1919, p. 194), committed to the following proposition: "Starting with premises which would be universally admitted to belong to logic, and arriving at results which obviously belong to mathematics, we find that there is no point at which a sharp line can be drawn with logic to the left and mathematics to the right." And as Russell says elsewhere, "By the name mathematical logic I denote any logical theory whose object is the analysis and deduction of arithmetic and geometry by means of concepts (such as order) which belong evidently to logic."

This, of course, is an ambitious program. The view that logic and mathematics are not two separate disciplines, but are one, is certainly made more plausible (but not proved) by the developments in symbolic logic. However, it is still controversial whether the attempted fusion of the two domains is successful, and we are not yet in a position to adjudicate the dispute. Before we can attempt that, we must pay some attention to the fundamental concepts and operations of symbolic logic.

Russell, in his definition of mathematics, refers to 'logical constants' and 'variables.' This provides us with a convenient starting point for our brief survey of some of the fundamentals of symbolic logic.

VI. Some Fundamental Concepts and Operations

Perhaps the best way to clarify the uses of these two entities of logic (*constants* and *variables*) is to exhibit them and then describe their function. The following is a table of the important *constants* and *variables:*

Logical Constants	Symbol (calculus of classes)	Symbol (propositions)
Relations:		
equality	$=$	$=$
logical product (multiplication)	$\times$ (and)	$\bullet$
logical sum (addition)	$+$ (or)	$\vee$
negation	$'$	$\sim$
inclusion	$<$	
		ϵ (epsilon)
implication		$\supset$ material $\prec$ strict
Logical Variables:		
individual classes	x, y, z	x, y, z
individual propositions		p, q, r
variable relations		R, S, T
variable properties		ϕ, ψ, x

According to this scheme, every proposition is completely expressible in terms of logical constants and logical variables. For example, the proposition, 'The class of white men is included in the class men,' in symbolic form is this:

$$\alpha \cdot \beta \supset \alpha \qquad (alpha \cdot beta \supset alpha)$$

$$\begin{matrix} \cdot & \cdot & \cdot & \cdot & \cdot \\ \cdot & \cdot & \cdot & \cdot & \cdot \\ \cdot & \cdot & \cdot & \cdot & \cdot \\ v & c & v & c & v \end{matrix}$$

(where v and c represent variables and constants, respectively)

The foregoing remarks add up to the conclusion that formal systems permit any number of matrices, and the 'laws' of logic are simply those rules of operation which regulate the appearance, or emergence, of the implications that follow from (or are validated by) the acceptance of a given set of definitions and rules. The Russell-Whitehead logic is a two-valued logic; the system of C. I. Lewis is a four-valued logic. But in either case, the much discussed 'paradoxes' of implication which occur in the Russell-Whitehead two-valued system of *material impli-*

cation and the Lewis four-valued system of *strict implications* are not really 'paradoxes.' There are no paradoxes (contradictions) in either case; the supposed paradoxes are necessary consequences of the definition of *implication*, subject to the limitations of the system in which such 'implications' are functioning.

These comments do not appear to contradict our general philosophy that implications always have to do with meanings *within a system*. Terms (i.e., the symbols representing concepts) are entry-points into systems, as Kattsoff puts it; and the function of the definition of such terms is to make it possible to deduce the theorems belonging in a given domain. Outside of a system of thought (a doctrinal function of system function) there is no meaning, no inference. Thus we escape a 'logical atomism,' and in this sense our theory of logic is 'organismic.' Fortunately, this idea of implication is neutral so far as ontology (a system of metaphysics) is concerned: it can be adapted to the tenets of 'idealism' or 'materialism' with equal ease.

VII. Pragmatism and Symbolic Logic

Some individuals fear and shun symbolic logic because they believe it to be formidable and useless. But actually the formalism of symbolic systems does not make the symbols less valuable, but more useful. The value of all formal generality, — whether of classes, propositions, linear order, areas, and the like, — is that it provides the ele ments of a methodology which is applicable to mathematics, esthetics, social phenomena, astronomy, and all the other special sciences.

These formal systems suggest hypotheses, which are elaborations of systems of implications. The formulations of theories of implications should outrun the empirical facts for the job of philosophy as a speculative enterprise is to frame visions of possible worlds. The recognition that the implications which come out are tautologies, does not mean that we *know* all the implications from the very beginning.

The fact that deductive system results in tautologies does not mean that all scientific thinking (including new empirical investigations) is composed of strings of tautologies. Scientific investigations in the natural sciences involve appeals to facts and employ inductive method as well as deductive. The technique for carrying forward the scientific enterprise in its totality is sometimes called the 'hypothetico-deductive method.' As already noted, this procedure is expounded in introductory textbooks in logic, frequently in relation to Dewey's well-known analysis of a complete act of thought from the origin of the problem to its final solution.

All purely deductive systems are in a sense logically uncreative; but they do not therefore exclude the novelty involved in formulating the premises, nor do they rule out the thrill of observations which validate or confirm our formal systems. Formal systems seem to stress *structural constancy;* whereas nature seems to present a world of *process*, with elements of novelty here and there. But there is no incompatibility between process and structure. To be sure, it requires *time* to bring out the novelties in nature, and it also requires psychological time to exfoliate the implications of a system.

There is a theory that the time required by the human thinker to reproduce what is wrapped up in a set of postulates reflects a psychological limitation of the cogitator. But in our view, time is an essential ingredient in mathematics from the very start, so that, as we shall see in coming chapters, time or temporal process appears as a kind of primordial prototype for both Brouwer's *intuitionism* and Hilbert's *postulational* approach to mathematics.

Now, in order to prepare the way for this notion of temporal process, and also to tie together some applications of ideas already hinted at, we advance another step in the present chapter by observing how the notions essential to logical structure have been incorporated into scientific theorizing.

VIII. Logical Structure and Dimensionality

The development of the notion of logical structure is due largely to Bertrand Russell.[3] These fundamental ideas were further generalized by C. J. Keyser in his theory of 'doctrinal functions' and by H. M. Sheffer in his theory of 'system functions.' While these ideas have thus far not yet succeeded in recasting the forms of natural science, a beginning in this direction is being made, and one may look for progress along these lines in the future.

The similarity of logical structure, or *isomorphism*, is well recognized in the domain of *group theory* in mathematics. The importance of this approach for scientific thinking has been demonstrated by Herman Weyl, in his book on *The Theory of Groups and Quantum Mechanics* (English translation in 1932). Also, in the form of *topology*, dealing with such non-metrical concepts as *continuity*, *ordered sets*, *dimensionality*, and the like, isomorphism shows us how to think logically about the analyses of physical events in space-time.

Obviously, the most fundamental idea presupposed by *isomorphism* is the concept of *order*. For our purposes, the most universal and important type of natural order is the ever-present order of space-time, which leads into the subject of isomorphism, since our notion of physical order presupposes a similarity of relation-structure between geometrical (conceptual) space and physical space. It is an interesting fact that the fundamental and universal orders of space and time appear also in the order exemplified by the series of natural integers, as some of the propositions from the 'science of dotology' indicated. For this reason the term *serial order* is appropriate. Serial order is based on what symbolic logic terms *irreflexive*, *transitive*, and *asymmetrical* relations, and deals with such relations as succession in time, positions in space, and quantitative magnitudes. The principles which express the facts about serial order are like the postulates of any deductive system, and may therefore be put into the following form:

(A) BASE: a class, K, of entities, x, y, z, etc., and a relation or rule of operation, R.
(B) POSTULATES:
  (1) xRx is false throughout the class K. This is the property of irreflexiveness: no element x has R to itself.
  (2) For any two elements, x and y, of K, either xRy or yRx. This states the property of asymmetry.
  (3) For any three elements, x, y, and z, of K, if xRy and yRz, then xRz. This states the property of transitivity.

If we let $f(x)$ mean that x belongs to the class, and specify that our relation, R, means specifically "is larger than" ($L = R$), and represent it thus: $L(x, y)$, then we may restate our postulates as follows:

(1) $(x) \cdot f(x) \supset \backsim L(x, x)$.
(2) $(x, y) : f(x) \cdot f(y) \cdot \backsim(x = y) \cdot \supset L(x, y) \vee L(y, x)$.
(3) $(x, y, z) : f(x) \cdot f(y) \cdot f(z) \cdot L(x, y) \cdot L(y, z) \cdot \supset xLz$.

The symbolic formulae read like the first set of postulates, except for the substitution of L for R.

While the notion of serial order is employed in the concept of isomorphism, the latter notion is especially applicable when we are comparing two domains, both of which have a 'base' and a set of postulates which obey the logical structure of serial order. Thus if two deductive systems have the same 'structure,' they are isomorphic and have similar properties. In other words, if every element of one system, S^1, matches an element of another system, S^2, and the generating relation of S^1 is similar to that of S^2, then the two systems have analogous logical properties. Instances of such isomorphism are as follows:

(1) A map and the territory which the map represents.
(2) The plot of a novel and the moving picture reproduction.
(3) The score on a musical sheet, the wavy lines on a phonograph record, the music as a series of air vibrations, the corresponding excitations carried by the auditory nerve, and the melody and harmony as experienced in consciousness.
(4) The external physical pattern, the corresponding retinal mosaic, and the phenomenal (conscious) visual pattern.
(5) The inverse square law as it applies to gravitational and magnetic attraction, and as illustrated by the spreading out into space of sound waves and light waves.
(6) Any *gestalt*, the elements of which can be *transposed* while yet keeping the same *form* or *logical structure*.

These examples illustrate the great importance of isomorphism for science. The fertility of this approach to the philosophy of nature will appear in the following chapters, especially in dealing with the important problem of the nature of scientific method in the physical and the social sciences.

Thus far we have been dealing with Logic. But within the last several years, the new science of cybernetics has appeared, making it necessary to integrate this development into our scheme for the formal foundation of all knowledge.

IX. Symbolic Logic, Cybernetics, and Semantics

If one were to summarize the historical development of logic up to the moment, one would probably find that the briefest epitome of the entire story is this: modern studies demonstrate that *there is no one, absolute, intuitively known science of reasoning implanted in the mind of man.* Just as there was a revolution in mathematics when non-Euclidian geometry dethroned the Euclidian-Cartesian geometry of three-dimensional space as the mathematics of God and Nature, so in a similar fashion has Aristotelian Logic been dethroned as the one and only rational system according to which nature and the mind of man are constructed. In the long run, this second revolution may prove to be of greater significance than the first.

The prevailing belief in current logical theory seems to be that reasoning, in so far as it employs symbolism, is the manipulation of meaningless (uninterpreted) symbols according to freely selected rules of operation upon these symbols. That is, deductive inference is regarded as a mechanical process of unraveling strings of tautologies,— bringing out the 'implications' wrapped up in a set of definitions and postulates. Until recently, these validating forms ('laws of thought' and 'rules of operation') were pretty well conventionalized and could therefore be formalized into the 'principles of inference' of Diagram XVI (p. 170). These *principles* correspond to the *postulates* as they appear in our Diagram VI.

Because the inferences of deductive reasoning can be formalized in this 'mechanical' manner, it is possible to construct machines that 'think',— at least in the sense in which thinking occurs in deductive logic. The modern discoveries about electronic calculating devices are inspired by Leibniz's calculus of reasoning (*calculus ratiocinator*), and it is for this reason that Leibniz is a key figure in current theories. Although the Russell-Whitehead system, as expounded in their *Principia Mathematica*, apparently provides the 'logic' for the new electronic machines, all these developments are in a sense an outgrowth of the Leibnizian scheme. In associating Leibniz and Russell in this manner, we do not disregard the differences in their general philosophies. In the field of logic, however, Russell is certainly carrying forward the program first mapped out by Leibniz.

Because the contemporary cyberneticists interpret brain behavior as physical mechanism, they naturally turn back to Leibniz for the *rationale* of this machine. There are three reasons for this: (1) the system promises the reduction of mathematics to logic; (2) the system is a two-valued pattern, providing the logical basis for the 'on' and 'off' circuits of electronic brains (though it should not be overlooked that Francis Bacon also pointed out in Book Six of *The Advancement of Learning* that any information could be conveyed by a 'biliteral code' which uses only two symbols); and (3) because the assumed validity of the *calculus ratiocinator* of Leibniz alone makes possible the complete 'mechanization of thought.'

Of course, the fascinating unification of concepts which culminated in the science of cybernetics did not come all at once. The story of this triumphant synthesis is important for its own sake as well as for our own subsequent purposes, and I shall therefore sketch briefly the major steps in the progress toward the mechanization of the human mind and the mentalization of electronic thinking machines.

Calculating machines that duplicate one or more features of human reasoning in logical and mathematical operations began with the early Chinese 'abacus' and momentarily culminate in such modern calculators as ENIAC (the initials stand for the electronic numerical integrator and calculator), a monster of 18,000 tubes which solves difficult mathematical problems with little time and trouble. Between these two extremes of early simplicity and modern complexity lies a chain of hesitating advances, — but always in the direction of bigger and better machines. Matthew Arnold's prayer, "More brains, Oh Lord, more brains!", is on the point of being answered, — by the electronic engineers!

As we have already noted, Leibniz was an early pioneer in inventing a calculus which would reduce reasoning to an automatic process, and in constructing a machine, still preserved at the Royal Library at Hanover, that would carry out this process in a manner akin to the operations of human thought. Before Leibniz, Blaise Pascal, in 1642, at the age of nineteen, constructed a machine for doing arithmetic. But yet earlier a contrivance for mathematical computations was conceived by Raymond Lully (1235-1315), who imagined a 'Great Art' whereby philosophical concepts could be fed as input and from which, he hoped, the various possible cognitions could be obtained as output.

Following these tentative gropings, the Englishman, Charles Babbage, in 1834, designed an arithmetic machine which became the prototype for Thomas J. Watson's *International Business Machines*, — even to the punch-card idea embodied in the I.B.M. contrivances. Then came the war, and with it came ENIAC, and later the new machines such as MANIAC, BINAC, UNIVAC, OROVAC, ERA, and the more recent 'brains' that have been devised.

The thing that distinguishes the newer types of 'think' machines is the incorporation of the feed-back mechanism, which regulates the activities of the machine as information is fed into the apparatus as it operates, this regulatory effect being negative or positive according to whether it slows down or accelerates the original process. The fundamental idea is simply the principle of the digital calculator, ticking off on the fingers the numbers that are being operated upon, with some device for more complex combinations of processes. It needs to be remembered that in the field of mathematics the four fundamentals of arithmetic, — addition, subtraction, multiplication, and division, — still constitute the basic means for solving problems. In a similar way, in the field of logic all complex propositional forms can be built up from the simple operations of disjunction ('or'), conjunction ('and'), negation ('not'), and affirmation. *In these two sets of parallel ideas we have the elements which make possible the new synthesis*, — the science of cybernetics, which promises to combine mathematics and logic in a single discipline, as Leibniz and Russell have envisioned it, with the immense power of generating all manner of deductive inferences.[4]

The Entymology of 'Cybernetics'

The term cybernetics was coined by Dr. Norbert Wiener from the Greek word *kybernetes*, which designates the 'steersman of a ship.' It comes from the same root as the word *governor* (e.g., of a steam engine). Dr. Wiener's studies of feed-back systems (sometimes called *servo-mechanisms*) began during the war when he and Dr. J. H. Bigelow at the Massachusetts Institute of Technology were assigned the job of working out a fire-control apparatus for anti-aircraft artillery which would be capable of tracing the curving course of an airplane and predicting its future position. The carrying out of this assignment is an excellent example of 'operational research' on a large scale, for this required the collaboration of physiologists, mathematicians, physicists, and electronic engineers. All of these fields are now tied together in this area of overlapping interests. At long last, — if one may believe the cyberneticists, — we discover that gun pointers, electronic calculators, and television sets use processes which nature has been employing in the living brain for tens of thousands of years.

Up to this point, one principle of human 'thinking' has not received adequate emphasis: that is, the role of *memory* in the processes of inference. Since the logical relations in a chain of inference extend backward into time, we must find a basis for memory in our calculating machines if the analogy between electronic and neural mechanics is to carry through. In the man-made computers information is stored in nets of relays, to be fed in at the right time in the ongoing process. Similarly, in the human nervous system there are feed-back or 'regenerative' circuits, which feed the information into the circuit in a temporally ordered series of operations. This is analogous to the influence of 'context' on 'meaning', — a well-recognized principle in semantics. Just as in the theory of probability there is a theorem covering situations in which past events influence present probabilities (known as the Markoff process), so does the historical background come in as a moderating influence in the understanding of meaning.

Therefore, the cyberneticists do not stand in awe of the phenomenon of memory, for it is not regarded as a unique characteristic of mind, or even of living systems. It must be noted, however, that while electronic calculating machines do perform complicated series of logical operations at a rapid rate, — based on sets of choices between alternatives, each set depending upon a set of earlier choices, — a very essential part of the whole apparatus is a clocking device which times the sequence, or sets the tempo of the choices. The whole scheme is well stated by Hudson Hoagland[5] in the following manner:

> "In such a machine there are devices to retain impulses until it is time for the appropriate circuit to act and relate them to other events in the process of computation. This may be done in the machine by systems of reverberating circuits and by electronic scanning devices, such as are used in television and also in the form of magnetization patterns of the molecules in iron wire after the manner of the well-known wire recorder. Thus, information can be stored until ready for use, and the machine quite literally possesses a functional memory in the form of patterns of dynamic electrical configurations or of molecular patterns which may be called upon to furnish information by appropriate stimuli arriving as timed pulses from other circuits in the apparatus. It is important to realize that this memory need not be lodged in any one locus in the machine, but belongs to its function as a whole. To ignore this is to commit the fallacy of Descartes in locating the action of mind on matter in the pineal gland."

The important thing brought out in the foregoing statement is the concept of 'reverberating circuits' which modify the rate of the original process by feeding back information into the machine as it functions.

This is similar to the psychological definition of 'purposive behavior': purposive behavior is behavior in which a possible future result of present behavior acts as a stimulus to present behavior. Here one finds that 'foresight' has made its appearance, and it is this adaptation of means to ends which the new mechanism claims to explain without the introduction of non-physical terms. This is a part of the great appeal of the cybernetics approach, — it claims to have solved the age-old argument of 'mechanism versus teleology.' Whether this claim is justified, we shall attempt to determine in a moment.

Electrical Communication Systems

In the foregoing synthesis we find that two lines of development have converged. Cybernetics is a science of communication in men and machines. However, since communication is the transfer of information, cybernetics is, — so to speak, — a bilingual science of communication engineering in its two phases of (a) the language of electrical circuits and electronic calculating devices, and (b) the language of neural networks or the biophysics of brain mechanisms. These two subdivisions, formerly independent, now coalesce into a unity that is enormously fertile in producing new progeny in the form of hypotheses. Before bringing these two parents together, let us study each of them separately.

In the process of communication a message is sent over a transmission system from an information source to its destination. In the case of telegraphy or telephony, this means that the signal which carries the message is a varying electrical current, and the channel of communication is a wire conductor. The message is first encoded in signals, sent over the channel, and then decoded at the destination.[6] In order to understand and improve upon electrical systems of communication, the engineer must investigate certain things: he must find a means of measuring the information content of messages; he must investigate the statistical structure of language, and discover how the structure of language may be changed in order to increase the information content per signal; he must understand the capacity of a channel for transmitting signals, and the effect of noise (distortions and static) on this capacity.

Those who have studied the physical sciences will observe in the literature in this field the appearance of certain ideas that seem familiar: the idea of *probability* and the concept of *entropy* are especially important in understanding the unusual interpretation assigned to 'information.' The 'entropy theory of communication,' as it may be termed, culminates in a redefinition of information as negative entropy. Among other things, as Warren S. McCulloch[7] puts it, "The second law of thermodynamics, which insures an increase in entropy, means that information can never increase as it passes through any computing machine." This, of course, is very intriguing; but whether the broadening of connotations of terms is legitimate, we shall examine later.

This brings us to the subject of the semantics of brain physiology. To this we now turn.

Neural Logic and Brain Semantics

The possibility of communication depends upon the transmission of signals. Signals involve the response to the presence of an accepted unit of something in space and time (a 'bit,' like dots and dashes) that can be transmitted over a channel. The presence or absence of these 'bits' in the circuit is indicated by the statement that the receiver is firing ('on') or not-firing ('off').

On the level of brain mechanics the nerve cells (neurons) correspond to the telegraphic relay. The human brain is made up of 10 billion such cells, and each cell is comparable to an electronic tube, operating on a voltage. In the brain the reception of a signal by a neuron corresponds to the 'tripping' of the relay in the electrical circuit.

In this remarkable manner it becomes possible to establish connections with the two-valued logic of George Boole, for the 'on' and 'off' of the neural circuit can be shown to correspond to a signal 'received' or 'not-received' by the nervous system. This quantum unit of action can then be regarded as equivalent to what in logic is termed an *atomic proposition,* — as McCulloch notes, — which is 'true' when a 'bit' of something (the signal) excites a neural response (*loc. cit.*). Thus the 'zero' and 'one' of the two-valued Boolean algebra of logic of 'true' and 'false' propositions turn out to be the operational basis for the neural logic of those electronic calculating machines which are man's brains!

The use of the binary digits 0 and 1 is the common denominator of the calculus of electronic brains and human brains. The numbers 1, 2, 3, 4, 5, and so on, in the binary system are simply 1, 10, 11, 100, 101, and so on. This translation corresponds to a parallel transformation in logic whereby the logic of relations is converted into the logic of classes (as indicated in Diagram XVI). Thus, the great aim of Russell and Whitehead of reducing the domain of mathematics to logic provides a formal basis for an analogous reduction of mind-patterns to brain-patterns.

An important paper by Pitts and McCulloch[8] on "How We Know Universals," demonstrates how a scanning mechanism in the cortex could furnish a basis for the recognition of *forms* as patterns of stimuli (an old problem in gestalt psychology). These authors summarize the idea that a rhythmic sweep of negativity up and down through the cortex, — the *alpha rhythm* of the electroencephalogram, in fact, — performs a temporal scanning of the cortex, 'which thereby gains, at the cost of time, the equivalent of another spatial dimension.' In connection with this most important phenomenon of the inter-translatability of spatial and temporal patterns, one should study also the work of L. A. Riggs and Floyd Ratcliff ("Visual Acuity and the Normal Tremor of the Eyes," *Science*, 1951, Vol. 114, 17–18), who believe that visual acuity is enhanced ten to twenty times beyond the limits set by the mosaic structure of the retina by a tremor effect. That is to say, the effect is a result of receptor cells which 'scan' the image and convey to the brain a pattern of nerve impulses in which there is a trading of time for space. Here discreteness in the spatial arrangement is again compensated for by continuity in time. For us, the profoundly significant thing about the above line of theorizing is the manner in which it lends support to the notion of 'emergence' and the isomorphism of an n and an $n + 1$ dimensionality as this was first outlined in my book, *Philosophy and the Concepts of Modern Science*, Chapter VIII, on 'Consciousness as a New Dimension."

Further advances in the field have come in rapid order. After Rosenblueth, Wiener, and Bigelow[9] had expounded some of the general implications of cybernetics, the philosophy of the program was put into coherent form by Northrop[10] in an article of rare vision. The discovery that conscious voluntary action and the brain processes through which they operate function by way of a negative feed-back mechanism led Professor Northrop to the conclusion that cybernetics has found a 'mechanism for purpose.' That is, according to Northrop, a teleological system can be, — and in the human nervous system is, — a mechanical system in which the behavior of the system is controlled by a negative feed-back over the goal. Thus the time-worn argument between the 'mechanists' and the 'teleologists' is an example of a problem that is wrongly stated. Both views are correct, and it is a matter of which language you prefer in expressing the facts, the language of physics or that of consciousness.

Contributions from Biophysics

Quite independently of the above developments, Dr. N. Rashevsky of the University of Chicago has been working out the general theory of biophysics. He eventually applied his biophysical approach to the problems of human perception and conception and dealt specifically with the biophysical basis of the Boolean algebra of logic.[11] Dr. Rashevsky's method of attacking the problem is quite different from Wiener's, though ultimately the two methods of analysis are likely to converge. In the first edition of his *Mathematical Biophysics*, many circuits are discussed which are essentially feed-back circuits, except that they are not called so. For that matter, for many years a number of theorizers (including the present writer) have used the notion of 'circular reaction arcs,' without realizing that these would eventually be dubbed 'feed-back mechanisms.' This is analogous to the case of the Frenchman who spoke prose all his life without realizing it.

A Critique of Cybernetics

The theory of cybernetics can be criticized on the following three counts:

(1) There is a dilution in the meanings of the terms employed, with a corresponding equivocation in the terms used.

(2) Cybernetics does not give a satisfactory explanation of creative thought and inductive logic.

(3) It does not provide an adequate interpretation of what it does attempt to explain, — the field of deductive reasoning.

Let us consider the first point of criticism. Whenever two formerly disparate sets of phenomena and their correlative explanatory concepts, — in this case electronic computing devices and living brain mechanisms, — are brought within the scope of a more inclusive set of categories, — in this case cybernetics, — so that the terms within each field become interchangeable (as *entropy* in thermodynamics and *information* in cybernetics become synonymous), there is a corresponding loss of precision. It seems inevitable that a gain in generality of viewpoint necessitates sacrificing the finer details of close vision.

In logic this kind of 'double vision' is not regarded as proper, and it is usually designated as the fallacy of *ambiguity in language*. When, for example, the cyberneticists use the terms 'signal' and 'symbol' as if they designated comparable processes, — in the electrical circuit and the brain circuit, respectively, — they are guilty of equivocation. Semanticists agree that in the living animal a *signal response* (e.g., Pavlov's dog that salivates at the sound of the bell) is quite different from a *symbol response* (e.g., the analysis of the meaning of the word 'bureaucracy'), although it is unfortunately true that some humans will behave like dogs and substitute conditioned responses when meaningful analysis is called for. The easy substitution of 'signal' for 'symbol' is an equivocation that sloughs over the whole *problem of meaning*, and this is 'synthesis' at the expense of 'analysis.'

A second criticism of cybernetics is that the machine theory does not provide an explanation of all types of reasoning. Cybernetic theory is on the right track so long as its application is restricted to deductive reasoning, though even here it has not gone the whole distance. Since mathematical reasoning is deductive procedure (once it has been formalized), the solution of mathematical problems by electronic calculating machines and by brains which duplicate them, — or *vice versa*, — is readily accomplished.

A machine, however, does not think up and solve new problems: and that is exactly what man is constantly doing. Creative thinking, where the element of originality enters upon the scene, calls for inductive reasoning, imagination, the formulation and testing of new hypotheses, — visions of territories not yet embodied in existing domains of fact.

A machine must operate according to the mechanics inherent in its own construction. It is not 'free' to change the rules or principles of its construction and operation. But the human mind does exhibit a measure of freedom to change its operations. One example of this creativity is illustrated by the passage from an Aristotelian to a non-Aristotelian framework of theorizing. This transition seems to have no analogue in present-day cybernetics. This same originality is illustrated in the passage from the Euclidian-Newtonian framework to a non-Euclidian and non-Newtonian scheme of reasoning. How will the mechanistic theory explain this transcendence of past models in favor of newly created patterns of scientific theory?

Our third criticism of cybernetics is that it does not give an adequate physiological explanation of the type of reasoning it has adopted as its very own: the mathematical-deductive form of reasoning. As we proceed, it must be kept in mind that our argument that machine logic does not provide a place for a non-Aristotelian logic is a subordinate part of our broader thesis that cybernetics does not provide a satisfactory neurology for the operations of reasoning.

Non-Aristotelian logic denotes a logic which sets aside the Aristotelian law of excluded middle (or *tertium non datur*) in favor of a more general, *multi-valued logic*. In place of the *two-valued* logic of *true* and *false* (which Boole and Russell took over from Aristotle, though they went far beyond Aristotle in other respects), the non-Aristotelian logic substitutes an *n-valued* or *multi-valued* logic of three values (true, false, and doubtful), or four values, or even an infinite-valued range which is the result of assimilating multi-valued logic to the logic of probability.

Just as non-Aristotelian logic is the Achilles' heel of the medieval form of Aristotelianism which is known as Scholasticism (or neo-Scholasticism in the contemporary Thomistic movement), so is it also the nemesis of current cybernetics. A non-Aristotelian logic would be very difficult to build into a calculating machine (following present blueprints) because the binary system of yes or no, one or zero, firing or not-firing, is necessarily committed to Aristotle's law of excluded middle. There are no intermediate values, and the effort to get a kind of *truth-gradient* out of the atomism of a two-valued system meets with difficulties. Moreover, the attempt to derive a multi-valued logic on a macroscopic level from the averaged effects of microscopic events cannot be justified by the conceptual equipment of present cybernetic theory. Since this is a crucial issue, at least in terms of our own formulation, it is necessary to pause for a moment and examine the problem.

On the microscopic level, — i.e., of individual neurons or channels, — the circuit of response is either 'on' or 'off,' 'firing' or 'not-firing.' Accordingly, the mathematics here is one of the finite differences, — quantum units of action which follow discontinuous laws. On the level of the brain-as-a-whole, which is described as the macroscopic level, the machine can solve partial differential equations where a mathematics of continuity is required. But how does one kind of mathematics come out on the macroscopic level, if it wasn't there in the elements on their own level as microscopic constituents?

The same problem comes up in connection with memory. The idea is implicitly assumed in the statement previously quoted from Hudson Hoagland that the whole machine, as a going concern, has the property of memory, which is not found in the individual neurons (or electron tubes). If we rule out the *emergence of non-summative properties* (as Northrop, McCulloch, and Wiener have), how can a machine have 'memory'?

If we use linear equations to describe the aggregate behavior of a mass of elements, there is not even memory, not to mention originality or creativity. Why should a statistical ensemble of elements contain properties (*continuity* in partial differential equations; *memory* in the brain-as-a-whole) when these are not in the parts? There is true emergence here, and no off-hand remarks about the 'mysticism' of emergence will exorcise the 'spirit' of the machine!

The fact is, — as Bergson pointed out some years back, — there are two types of memory we must take into consideration: (a) memory for individual meaningful events, and (b) rote memory which is comparable to habit. The machine has rote memory in its magnetic tapes, reverberating circuits, and on the image face of its cathode-ray tubes, but machines are unable to step from this type of 'memory' to the recollection of meaningful experiences. To use the word 'memory' to cover both types of phenomena is to commit the same fallacy we considered in connection with the substitution of 'signal' for 'symbol.' Gestalt recognition of meaningful forms implies an integrative action which is responsible for the perception of wholeness in the relation of memory patterns, and such gestalt integration is not accounted for by the 'nothing but' type of physicalism when it excludes field forces.

The trouble originates in the elementalistic postulate of atomic constituents in behavior, when in reality what is required is an organismic approach to brain physiology. We need a relativistic neurology, as I pointed out in my *Promise of Scientific Humanism* (see Chapter XIII and the articles there referred to).

The assumption of current atomistic brain physiology is that any neuron, like any relay or bank of relays, is either 'on' or 'off', — that is, two-valued choices based on previous two-valued choices; but the elementalistic assumption that 'this neuron is active,' and 'that neuron is passive,' is false to the field-organismic situation. The real situation is that *the same neuron may be both active and passive at the same time, with reference to different points on the cortex.* From a macroscopic point of view, on our theory, there is no contradiction in the concept of a statistical ensemble with properties of novelty not found in the parts, for our theory of emergence in terms of field-physics specifically provides for the gestalt properties transposable across the emergent social whole. Here a function of the sum is not a sum of the functions.[12]

And if, in relativity theory, the field supplies the non-linear manifold wherein the familiar formula for the compounding of velocities (addition of vectors) is not applicable, how much more so do brain processes and social phenomena manifest the non-additive or gestalt properties of the mental and cultural life of mankind? The significance of this question and the full import of our own answer to it will appear subsequently, especially in the last chapter of this volume. Here we shall see how the field-theoretical approach to psycho-social phenomena culminates in a theory of the emergence of a social cortex for a coming planetary civilization. In such a framework the data of parapsychology, — such as *ESP* and *PK* effects, — will perhaps find their explanation. What I am working toward is the exfoliation of a three-level isomorphism between electronic computers, human brains, and the embryogenesis of a giant organism, with a world sensorium. To establish the validity of this proposed isomorphism is the goal that lies before us.[13]

FOOTNOTES CHAPTER V

[1]Quoted from Bertrand Russell's *The Philosophy of Leibniz*, pp. 169-170. An excellent selection from Leibniz's writings appears in English translation in Philip P. Wiener's volume on *Leibniz*, in the modern Student's Library, 1951, Charles Scribner's Sons.

[2]In this chapter (Section III), I am using material which first appeared in my article on "Symbolic Logic and the Frontiers of Social Science," *Psyche* (London), Vol. 16, 1936, pp. 138-149. I have also made use of the following volumes: *Symbolic Logic*, by C. I. Lewis and C. H. Langford; *A Modern Introduction to Logic*, by L. S. Stebbing; and the *Introduction to Symbolic Logic*, by Susanne Langer. Wherever, in the present chapter, reference is made to these authorities, the reference is to the above-named books.

Later sections of this chapter have been considerably influenced by the doctrines of Professor Charles W. Morris as presented in his book, *Signs, Language, and Behavior*.

[3]See his *Introduction to Mathematical Philosophy*, Chapters IV and VI; and *Principia Mathematica* (Whitehead and Russell), Vol. 11, Part IV.

[4]Cf. "The Relations Between Symbolic Logic and Large-Scale Calculating Machines," by Edmund C. Berkey, *Science*, 1950, Vol. 112, 395-399.

[5]"Rhythmic Behavior of the Nervous System," by Hudson Hoagland, *Science*, Vol. 109, 1949, 157-164.

[6]See "The Mathematics of Communication," by Warren Weaver, *Scientific American*, Vol. 181, 1949, 11-15. A more detailed and technical summary will be found in Dr. Weaver's volume, *The Mathematical Theory of Communication*, 1949.

[7]Cf. "Machines That Think and Want," by Warren McCulloch, *Comparative Psychology Monographs*, Vol. 20, 1950, 39-50. The problem of *information* in relation to *entropy* and the second law of thermodynamics is discussed in a series of articles in the *American Scientist*. See L. Brillouin's article, "Life, Thermodynamics, and Cybernetics," *American Scientist*, Vol. 37, 1949, 554-568; Richard C. Raymond's, "Communication, Entropy and Life," *Ibid*, Vol. 38, 1950, 278ff.; and Brillouin's reply, "Thermodynamics and Information Theory," *Ibid*, Vol. 38, 1950, 594ff. See also, "The Theory of Open Systems in Physics and Biology," by L. von Bertalanffy, *Science*, Vol. 111, 1950, 23-29.

[8]Cf. "How We Know Universals," by McCulloch, W. S., and Pitts, W., *Bulletin of Mathematical Biophysics*, 1947, Vol. 9, 127-147.

[9]Cf. "Behavior, Purpose, and Teleology," by Rosenblueth, A., Wiener, N., and Bigelow, J., *Philosophy of Science*, 1943, Vol. 10, 18-24.

[10]Cf. "The Neurological and Behavioristic Psychological Basis of the Ordering of Society by Means of Ideas," by F. S. C. Northrop, *Science*, 1948, Vol. 107, 411-417.

[11]See his two articles, "Some Remarks on the Boolean Algebra of Nervous Nets in Mathematical Biophysics," *Bulletin of Mathematical Biophysics*, 1945, Vol. 7, 203-211; and "The Neural Mechanism of Logical Thinking," *Ibid*, 1946, Vol. 8, 29-40.

[12]An alternative way of analyzing the facts of wholistic emergence is provided by Stuart Carter Dodd. Professor Dodd's approach does not contradict my own analysis and in fact supplements it at many points.

[13]A conception of neurophysiology in terms of the plastic phases of synaptic changes as functions of use and disuse is set forth in J. C. Eccles' book, *The Neurophysiological Basis of the Mind* (1953). This is a current substitute for the earlier doctrine of neurobiotaxis or neurotropism (of Kappers and Rashevsky), which I shall utilize later on in my theory of the emergent evolution of a world sensorium, still to be exfoliated.

6

THE MATHEMATICAL BASIS OF KNOWLEDGE

"The true philosophy is written in that great book of nature which lies ever open before our eyes but which no one can read unless he has first learned to understand the language and know the characters in which it is written. It is written in mathematical language, and the characters are triangles, circles, and other geometrical figures."

— Galileo Galilei, *Saggiatore*

I. Types of Science

There are several ways in which the sciences are classified: normative and descriptive, pure and applied, and so on. As we noted in the preceding chapter, one of the most important of these distinctions occurs between the empirical or natural sciences and the non-empirical or formal sciences. That is:

Sciences	Empirical (or Natural)	Physical Sciences Biological Sciences Social Sciences
	Non-empirical (or formal)	Logic Mathematics

According to a generally accepted way of stating this distinction, the non-empirical sciences are concerned with the purely formal and necessary implications, whereas the empirical or natural sciences are concerned with the existence of things and their inter-relations in space and time. From this viewpoint, therefore, mathematics and history represent the extremes in two groups of sciences, mathematics yielding *certainty* in its conclusions, but having no material *content*, whereas history possesses *content* but has no *certainty* or *predictability*. That is to say, mathematics and logic deal with questions of formal implication, have certainty but no empirical content; history deals with questions of existence, has rich content, but does not attain certainty about the future. For this reason, a science such as physics, which is closer to mathematics and farther from history, achieves more certainty or predictability than the social sciences, where history figures more prominently. In general, the natural sciences fall somewhere between pure mathematics and sheer history, and have many of the values and limitations of each.

The relationship between the two groups of sciences raises difficult questions. One wonders, for example, how a non-empirical science can have meaning if it has no 'content.' Other questions also come to mind. We shall have to postpone most of them and content ourselves with pointing out the obvious: that however they may have come into being, the non-empirical sciences *do* exist and have, at the present time, a considerable measure of independence of the natural sciences. Moreover, in their contemporary highly developed form, these 'pure' sciences have evolved a mode of procedure that is broadly described by the term *deductive system*. We shall study this system in more detail in the present chapter.

II. Postulational System

In a general way, the technique of procedure in mathematics and symbolic logic is termed *postulational procedure*. The structure of a deductive system gives us the three-level affair that was outlined in the previous chapter. A condensed form of the same scheme may be presented thus:

TERMS:	*Terms* are the symbols which represent
1....	the fundamental entities of the system.
2....	These are the primitive concepts of a
3....	thought-structure.
POSTULATES:	*Postulates* are the statements of the re-
1....	lations which obtain among the terms.
2....	
3....	

THEOREMS:	*Theorems* are statements of the more complex relations, logically dependent upon the postulates.
1....	
2....	
3....	

Every formal deductive system consists of (1) *terms* which serve as symbols for primitive concepts; (2) *postulates*, which define how the terms are related among themselves and what operations are permissible on them; and (3) *theorems*, which develop the logical consequences of the postulates and are completely deducible from them. First let us focus our attention upon the concepts.

If one consults a treatise on geometry, such as Euclid's *Elements*, he will find the definitions of certain elementary concepts stated in appropriate terms. Let us take the concept of *angle* as an example. The definitions given are usually stated in terms of other elementary ideas: *lines*, *planes*, *intersections*, and so forth. Now if we ask for the definition of these new terms (concepts), we find that we must either employ the earlier terms or introduce an additional vocabulary. The only way out of the resulting dilemma, — i.e., the alternatives of an infinite regress of definitions or of using definitions that are circular, — is to tell the reader that he has an 'intuitive' idea of what an 'angle' (or other notion) is and thus leave it undefined. Given these 'undefined' elements, other terms can be defined in terms of these 'primitives.' This procedure has the sanction of deductive system-makers. As Professor C. J. Keyser states it in his book on *Mathematical Philosophy*, "If he [the thinker] contends, as sometimes he will contend, that he has defined all his terms and proved all his propositions, then either he is a performer of logical miracles or he is an ass; and, as you know, logical miracles are impossible."

In the deductive system one has the freedom to choose his primitive concepts and postulates, but from that point on, one's logical freedom ceases and one is the victim of 'fate', — one can get out only what is wrapped up in these elementary concepts and postulates. Different systems take different ideas and postulates as basic; but these must be internally consistent, else the system destroys itself. Those whose minds seek unity like to believe that behind the various systems of mathematical logic lies a super-system that includes them all; and, indeed, as previously noted, there are indications that for every system there is a more inclusive system that embraces it. This supports the doctrine that a viewpoint which integrates three sets of ideas is superior to one that reconciles two sets of ideas, and so on.

The question of what decides the choice of primitives is interesting. The earlier view, contained within the philosophies of Pythagoras, Plato, Aristotle, Descartes, and others, was that certain self-evident truths, supply the inescapable principles ('laws of thought' and 'axioms of mathematics') for rational procedure. This view is not generally accepted today. Because of the difficulty in finding such intuitively known principles, the tendency is to regard 'axioms' as 'postulates' which may be accepted or rejected at will.

Since Russell was interested in deriving arithmetic from logic, his problem was governed by this concern. Accordingly, as we shall see later, he attempted to show how the concepts of *zero*, *number*, and *successor*, could be derived from such strictly logical concepts as *class*, *membership in a class*, and *similarity*. If this could be accomplished, arithmetic could be shown to be a branch of logic, an achievement of no mean proportions. In a moment, we shall see how this synthesis was attempted. But before doing that, let us say a word about the rôle of postulates in formal systems.

III. The Role of Postulates

It is apparent from the preceding breakdown that the distinctive characteristic of any formal system is to be found in the postulates, for the terms have no properties except those declared by the postulates, and since the theorems only elaborate what has already been stated by the postulates, they must therefore depend on the latter for significance in the system. Such mathematical creations may appear at first sight to be so arbitrary and artificial as to be insignificant for human problems. But the great advantage of such abstractness is that misunderstanding is thus reduced to a minimum and the communicative capacity of ideas is raised to a maximum.

Postulate systems provide a framework for thought in which the conclusions will hold whenever the system's postulates are admitted, regardless of what particular referents may be correlated with the primitive concepts (symbols). When concrete meanings *are* given to the previously undefined terms, the result is a special *interpretation* or *model* of the abstract system. In this case, the definitions come from outside the system itself, being specified for the postulate set by the experiential referents which give the significance to the system, but at the same time introducing a degree of vagueness and a consequent possibility of misinterpretation. This 'significance,' or reference of the statements of the system to something outside the system itself, is what determines the 'content' of that system. When we say that a purely formal system has no content, we mean that it has no content of the same level as any given interpretation of it may have; that is, the 'content' of any formal system is the 'form' of its special 'interpretations.' In a sense, the experiential contents of thought-systems are contingent, for their 'contents' are the 'forms' of those particular segments of the world which the systems organize. As we have seen, this type of defining can lead to an endless chain, since the words of the definitions call for further definitions, which again means reference to more fundamental levels of experience. Logically, this regression is infinite, and thus it appears that we can make 'precise' statements only in an ultimately undetermined world. *This is but another instance of the thesis that we live in an 'open' world, capable of indefinite development and expansion.*

Turning now to the postulate set itself, let us consider in more detail the conditions which limit the mathematician in his choice of postulates. Since the postulate set is the foundation of a formal system, considerations of physical reality do not enter in. And in the case of a general system (not a *model* or *interpretation*), there are no empirical referents for the primitive terms which might restrict the postulates to those statements which would be significant for those referents. Therefore the postulates can only be limited by each other; that is, the primary condition placed upon them is that they be *consistent* with each other. Of course, no postulate can be logically dependent on any other, for it would then be a theorem and not a postulate. Other properties are desirable, such as simplicity and conciseness, but these are not as essential to a deductive system as *consistency* and *independence.*

To say that a postulate system is consistent is to assert that no theorem deducible from it shall ever constitute the negation of one previously deduced. That seems reasonable, until we consider that this requires that each individual theorem should be checked against every other. The difficulty of this becomes obvious when we recall that there are an indefinite (perhaps infinite) number of theorems deducible from a postulate set. There is no way by which we can know *a priori* how many theorems may be proved by our postulates, nor can we be certain at any point in the process of expanding a system that we have made all possible elaborations. Thus the method of individual checking can give negative results only; it can demonstrate that the system contains an inconsistency, by presenting an instance of contradiction, but it cannot prove that the postulates are mutually consistent because it can never reach all possible theorems in order to check them.

If, therefore, we wish to assure ourselves that our axiom set is completely self-consistent and will never, in any of its possible deductions, present a contradiction, we shall either have to take another way around or restate our problem. Here we get into very deep waters, and only the strongest swimmers will stay afloat. Nevertheless, we cannot avoid the issue, which brings us into new regions of the philosophy of mathematics.

At the present time there are three main approaches to the resolution of the problems we have come upon, each of which is associated with a distinctive school in the philosophy of mathematics. These three schools are termed *Logicism*, *Formalism*, and *Intuitionism*. Each presents a unique view of the nature of mathematics, and thereby helps in a measure to clarify our understanding of what we are doing when we build any kind of formal thought-system. Since our goal is to show how various fields of inquiry can be made tributary to an integrated knowledge of the world, it will be necessary to enter into a rather detailed analysis of the foundations of mathematics. We consider first the school of logicism.

IV. The Logistic Approach to Mathematics

Everyone knows that mathematics is logical, but the thesis with which the name of Bertrand Russell is associated is that mathematics *is* logic. Another way of stating the thesis of logicism is that, given the postulates of pure logic, all of mathematics consists of theorems derived from these postulates. For example, a straight line is not merely a notion from which theorems are deduced by logical methods, but is a concept that can be defined in purely logical terms. Russell's work, *The Principles of Mathematics*, expounds this view to show how mathematics had helped to simplify this problem by reducing much of mathematics to arithmetic, and how logicians had, in parallel fashion, expanded traditional logic so as to be able to handle mathematical questions. In *Principia Mathematica*, Russell and Whitehead stated certain postulates of logic and then proceeded to deduce enough mathematics to demonstrate the thesis. As the authors of the *Principia* state it in their Introduction, "There is no point at which a sharp line can be drawn with logic to the left and mathematics to the right."

The school of Logicism has sought to show that not only is it true that mathematics can be derived from pure logic, but also that the problem of consistency in mathematics must be referred to the domain of logic. The resulting postulates will not be completely free from limitation by the significance inherent in the primitive terms, since these are now to be defined by something outside the mathematical system itself, — in this case in terms of variables and logical constants. As we have already noted, a variable is any symbol whose meaning is not specifically determined, but is limited in such a fashion that it can preserve a recognizable 'identity' throughout a context, without danger of confusion with other symbols; while logical constants are such words as 'implies,' 'contains,' 'not,' 'or,' 'some,' 'all,' and so forth, which have unique meanings enabling us to make precise statements about the variables.

In the system of Logicism, as Kattsoff[1] points out, three distinct tasks must be met and overcome: it must be shown (1) that every mathematical concept is a logical concept; (2) that all methods of proof used in mathematics are purely logical methods; (3) that every mathematical proposition can be deducted from the fundamental assumptions of logic alone. We shall see how Logicism faces up to each of these tasks.

The first step in this program was the reduction of all mathematics to one particular branch of it: arithmetic, or the fundamental relations of the natural numbers (positive integers). This part of the project was carried out in great part by the Italian mathematician, G. Peano,[2] who succeeded in setting up a group of five postulates, relating three primitive terms, from which the entire body of arithmetic could be derived by construction. The primitive terms are *zero*, *number*, and *successor*. The five postulates are:

P_1: *o is a number.*
P_2: *The successor of a number is a number.*
P_3: *No two numbers have the same successor.*

P_4: *o is not the successor of any number.*
P_5: *Any property which belongs to o, and also to the successor of any number which has the property, belongs to all numbers.*

This last postulate is the famous principle covering *mathematical induction*, and, as we shall soon see, it raises a crucial issue in the proposed reduction of mathematics to logic.

It was through the use of mathematical logic that Peano set out to 'reduce' mathematics to arithmetic. Therefore, the next step toward the logistic goal was the replacement of the undefined terms (primitives) of Peano's framework by definitions in terms of logical constants and variables. The first term to be so defined is 'number,' and it is at this point that a very important decision had to be made, affecting the entire conception of the nature of mathematical thinking.

It is commonly recognized that there are two aspects to the idea of number, namely, 'cardinal' and 'ordinal,' expressed respectively by the words 'one,' 'two,' 'three,' and so forth, and the words 'first,' 'second,' 'third,' and so on. The *cardinal* aspect of number refers to *quantity*, while the *ordinal* aspect refers to the idea of *succession*. It should also be noted here, since the point will be of importance later, that cardinality is a *spatial* notion, whereas ordinality is a *temporal* notion, implying the involvement of the agent or knower. It may also be observed that the notion of *order* is prerequisite to the ordinal concept of number, whereas the notion of *unit* is prerequisite to the cardinal concept. In defining the three primitive terms, therefore, two of them must be defined simultaneously or interdependently: if the cardinal aspect is regarded as the more basic, 'zero' and 'number' will be interdependent, and 'successor' must be subsequent and dependent; but if the ordinal aspect assumes priority, then 'number' and 'successor' must be defined together, and 'zero' afterwards.

Since Russell's thesis was the demonstration of the complete derivation of mathematics from logic, he assumed that the cardinal concept of number is prior to the ordinal, because ordinality could not be directly expressed in terms of logical constants without using the notion of cardinality. Cardinality is recognizable only when there are two or more sets of objects having the *same* number of members; that is, the 'cardinality' of the members of a basketball team, the fingers on one hand, the pennies in a nickel, and so forth, is that property which they all have in common of containing the same quantity of instances.

That they have the same quantity of members may be checked by putting the members of each class into one-to-one correspondence with those of each other class. Every class which can be put into such one-to-one correspondence with any given class will have the same cardinality as the given class, and there will thus be a class of such classes, all having the same cardinality. The classes are said to be similar to one another, a property which they share among themselves, and which is the only property necessarily shared by them. The cardinal number of any one of such classes is defined as that class of classes similar to a given one. In this manner, 'number' can be defined to be the class of all classes similar to a class F having the following properties: an element x is in F, and if any other element y is in F, y is identical with x. And the 'successor' of a number N becomes the class of classes similar to the class which contains both the class whose number is N, and the class F, and nothing more.

Central to this procedure is the notion of 'class,' or as it is often called, 'aggregate.' It is characteristic of this notion that it represents something static, unchanging, finished; belonging to an external, objective world; something given and not constructed. An aggregate, or class, is simply a set, or collection, of any elements whatever which have some well-defined property in common so that, for any object presented, it can be decided whether or not it belongs to the class. Unfortunately, this notion, which apparently defines the numbers so well, has internal flaws of its own. For consider the class of all those classes which are not members of themselves: is this class then a member of itself, or is it not? Obviously, it is impossible to decide the question. Another example of the same type of paradox is presented by the famous case of the barber who shaves every man in town who does not shave himself.

There are two problems involved in these paradoxes, both of which provide opportunity for difference of opinion as to their proper solution. In the first place, it is immediately apparent that the definition of 'class' must somehow be at fault, so that either it must be modified and limited in its application or an altogether new definition must be sought. Perhaps the notion of aggregate just is not valid at all. Secondly, it is clear that the paradoxes develop only if it is assumed that the object in question either has the given property, or does not have it, so that the truth of one assertion can be proved by demonstrating the contradiction to which its negation would lead. For example, the barber in the above case must be a man who does shave himself, for if we assume that he is a man who does not shave himself, then the barber will shave him; but since he *is* the barber, this means that he *does* shave himself, contrary to the first assumption. This type of reasoning is what is known as an 'indirect proof,' and is dependent on the so-called Law of Excluded Middle (LEM), according to which an entity either has the property a, or it has the property $\backsim a$. Of course, one wonders what good it is to have such a 'law' if one can't decide in every particular instance which alternative is the correct one.

Instead of questioning the law of excluded middle, Russell followed the first course of correcting the inadequate definition of aggregate by inventing his 'theory of types,' which distinguishes between a class, considered as a unity, and a class considered as a collection of other unities. The chief principle of the theory of types is the stipulation that whatever involves 'all' of a collection must not itself be one of the collection. This is a recognition that there are collections about whose 'totalities' no significant statement can be made. For example, no significant statement can be made about *all* propositions, for such a statement would itself be a proposition. But Russell's redefinition of aggregate is not the only possible approach, and other philosophies of mathematics also have something to say on this matter.

Thus the *first task* of Logistics, the demonstration that every mathematical concept is a logical concept, led to the study of the logical paradox of the theory of aggregates. The *second task*, that of showing that all methods of proof are logical methods, has brought up the question of the conditions under which such methods are applicable at all, as just shown in the case of the LEM. This becomes an even more crucial question when attempts are made to deal with infinite collections of objects in terms of the ordinary logic. Since the greater part of the difficulties in the philosophy of mathematics, as well as its significance through analogy for the rest of our thinking, is involved to some extent in the notion of infinity, it will be pertinent to our purpose to discuss briefly the main aspects of the concept of infinity.

Two different notions of infinity occur in mathematics: the *potential* and the *actual*. 'Potential infinity' refers to an endless chain of operations, a process; 'actual infinity' refers to a set which can be put into one-to-one correspondence with a proper part of itself, — thus it is thought of as an *entity*. Therefore, potential infinity associates itself with the counting process, with the ordinal concept of number, and is indeterminate in the sense of being unfinished or still becoming; whereas actual infinity is closely related to comparison, to cardinal concepts, and to determinacy (completeness) of being. One example of potential infinity is the endless divisibility of any line segment into halves, where attention is directed not to the measure of the segments involved, but to the repetition of the operation of halving as equivalent to counting. An example of an actual infinity is the set of natural numbers, which can be put into one-to-one correspondence with the set of odd numbers, a proper sub-set of itself.

Now the Russell definition of cardinal number has an advantage in that it serves equally well for both finite and infinite aggregates, and provides us with a criterion for comparing infinite collections with one another. Common-sense seems to indicate that there is no possibility for comparing orders of infinity. But the Russell definition of cardinality claims that some infinite classes are greater than others in a sense made significant by definition. Thus, if the cardinality of the natural numbers is $\aleph_0$, then any other class which holds a one-to-one correspondence with the set of natural numbers will also have the cardinality $\aleph_0$. These classes are said to be denumerable, or countable, since the operation of putting into one-to-one correspondence with the positive integers is essentially counting. The rational numbers, for example, can be put into one-to-one correspondence with the natural numbers, and therefore constitute a denumerable set. Cantor's 'diagonal procedure' proves this fact, as the following device indicates:

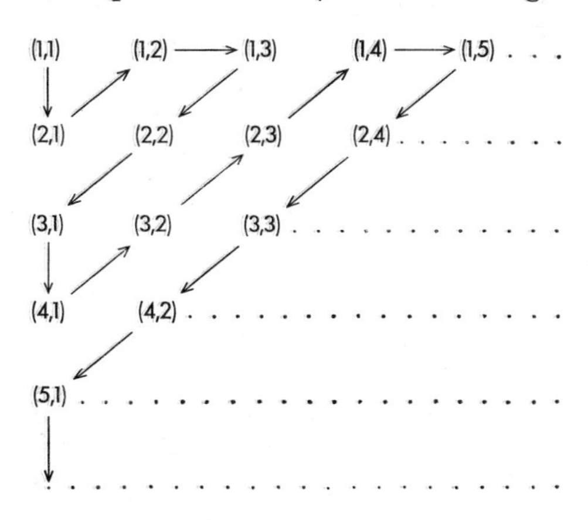

The denumerable infinity of pairs of numbers

However, if we attempt to write in a countable array all of the real numbers (all possible non-terminating decimals), we find that a number not included in the array can always be constructed for we have only to take as its first digit one that is different from the first digit of the first number in our array, its second digit different from the second digit of the second number in the array, and so forth, and it will differ from every number in this supposedly complete collection. But it will itself be the kind of number assumed to belong to this collection, thus contradicting our assumption that we have already collected them all. This is the classical proof that the real numbers form a non-denumerable set, and that therefore their cardinality is 'greater' than that of the natural numbers.

It would be well to point out a certain distinction in the type of infinity recognizable in the non-denumerable, as contrasted with the denumerable sets, a distinction which will be useful later on when we attempt an analogy with the nature of knowledge in general. Denumerable infinite sets have an infinite extension in that they are composed of completely defined and determinate elements of which there are an infinite number. But there is no possibility of confusing one of these elements with another, for the characteristics which distinguish them from one another are finite in number and available to observation. The continuum, on the other hand, has an intensive infinity because, in addition to containing an infinite number of terms, each number contained in it is itself written as an infinite sequence of digits. It would therefore be necessary to exhibit *all* of these digits in order to distinguish between two real numbers. A great deal of controversy in the philosophy of mathematics can be traced to the indeterminacy inherent in this situation. The essential question is this: how can you prove, or even discuss, the determinate properties of those numbers which are themselves not fully determined?

As an example of this problem, consider the question: does the sequence 0123456789 occur in the decimal expansion of π? π has been developed to several hundred digits and this particular sequence has not yet been observed. But π is a non-periodic and non-terminating decimal, so that it is impossible to predict what sequence of digits will appear next. Under such circumstances, are we justified in saying that this sequence from 0 to 9 *either* does *or* does not occur? The indeterminacy of π is not an accidental feature of our knowledge of number, but an essential and characteristic property of the number itself, resulting from its definition. No matter how far the development has been carried, if the sequence sought has not been found, our knowledge of number is still indeterminate; that is, we are not justified in saying that *if* we could carry the expansion far enough we would eventually find the answer. What sense does it make to say that the sequence exists, or does not exist, as the case may be, regardless of whether we can find it? This is the problem of LEM again. Just what does it mean for a mathematical statement to be true, so that we can discuss its truth or falsity independently of our having determined which one of these values characterizes our statement? The assertion that the *LEM* can be applied here amounts to affirming that a number 'in its own right' is a determinate entity, even though we express it as essentially indeterminate. But we shall return to this point later.

The question of truth in mathematics is always associated with the question of the existence of mathematical objects. Therefore, we must ask ourselves just what it means for a mathematical object to 'exist.' In the empirical sciences, the problem of the existence of the subject matter is a relatively easy one, for there is here an independent realm of objects (even if it consists only of 'pointer-readings') which immediately registers whether or not statements predicated of the realm are true. If mathematics could likewise be assumed to be a system of statements about some independent reality, objective to the operations of the mathematician, it would be quite simple to agree on what it means for a mathematical statement to be 'true.' This is not a question however of mathematics being independent of the mathematician's mind, but rather a question of the independence of mathematics from the operations of the mathematician, some of which are necessarily unfinished operations. In other words, the relation of independence is questioned, not because the mathematician is a human being with a finite life-time, but because of the logical impossibility of achieving the infinite through successive reiterations of the finite.

The purpose of this digression into the infinite was to discover the difficulties inherent in the second part of the Logistic thesis, and also to bring out the inner core of the controversy over the foundations of mathematics in the question: *when may a mathematical statement be said to be true?* What does it mean for a mathematical object to exist? The answer of the Logistic school on questions of truth is to regard 'true' as an undefined value which is assigned to certain statements in accordance with definite postulates. Thus the concept 'true' has no connotation through reference to something outside the postulate system in which it occurs.

The *third task* set for Logicism, the demonstration that all of the postulates of mathematics are purely logical postulates, grew out of the foregoing considerations. For instance, one of the main points in the contention between the Logistic school and its critics is the status of mathematical induction, the fifth Peano postulate. According to the thesis of Logicism, this 'postulate' should appear as a theorem when Russell's logical definitions for Peano's three primitive terms are accepted. But any attempt to prove the principle of induction turns out to be circular, for the conclusion of the principle involves an infinite cardinality in saying that the property under consideration shall be true for all members of the set. Now the notion of an infinite cardinality depends for its definition on the possibility of putting into one-to-one correspondence all those sets having the same infinite cardinal number, which is itself an infinite operation, and thus requires the use of the principle of induction for the validation of its own possibility. This situation makes it evident that the principle of induction must be an independent assumption, not reducible to a purely logical principle. Such, at any rate, was the conclusion of Henri Poincaré, one of the greatest mathematicians of the nineteenth century, who urged a rather intuitionist view of mathematics. But we can discuss that view to better advantage later, when we consider the question of whether mathematics is a purely analytical, or an essentially synthetic, discipline.

In conclusion, however, we can say that the work of the Logistic school has been of great value, especially in clarifying the relations of logical and mathematical concepts by developing symbolism techniques for dealing with these fundamental issues. But it is now generally conceded that, in the strictest interpretation, Logicism has failed to prove its thesis.

V. The Formalist Analysis of Mathematics

A second approach to the philosophy of mathematics occurs in the Formalist (or Axiomatic) school, the foremost exponent of which is David Hilbert, in Germany. It differs chiefly from the Logistic school in that it abandons what might be called Russell's metaphysics of logic, observing that the Logistic attitude toward mathematics met its difficulties at the point where it attempted to refer mathematics to something outside itself, such as 'logical constants.' The Formalist program, as Hilbert presents it in his volume on *Die Grundlagen der Geometrie*, finds mathematics and logic as two completely independent enterprises. In this system, mathematics is the science of the possible *structures* of objects only, that is, any sets of arbitrary operations performed according to arbitrary rules on arbitrary symbols. Logic, on the other hand, is the science of passing from one statement about a mathematical system to another. In other words, the postulates define what may be done with the symbols, but logic judges whether or not the postulates are being properly applied. Thus logic serves as an 'umpire,' outside the game itself, rather than as a member of the 'family' to which all the objects in play belong. The fundamental mathematical objects are themselves completely meaningless symbols and, having no reference to anything beyond themselves, they are characterized only by those axioms (postulates) which explicitly award them certain properties. Since mathematics has no external reference, the proof of a statement *about* the system has to be based *on* the system, which poses recurrent problems of proof of consistency for the Formalists.

One interesting feature of the Formalist program is its conception of the nature of mathematics and of mathematizing. Although it is a strictly formal, supposedly self-contained system, mathematics is left hanging in mid-air as it were, since it is not itself immediate experience, nor is it allowed reference to any immediate experience. It is the articulation of pure *possibility of structure*, with no limits prescribed by content, not even to the extent that a reference to logical constants would constitute content. An empirical system may also be self-contained in the sense that statements can be made about any of its objects only in terms of some other of its objects. However, in answer to the question of what *is* the object, it presents an immediate experience by saying 'this is it,' something which Formalist mathematics can never do.

This means that mathematics is static, a finished system, all of whose statements already exist, and that the truth or falsity of any proposition is determined automatically by the axioms with reference to which the proposition is constructed. Once the mathematician has selected his axioms and fundamental symbols, the whole system is in determinate existence, and he has only to unravel it. For the Formalist, mathematical reality is independent of the mathematician's activity, independent of immediate experience, and hence independent of time. Such an attitude, of course, accepts without question the law of excluded middle. Regardless of whether we are clever enough to prove it, a given proposition either is, or is not, 'true' (i.e., consistent with the axioms of the system).

This approach permits the Formalist to indulge in what some other mathematicians regard as a very dubious procedure: the use of the indirect proof. Indirect proof consists of an assumption that the proposition in question is not true, followed by a demonstration that such an assumption, in conjunction with the original axioms of the system, leads to a contradiction. The principle of the method rests on the assertion that if the denial of the proposition is not consistent with the axioms, then the affirmation of the truth of it is.

It is apparent, of course, that this attitude makes sense only when the proposition in question is susceptible to judgment as consistent or inconsistent with the axiom set. For instance, in our previous example, the number π was not sufficiently limited to define the operation of locating the sequence 0 through 9 in it. It would seem, however, that if the only symbols used in a proposition are the fundamental symbols of the system, and the only operations inherent in the proposition are those defined by the axioms, then the proposition should be either true or false with respect to this system. However, even this is not the case, as we shall see presently. There is another difficulty with the method of indirect proof. The contradiction, which is expected to establish the falsity of the assumed proposition and the consequent truth of its negation, only indicates that the entire set of propositions, — i.e., the original axioms and assumed proposition, — is not self-consistent. In order to be certain that the error is in the assumed proposition, it must first be established that the original set of axioms is self-consistent.

Proving the self-consistency of the original axiom set therefore becomes the center of all of the Formalist's problems. Although the attempts to achieve this have proved fruitless in the end, they have at least been valuable in revealing the sort of problem involved in mathematical thinking. One of the difficulties in the situation was brought to a focus by L. E. J. Brouwer[3] in his article on "Intuitionism and Formalism," where he showed clearly the circularity involved in proving consistency by means of complete induction. The axiom set, whose consistency is to be established, contains this very postulate of complete induction, so that it is not permissible to use it in order to prove an assertion about the axiom set as a whole. Even if the inductive axioms were known independently to be true, they would be 'true' only under certain conditions, and it would then be necessary to prove that those conditions were satisfied by the consistency principle.

It was Hilbert's plan to establish first the consistency of his axioms for finite sets, by reference to arithmetic models, and then adjoin to these a 'transfinite axiom,' which would permit him to extend his operations to infinite sets and their properties. Leaving aside for a moment the question of the consistency of axioms about finite sets, Hilbert proposed to prove that *if* the finite axioms are consistent among themselves, then the transfinite axiom will be consistent with them, and hence it will be legitimate to use it in connection with all infinite collections, thus overcoming the handicap of our finite and incomplete thinking operations.

The transfinite axiom itself asserts that if a certain property is true of a certain member of a given class, then it is true for all members of that class. Hilbert's example is the property of being venal. Then the 'certain member' would have to be a definite individual with a sense of justice so incorruptible that if he were venal, it must follow that all mankind is venal. By means of this postulate, Hilbert proceeded to prove the various properties of the infinite sets constructed by Cantor, maintaining that their mathematical existence is demonstrated by their failure to contradict previously established theorems. But there seem to be some difficulties with this program. For one thing, the axiom is dependent for its truth, and even for its significance, on the selection of that 'certain member,' and it would appear likely that if the conditions restricting the choice of that member were articulated, the result would be the usual form of the postulate of complete induction. Also, the whole problem of the meaning of the 'existence' of infinite aggregates is again to the front.

Turning now to the demonstration of the consistency of the axioms for finite sets, we find that the method of proof is based on the property of the axiom set of being *categorical.* A set is said to be categorical when any two sets of objects which satisfy the axioms are isomorphic to one another with respect to the operations indicated by the axioms. Therefore, if a certain set of objects previously known to be consistent satisfies all of the axioms, one is assured that the more general set is likewise consistent. This is the argument behind the use of a 'model,' wherein its very existence demonstrates its consistency. More often, arithmetical rather than physical models have been used, because of their simplicity and precision. But arithmetic is dependent upon the concept of natural number, and the Formalist scheme therefore collapses.

After insisting that Russell's definition of 'one' is circular because the definition of the cardinal 'one' depends on the setting up of a one-to-one correspondence, which presupposes the notion of 'one,' Hilbert concludes that mathematics and logic must be developed simultaneously, not deriving one from the other, and that the natural numbers are to be constructed from more primitive 'thought-things' by methods no more complicated than that by which we recognize that 2 and 2 are 4. But for us this means ultimately that immediate experience must come in somewhere.

The foregoing difficulties have led to the conclusion that *a mathematical system cannot be self-sufficient*; that is, we cannot set bounds to our mathematizing and expect to be able to prove everything about a closed system in terms of that system. Therefore, the original aims of the Formalist school must remain unattainable, a fact which may seem surprising until we recall that any proof of consistency is dependent on the decidability of the various propositions involved in a system. Given a proposition stated in terms of a certain system, is it possible to decide whether it is true or false by reference only to the axioms and previously proved theorems of the system? This is the essential question, for a consistency proof would develop as a demonstration that for any proposition *P*, which was demonstrable in the system, *not-P was not* demonstrable. Of course, for the consistency of the whole system, it would be necessary to prove this for *any* proposition *P* of the system, and we have already seen the difficulties involved in this aspect of the attempt. The inability to do this was formally stated and proved by Kurt Gödel.[4]

The proof of Gödel's remarkable theorems cannot be given here, but the general significance of his work may be pointed out. Summed up, *Gödel's theorems mean that mathematics, and therefore any intellectual system constructed on the postulational (or 'axiomatic') pattern, can never be regarded as a closed system, completely formalized.* Some interpreters would hold that this undecidability does not necessarily result in an abandonment of LEM, but rather calls for a redefinition of truth. It may be argued that any proposition may still be regarded as either true or false with respect to a given system, but in order to find out which it is, it is necessary to refer to something outside the system.

Again, it may be pointed out, this situation does not imply that there are mathematical thoughts which cannot be formalized at all. Rather it means that for any given system of mathematical thought there are certain principles which cannot be formalized within that system, but which, when expressed, constitute a meta-system with respect to the given system. This latter, which is our interpretation of Gödel's research, bears a certain analogy to Russell's theory of types, except that we have here an explicit denial of the axiom of reduction, an exclusion which is important for us in the development of our dimensional theory of thought-systems.

We discover, therefore, that in order to state formally every principle in use in our mathematizing activities, we are led to an infinite regress of 'meta-systems,' a chain which is incomplete at any finite stage. In the thesis to which we are committed, this situation is accepted as genuine and workable. If we were to hold that any nonterminating regression invalidates each individual step in it, we would simply have to abandon formal logic as fruitless and fall back on nonrational methods for solving problems. Instead of doing that, let us rather approach the dilemma from the other point of view and admit that, *since formal logic is obviously an exceedingly valuable instrument in our intellectual lives, its necessary incompleteness is not an absurdity, but merely a characteristic to be taken into account as we employ it.* To see why this viewpoint is proper, we consider now the final approach to a philosophy of mathematics.

VI. The Intuitionist Approach to Mathematics

Intuitionism represents quite another approach to mathematics from that shared by Logicism and Formalism. For these latter two, mathematics is a game played with symbols, and consists in the manipulation of these symbols (logical and/or mathematical). But the intuitionist has another goal. For him, mathematics deals with certain kinds of objects, or certain aspects of objects, and the symbols merely aid the mathematician in his highly abstract and intricate ways of thinking about them. That is, he feels the close relationship of mathematics to the activity of thought, and he wishes to carry on this natural function as a free, living activity. In addition to Brouwer's form of intuitionism, a calculus of intuitionist logic has been developed by A. Heyting,[5] who argues that the Formalist system results in statements about language, not statements about objects, and is, therefore, not mathematics.

Max Black[6] describes this difference in approach as the distinction between 'static' and 'dynamic' attitudes toward mathematics. A static attitude stresses the certainty and completeness of mathematics, its ability to accumulate truth indefinitely without ever contradicting itself. The dynamic attitude, on the other hand, emphasizes the growth of mathematics as a cultural achievement produced by our fallible human minds. The former attitude is compatible with realistic philosophy in general, since it wishes to deal with mathematical results as if they existed independently of minds thinking them. The dynamic attitude is more closely related to idealistic philosophy in that it regards the reality of human experience as the point of origin of all thought-systems. As an example of this latter attitude, it is interesting to note how the principle of mathematical induction, which Poincaré regarded as the key to the whole of mathematics, proceeds from the idea of growth, just as Brouwer's concept of natural numbers does. That is to say, both are 'becoming' operations, meaningful only when defined as constructions which require *time*, — time in the sense of a linear sequence of 'present moments,' with a definite direction and a real distinction between 'past,' 'present,' and 'future.' This stands in contrast to the formalist conception, where there is no sense of time at all because mathematics exists in an eternity where past, present, and future coexist simultaneously.

Intuitionism harmonizes best with the idealist, dynamic emphasis. All mathematical objects are products of human thought and, as such, are subject to the errors and limitations of human thinking. This means, among other things, that properties of mathematical objects are limited to thinkable properties. As Black points out (*loc. cit.*), this is the philosophical motive which lies behind the Intuitionist's insistence on constructibility as the criterion of existence. Kant may be said to be one of the earlier of the modern Intuitionists, for ideas were to him subjective, since they depend on the activity of the mind or on its structure. This does not mean that they were subjective in the sense of being completely arbitrary or created freely, but that they were conditioned by the primary intuitions of the human mind. In this manner, Kant sought to account for *synthetic a priori* judgments. So far as mathematics is concerned, the Formalists and the Logical Positivists do not admit that there are any synthetic *a priori* propositions, but hold that mathematics is a vast tautology, completely analytical in character. The Intuitionists, on the other hand, hold that mathematics is based on an intuition of a process which is not capable of deduction from tautologies. In this sense, Intuitionism accepts a synthetic feature.

The great challenge to the Formalists is that of demonstrating the complete consistency of the system within its own terms. This, as we have seen, cannot be done. But even if the mathematical system were completely consistent, and demonstrably so, that would not account for our having one mathematical system rather than another, *nor would it account for the applicability of that system to the physical world.* If mathematics reduces to a postulate system, then the choice of the particular postulates is itself an act of mathematical creativity; surely, therefore, the assertion of these first axioms cannot be an analytic statement. Postulate systems usually are built upon preestablished doctrines, and the consistency of the system is then made to rest on the consistency of this foundation. As the Intuitionists observe, we must make a synthetic judgment which cannot be accounted for in any other way than by simply admitting it as a primary intuition.

These remarks indicate that the Intuitionists are much concerned about the source of mathematical reality, which they regard as a more fundamental problem than the question of the formal consistency of mathematics. It is difficult for us to believe that 'reality' should be inconsistent, so if we can trace our mathematical thinking to something that we can admit as 'real experience,' the consistency of our mathematics would follow automatically.

The earlier idealist position of modern philosophy supplied a basis by asserting that mathematics is an exposition of the necessary laws of the mind, an expression of the structure of the mind itself as a static entity of intuitions and categories. This was the view of Kant, who held that number is not a concept, but a category in terms of which concepts can be framed. Thus, mathematical propositions, though undeniably synthetic, are also *a priori*, and can be stated by the mind on the basis of its own nature without recourse to experience.

The current form of Intuitionism is derived from Kant's position, but with considerable modification. It traces mathematics to the creative activity of the mind, rather than to its structure, and finds the reality of mathematics residing in its constant evolution to ever higher forms of thought. This attitude is well expressed by Brunschvig,[7] as follows:

"The truth of the science does not imply the existence of a transcendental reality; it is bound to the processes of verification which are immanent in the development of mathematics. It is this verification that we have believed we could uncover at the root of the constitutive notions of knowing. . . . Mathematical philosophy has ended its task by setting itself to follow the natural order of history, by becoming conscious of the two characters whose union is the specific mark of intelligence: indefinite capacity for progress, perpetual disquietude as to verification."

Present day Intuitionism, as defined by Brouwer, represents this last explanation of the reality of mathematics. But Brouwer's Intuitionism differs greatly from the original Kantian philosophy with which it has historical continuity. Of the two primary intuitions of Kant's philosophy, — space and time, — Brouwer rejects that of space, and retains that of time. This is related to his belief that the primitive conception of number is ordinal rather than cardinal, which makes the conception of succession more basic than that of magnitude. The recognition of succession, Brouwer feels, cannot be adequately accounted for without referring to an original intuition of succession in time, an unending sequence of numbers from which all valid mathematics is derived. In Brouwer's[8] own words:

"The neo-intuitionism considers the falling apart of moments of life into qualitatively different parts, to be reunited only while remaining separated by time, as the fundamental phenomenon of the human intellect, passing by abstracting from its emotional content into the fundamental phenomenon of mathematical thinking, the intuition of bare two-one-ness. This intuition of two-one-ness, the basal intuition of mathematics, creates not only the numbers one and two, but also all finite ordinal numbers inasmuch as one of the elements of the two-one-ness may be thought as a new two-oneness, which process may be repeated indefinitely."

As this quotation implies, this intuition is a fusion of the continuous and discrete, a possibility of grasping simultaneously several units, connected by a *between* that is not exhausted by the interpolation of new units. In this manner, Brouwer dispenses with the three-dimensional space continuum as a prerequisite of conceptual life and builds his intellectual structure on a primary intuition of a one-dimensional time continuum wherein the observation of change and repetition occupy correlative positions.

There is a similarity in Brouwer's view to the doctrine of Kant in that in both notions the fundamental intuition is not itself regarded as a concept, but rather as something more elemental in terms of which all the undefined terms of all mathematical systems are to be conceived.

It is important to note that this doctrine, although called 'Intuitionism,' is not a 'mystical' approach to mathematics, — nor is it a logically loose one either. On the contrary, it is more insistent on rigorous proof than is either Logicism or Formalism. Such an attitude simply means that the source of mathematics is an intuition that presents mathematical concepts as immediately clear. Mathematics is simply the exact part of our thinking.

The foregoing discussion should make clear why Brouwer insists on the distinction of mathematics from the language of mathematics. The language, as previously intimated, is only a make-shift aid to our memories and a tool for communicating our mathematics to the minds of others. Brouwer feels that the paradoxes of mathematics are due to our taking too seriously the regularities in our language about mathematics, which we observe after the mathematizing proper is finished.

This brings us to what is probably the most significant point in Brouwer's program: the notion of what constitutes mathematical existence. Here we come upon a fundamental difference between Intuitionism and Formalism. Formalism insists that consistency alone implies existence, whether or not the entity in question can be constructed in finite time. Intuitionism, on the other hand, holds that consistency implies only the *possibility* of existence, and that constructibility in a series of steps is necessary to establish existence. This means that the existence of an infinite aggregate cannot be demonstrated by proving that the denial of its existence leads to a contradiction, but can only be established by giving explicit statement of the rule of its construction. Thus an aggregate (*Menge*) is a law of construction, the statement of the performance of certain operations, rather than the objective and external set of entities themselves. Here, Brouwer denies the 'law of excluded middle', and his position insists on the principle that if an explicit rule for constructing the solution to a mathematical problem in a finite number of steps cannot be given, then the answer to that problem must remain indeterminate. From this point one may then proceed to the construction of a third possibility, and here Brouwer's view falls into line with the so-called 'modal' logics (i.e., multi-valued logics in which three or more truth values are recognized).

With his insistence on constructibility in a finite number of steps, the question arises as to how Brouwer deals with real numbers, since to pick out one real number as distinct from every other requires determining the value of every decimal place of it, — and there are an infinity of decimal places. The problem is overcome by asserting essentially that the rule of constructibility applies to propositions about real numbers. A real number is an infinite sequence of integers, generated by a succession of arbitrary choices, but only those propositions are significant which can be verified in a finite number of operations. Therefore, any proposition which requires for its verification the successive examination of all of the digits of the number is neither true nor false.

The construction of a real number employs a process quite compatible with the intuitionist insistence on grounding all our more abstract thoughts *on those simple thought experiences which we cannot escape.* Limiting a real number to a specific value is like measuring a physical object: its length (let us say) is between 1 and 2 units, between 1.5 and 1.7, between 1.54 and 1.68, and so on. Constant narrowings of the range of error in this way builds what is called a 'nest of intervals', — a sequence of intervals, each lying inside the previous and contracting indefinitely. Each such nest picks out a real number from the continuum which is constructed by arbitrary choices of the integers for each place in the sequence. Thus a real number is always an approximation to a certain degree of accuracy, depending on how far the finite sequence of choices has been carried. And the continuum is only the concept whose denotation is all such sequences. But the continuum can in no sense be said to be a complete totality, for no matter how well we specify its characteristics, we cannot exhaust it. That is why Brouwer calls it a 'medium of free becoming.'

To sum up the intuitionist position, it should be pointed out that while this attitude gives freedom and a consequent real significance to our mathematical creativity, like all freedoms, it carries with it a responsibility. An intuitionist proof must be more rigorous than a formalist demonstration. Indeterminism is always accompanied by the necessity for labor in construction. Nothing comes easily, but what is achieved must be established on the firm foundation of the reality of our experience.

VII. The Mathematics of Space-Time

It is evident from the foregoing survey that the philosophy of mathematics is controversial. The foundations of mathematics still remain to be established. Various theories of the nature of mathematical reasoning are available, and these justifications of abstract thought-systems have settled down into the three types of mathematics we have placed under scrutiny. The Logistic method of Russell and the Formalist (Axiomatic) method of Hilbert have appeared to be defective in one way or another, and so we have finally concluded that Intuitionism is the most satisfactory of the existing philosophies of mathematics.

In the history of the subject, two questions have been uppermost in the minds of those who have investigated the nature of mathematics. In the first place, since the time of the ancient Greeks there has been the standing problem, "Why does mathematics work in natural science?" In the second place, and of more recent origin, we have the question, "How is mathematics possible?" If we treat these as two separate questions, the issues are indeed complicated. If, however, we treat them together, then both questions, "why are mathematical physicists able to make reliable predictions on the basis of mathematical manipulations?", and "how is mathematics logically possible?" may be susceptible of simultaneous solution.

Our proposed solution to these problems is based on the conviction that the insolubilia of mathematics come from the fact that the thinker omits from mathematics an essential feature, — *time!* Many mathematicians are inclined to be space-conscious rather than time-conscious. And so we have sought to restore time to mathematics and regard it as a common denominator of both thought and reality. It is the supposed divorce of mathematics from physical reality that is responsible for at least some of the present dilemmas of mathematics, and to overcome this dualism we have erected a bridge by way of a process-philosophy. In support of this view, we appeal to the argument of E. R. Hedrick,[9] who has proposed that a possible basis for agreement between the intuitionism of Brouwer and the formalist approach of Hilbert may be found in the inherent properties of *time*, namely: the indefinite divisibility of it, and the occurrence of a time between any two other times. Here the idea of unit is introduced, and this is another of the fundamental properties of *real number*. This recognition of time as the 'primordial prototype' is valid for intuitionism and could also be valid for a suitably modified formalist method, thus confirming Hamilton's definition of mathematics as the 'science of pure time.'

It is true that when we focus upon empirical reality, space becomes an important ingredient of our purview. In dealing with the resulting epistemological problem of the relation between the mental space-time of the knower and the objective space-time of the things known, we have found the concept of isomorphism of peculiar value. But this does not introduce any discordant note into our philosophy of nature. However, in order to see more clearly how time does enter into such an apparently 'static' notion as isomorphism, let us retrace our steps a bit.

The mathematician, we have seen, can construct *n*-dimensional manifolds of any degree of complexity. Among such manifolds, as Weyl[10] makes clear, the physicist finds that a certain 4-dimensional topological manifold for the representation of physical events works very well. The elements of the space-time manifold of physics can be put into contact with the 'here-nows' of the observers through the use of world-lines of the objective physical facts, the postulate of the causal structure of the universe, and the position of the observer and the direction of his world-line at the moment of the observations. In such a scheme, a continuous deformation leads to the same result concerning observable facts. *This one-to-one transformation of the whole picture is an example of isomorphism.* In brief, topology is a non-quantitative geometry (unlike the metrical geometry of Euclid) that studies the properties of bodies which remain invariant even when they are distorted, — hence the name 'rubber sheet' geometry.

Now, from this point on, we make our own extrapolations. In order to recall what these extensions are, it is necessary to refer only to our concept of the emergent time-axis as the basis for the increasing richness of dimensionality beyond the 4-dimensional space-time of the physical matrix. In our own approach, we have used the conception of 'mind' as the temporal aspect of the spatio-temporal unities that emerge in the creative advance of nature from 'matter' to 'life' to 'consciousness.' Thus, apparently, we find ourselves in line with S. Alexander's profound and unique theory that time is the moving principle of space, that is, that *time is the mind of space*, so that space is the body of time.

Before we are through with our exposition of the formal foundations of knowledge, we shall have to relate our theory to the general notions of topology and the field-theoretical approach to scientific synthesis. In order to do a thorough job on this, we shall take a fresh hold on field theory and topology in the next chapter. In the remainder of the present chapter, and by way of preparation for this, let us bring together the scattered conclusions we have assembled in this chapter on mathematics and the preceding chapter on logic.

VIII. Logic and Mathematics in the Integration of Knowledge

In a general way it can be said that logic and mathematics have been emancipated from their ancient bondage: it is as if they had been given wings and freed from traditional limitations. On the one hand, the perspectives of the mathematician have been so widened and enriched that the mathematician can now operate with a much larger assortment of notions: in the number system he has natural, rational, irrational, negative, complex, and transcendental numbers; and in algebra he has non-commutative as well as commutative operations; while in geometry he has not only Euclidian geometry, but the various types of non-Euclidian geometries to work with. In a parallel fashion, a dramatic emancipation has taken place in logic. After setting aside the traditional Aristotelian 'law of excluded middle' as something written in the heavens, the logicians have discovered logics of three, four, five, and more modalities, and these modal logics give a flexibility to thought which fits in with the scientist's demands for a fuller equipment of intellectual tools with which to attack nature's mysteries.

These two series of developments proceeding side by side have eventually converged, presenting us with the contemporary problem: what is the relation of the one to the other? Our answer is that mathematics is not to be deduced from logic, nor is logic to be deduced from mathematics. Any formal system is either a logic or a mathematics, depending mainly on historical antecedents. A formal (deductive) system appears as a logic (e.g., the Boole-Schroeder algebra of logic) when it is interpreted as applying to classes, propositions, and inferences as such. But when we deal with a manifold of elements which have been ordered according to transitive, asymmetrical relations (serial order), we enter the domain of what has traditionally been considered as a mathematics. The most elementary and ubiquitous example of such an ordering is the number system, and this introduces us to arithmetic. This linear order becomes a geometric manifold when it becomes an area, that is, when a manifold is a range of functions of two or more variables. In this manner we pass from an ensemble of points to lines as a higher type of order than points, to planes as higher types than lines (since planes are classes of lines), and to solids as higher manifolds of planes. Beyond this, we rise into the domain of projective geometry, a boundless field wherein, — as C. J. Keyser claims, — real numbers and imaginary numbers, finites and infinites, enter on equal terms. This gives us a kind of stratified language of dimensions in which (as Russell's theory of types might be extended to mean) any aggregate of presupposed individuals is of a higher type than the individuals in it.

Therefore, our conception is that neither mathematics nor logic is derived from the other, but one (mathematics) is a formal structure that applies to those branches which by tradition have belonged to what was called mathematics (arithmetic, geometry, algebra, and so forth), while logic is a system in which, by tradition, concepts, propositions, and inferences, are the objects of formal analysis. Of course, there is overlapping of content; and behind both is the experience, the temporal flow, of the human thinker who meditates on the objects of his apperceptive synthesis.

If we now relate these formal thought-systems to empirical reality, we observe first of all the historical fact that mathematics and logic came into being as abstractions from man's experiences and reflective processes in those fields which later came to be known as the 'natural sciences' (of our LEVEL II in the *Temple of Knowledge*). For example, the origin of geometry is associated with the 'rope stretchers' of ancient Egypt who surveyed the land annually (after the overflow of the Nile river). These operations were then lifted out of their concrete contexts into the rarefied atmosphere of an independent discipline by Pythagoras and others, who generalized the mental processes actually being employed, and thus an autonomous science of pure geometry arose. In the process, empirical generalizations were transformed into definitions (e.g., a triangle is now, by definition, a figure the area of which is equal to two right angles, and 2 plus 2 equals 4, by definition). Today, such 'pure' systems of mathematics have been dissociated from physics and psychology, and they can be put on the basis of postulational treatment wherein the free creativity of the human mind has full play. But new systems of logic and mathematics continually come into being to fertilize physical theories, and new discoveries in natural science by analogy call forth the new developments in the formal sciences of logic and mathematics. This is the dialectic between experience and nature, thought and its objects.

One great lesson that man has learned is that in nature we never find space as such, as an absolute entity in itself, nor do we find 'things' in space as though space were an empty vessel or container. Space is not antecedent to matter. In the natural order we find the physical elements ('particles' of 'matter') ordered according to spatio-temporal patterns. Nature is an indissoluble unity of space-time-matter patterns, and on this planet there has been added an emerging hierarchy of levels of living creatures, the new levels pyramided upon the cosmic base of the Minkowski-Riemann-Einstein matrix of space-time. In our logic, therefore, we set aside the principle of excluded middle, at least in so far as emergent evolution indicates an 'open' universe, one in which 'consciousness' represents the field property of the macroscopic whole that emerges from the microscopic constituents. Thus our logic and our mathematics start from the experience of duration, or temporal passage, and it is in this sense that our formal systems grow out of an 'intuitionist' basis (although in stating this we do not necessarily imply that we accept the additional connotations of the term as used by others).

To repeat: the manifest universe is a space-time-matter trinity (unity), a hierarchy of levels reaching into higher dimensionalities which emerge according to a principle of isomorphism (perhaps homomorphism is a better term). In mathematics, one can deliberately disregard the 'matter' and the 'time' aspects of nature (the *energy-knots of behavior stuff, in the language of our monism of action*), and think of space as divorced from physical reality. But this involves an abstraction from empirical reality, a separation of what in nature has been united, — the marriage of space and time. In treating them in an elementalistic fashion man has put asunder what nature has united, this does no harm, — indeed, is very useful, — so long as one knows what he is doing; but all sorts of problems of reconciliation are created if nature's fertile union is thought of as illegitimate.

FOOTNOTES CHAPTER VI

[1]Cf. *A Philosophy of Mathematics,* by Louis O. Kattsoff, 1948, p. 31. In this connection Dr. Kattsoff is relying on *Die Philosophie der Mathematik der Gegenwart,* by W. Dubislav, 1932, pp. 38-39.

[2]Cf. *Formulaire de Mathematiques,* by G. Peano, Turin, 1895. In subsequent statements Peano presented alternative formulations of this postulate set, but the variations are not significant.

[3]This is Brouwer's Inaugural Address at the University of Amsterdam in 1912, reprinted in the *Bulletin of the American Mathematical Society,* Vol. 20, 1913.

[4]K. Gödel, "Ueber formal unentscheidbare Sätze der *Principia Mathematica* und verwandter System," I, *Monatshefte für Mathematik und Physik,* Vol. 38, 1931; and "Ueber Vollständigkeit un Widerspruchsfreiheit," *Ergebnisse eines Mathematischen Kolloquiums,* Heft 3, 1932, pp. 12-13.

An excellent semi-popular account of Gödel's reasoning and conclusions is given by Ernest Nagel and James R. Newman in their article, "Gödel's Proof," *Scientific American,* Vol. 194, 1956, 71ff.

[5]Cf. A. Heyting, "Die intuitionistische Grundlegung der Mathematik," *Erkenntnis,* Vol. 2, 1931, p. 106.

[6]Cf. *The Nature of Mathematics,* by Max Black, 1934, p. 169 ff.

[7]Cf. L. Brunschvig, *Les Etapes de la Philosophie Mathematique,* Paris, 1929. Quoted from James Byrnie Shaw's volume, *Lectures on the Philosophy of Mathematics,* p. 168.

[8]Cf. *Monatshefte fur Mathematik und Physik,* Vol. 41, 1934, p. 274.

[9]Cf. "Tendencies in the Logic of Mathematics," by E. R. Hedrick, *Science,* 1933, Vol. 77, 335-343.

[10]Cf. "The Mathematical Way of Thinking," by Hermann Weyl, *Science,* 1940, Vol. 92, 437-446.

7

DIMENSIONS IN NATURE AND IN THOUGHT

"Euclidian space may be compared to a crystal, built up on uniform unchangeable atoms in the regular and rigid unchangeable arrangements of a lattice; Riemannian space to a liquid, consisting of the same indiscernible unchangeable atoms, whose arrangements and orientation, however, are mobile and yielding to forces acting upon them."
— Hermann Weyl, *Philosophy of Mathematics and Natural Science*

"The recognition of the new concepts grew rapidly, until substance was overshadowed by the field. It was realized that something of great importance had happened in physics. A new reality was created, a new concept for which there was no place in the mechanical description. . . .The electromagnetic field is, for modern physics, as real as the chair in which one sits."
— Einstein and Infeld, *The Evolution of Physics*

I. What is a Dimension?

In the preceding chapter we have observed that mathematics deals with manifolds which are ordered according to dimensions. In the *dimensional theory of thought-systems,* — as the present approach may be termed, — we start conceptually with a linear ordering of points exhibiting the transitive, asymmetrical relations of serial order. This elementary ordering of points is the basis of the concepts of arithmetic and thus introduces us to number theory. In turn, a linear order with one dimension becomes a geometric manifold (area) when the manifold becomes a range of functions of two variables. Thus we pass from points to lines, and from lines to planes, on to solids and polyhedra, in a hierarchy of ordered aggregates. The procedure for creating a geometry of n-dimensional space is inherent in this process, and because of the central importance of the idea of hyperspace in modern science, it is desirable that we examine the process whereby one climbs the dimensional ladder.

The geometry of space begins with the postulate that the system of real numbers can be put into one-to-one correspondence with the points on a straight line. Taking two intersecting straight lines, perpendicular to each other, and calling one of them the x_1 axis, and the other the x_2 axis, we then discover a one-to-one correspondence between the points of a plane and the number pairs (x_1, x_2). We may then use the term 'number pair' and 'point of a plane' interchangeably and build up the analytic geometry of the plane.

The subject of two dimensional analytic geometry leads naturally to the subject of three dimensional analytic geometry. By erecting a line perpendicular to both the x_1 and x_2 axes, we obtain three mutually perpendicular lines whose points may be put into one-to-one correspondence with each of the three variables, respectively, giving us a one-to-one correspondence between the points of three-space and number triads (x_1, x_2, x_3). With this as a basis, analytical geometry of three dimensions is built up after the fashion of the geometry of two dimensions.

It happens that the mathematician is often interested in problems involving more than three variables. Fortunately, it is possible to invent conceptual spaces of any number of dimensions, provided these are constructed in a consistent manner. Thus, after constructing a space of three mutually perpendicular axes, we may construct a fourth axis perpendicular to each of these, giving a set of four mutually perpendicular lines. Thus we have a one-to-one correspondence between the sets of four numbers (x_1, x_2, x_3, x_4) and the points of four-space.

The generalization we have employed in the above cases is simple: taking a set of n lines, each perpendicular to each of the n-1 others, we have a space of n dimensions. The points of this n-space are placed in one-to-one correspondence with the sets of n numbers $(x_1, x_2, x_3, \ldots x_n)$. We are now equipped to employ geometrical language in problems involving n variables. An essential principle in such dimensional thinking is the *principle of duality* which, given this one-to-one correspondence, makes it possible to interchange the word 'point' and 'line' in any theorem about points and lines and thus obtain a theorem concerning lines and points. For example, the theorem 'two points of a plane have one and only one line in common' becomes 'two lines in a plane have one and only one point in common.'

From such elementary beginnings a generalized science is perfected whereby it is possible to move up or down, from a space of fewer to a space of more dimensions, or vice versa. This type of geometry results in the four-dimensional Euclidian regularities, and these have been discussed by H. P. Manning and others. But when we deal, not with static structures such as are exhibited in crystallography, but with the processes of a dynamic world, the 'restless universe' of physics, where incessant motions are displayed, a space-time geometry, a non-Euclidian (e.g., Riemannian) analysis seems most suitable. Here we find that the type of approach previously referred to in connection with *quaternions* may provide the best 'fit.'

This last remark is especially pertinent in connection with the field-theory approach. This new formulation bears some relation to the significant changes in our ideas about space-time manifolds. We therefore devote the present chapter to an examination of the role of field theory and dimensional analysis in fashioning a satisfactory theory of the universe.

One of the impressive features of the evolution of scientific thought is the growing recognition that the older $3 + 1$ space and time framework is not adequate for dealing with physical reality in all its complexity. Accordingly physicists have experimented with five- and six-dimensional formulations. And if such multi-dimensional manifolds are not sufficient for the systematization of physical events, how much more difficult is it to squeeze mental events into them?

I well remember how one of my former teachers in philosophy, strongly influenced by the empiricism of John Dewey, would exclaim that there is something wrong with any philosophy which seeks refuge in a fourth dimension. In those days this remark seemed to contain much wisdom. Today, in the light of new developments, this observation seems to reflect a flatland view of reality. No one, of course, wants a lot of loose dimensions rattling about; but when the facts drive us out of our ancient limitations, we should be ready to expand our horizons and move into higher degrees of freedom. This is surely so when no less an authority than physics informs us that the time has come to enlarge our assortment of dimensional concepts.

On other occasions I have presented the idea that the four-dimensional space-time manifold of physics, satisfactory as it may be as the continuum for 'particle' physics, is not sufficient for psychical (mental) events. The additional dimensions that are required have a genuine meaning as regards consciousness, since it is consciousness which thinks them. Still more important, however, we note that on the purely physical level, as conceived by classical mechanics, the human solidarity we envision as coming into existence (*via* the 'electromagnetic society') is altogether inexplicable; but with the generous allowance of extra dimensions, of a number still to be determined, the reality of human solidarity can be made more plausible.

So important is this matter for the development of our thesis that, at the risk of becoming repetitious, we pause and give added consideration to this topic of the 'dimensions' of the universe.

II. Dimensionality and Field Theory

Originally the term dimension was applied to the three dimensions of Euclidian space (geometry), and later these dimensions were represented analytically by the three rectangular coördinates of Cartesian geometry. Now, however, the word dimension has been generalized so that it designates a manner of arranging data, a way of treating any given set of entities. This more general usage is illustrated, for example, by the employment of 'dimension' in physics as referring to a 'degree of freedom,' and even more frequently as an 'independent variable.'

In its most general sense the term *dimension* is no longer limited to what we call 'space.' A 'dimension' refers to any *manifold* which can be *ordered.* The particular way in which the elements of any dimensional aggregate are arranged is known as *serial order.* As noted in a previous chapter, serial order covers such relationships as succession in time (therefore time is a dimension), positions in space, the series of natural numbers, a temperature gradient, and many other important relationships which exemplify what mathematical logic terms transitive, asymmetric relations.

Some physicists have contributed to confusion in the field by occasionally treating the 'higher' dimensions of space as real aspects of nature, while at other times referring to multi-dimensional space as a 'mathematical trick' which has no genuine physical significance. For example, James H. Jeans seemed to pass from the one interpretation in his earlier book on *The Mysterious Universe* to the second interpretation in his later book on *The New Background of Science.*

Our own conception of dimensionality, as related to the philosophy of emergent evolution, is connected with the idea that dimensionality is a feature of a behavioral organization of 'particles' wherein the old *law of identity* ceases to apply as the 'material' constituents interact with each other to produce a new whole. This is one important formulation in our non-Aristotelian approach to nature.

We find a partial confirmation of this conception in the new quantum theory (Dirac), where the 'spin' of the electrons has the property of turning 'space' into 'time.' When we deal with transitions from lower levels of nature to the next above, where the new simplicity (behavioral unity) emerges out of the interacting parts of the ensemble, *time plays the role of the next higher dimension.* In the case of the transition from the level of electrons-protons-neutrons to organized atoms, the spin is connected with the indistinguishability of the electrons. The 'interchange energy' by means of which a new whole is produced adds a new dimension to reality, and this dimension gives rise to gestalt properties, — field properties of the new whole which, like public time, are transposable across the parts. In this view the distinction between 'space' and 'time', — like the distinction between the 'static' and 'dynamic' aspects of nature, — is to some extent relative, for what appears as a space-interval from one point of view is a time-interval from another, except that in terms of the ladder of emergent evolution the time-series is absolute.

It is most important to realize that in the scale of evolution from *atoms* → *molecules* → *living cells* → *multicellular organisms* → *humanity*, this time-direction is not relative. The test of growth is absolute, being in terms of complexity of structure and unity of function. The significance of this fact for the coming unity of mankind has already been hinted at. This property of emergent evolution of turning time (function) into space (structure) by congealing the products of evolution into the 'matter' of the next higher level is, for us, what makes it necessary to adopt a non-Aristotelian logic and metaphysics.

Suppose we are considering two or three elements of nature, — let us say electrons and protons and neutrons, — and we deliberate as to what can happen as these entities interact with each other on the bottom-most level of unorganized matter. In terms of three-dimensional space we would predict that as a result of mutual influences the particles could do *this* or *that,* — move in this direction or that in the three dimensions of space, — but we would then be overlooking another possibility, something not provided for by the Aristotelian two-valued logic of individuality, namely, that the particles may combine with each other and cease to behave as individual particles going their own isolationist ways.

The newly emerged organization, — the atom, — has an additional dimension of reality which may be symbolized by $\sqrt{-1}$, in the sense that the emergent novelty is like an imaginary number in a complex domain. Just as the electric and magnetic vectors of electrodynamics are at right angles to each other — and for that reason the alternating current employs $\sqrt{-1}$, — so the process whereby time is changed into space can similarly be represented. It is for this reason that $\sqrt{-1}$ is so important in relativity theory, for that is the method whereby Einstein treats non-Euclidian geometry as equivalent to a Euclidian geometry of a radius $\sqrt{-1}$.

The Euclidian-Newtonian assumption that the only 'real' spatial dimensions of the physical world are the three coördinates of classical science, as represented by Cartesian coördinates, is a naive view which came, perhaps, from the ancient doctrine that 'God geometrizes,' and does so only in accordance with the scheme of Greek logic and mathematics. It is no accident that the Greeks had no concept of *zero* or $\sqrt{-1}$, and that it required the Western mind in revolt to invent these ideas and employ them to such advantage in science and electrodynamics. When electricity entered, the tyranny of classical physics and logic made its exit.

In logic one of the first to break away from slavery to ancient habits of thought was George Boole. Boole introduced zero into logic (but not into mathematics, — the Hindus did that), and thus he paved the way for the next step. Among other things, Boole helped make it possible to employ cross-classification in nature, and this provides an escape from the alternatives of a two-valued choice, an escape into a higher dimension of thinking by way of an orthogonal intersection with the existing alternatives. For example, traditional logic would classify human mental faculties into, e.g., rational and non-rational (this being an application of Aristotle's law of excluded middle, that *A* is either *B* or *non-B*, as pictured in the 'tree of Porphyry'), and the class of *non-B* would then be further subdivided; but there would be no cross-classification, i.e., if a response were rational, it could not include any element of the non-rational, such as emotional content. But when Boole introduced zero into logic, it became possible for De Morgan to arrange for the sharing of such hitherto mutually exclusive properties. We have on occasion made use of this idea in supposing that 'facts' and 'values' need not be exclusive of each other: there is no reason why judgments of fact may not also be judgments of value, though in Aristotelian logic it appears that if we classify judgments into factual and non-factual, there is no way to get valuational judgments (one variety of non-factual) into conjugate relation with factual judgments. In symbolic form, Boole expands what he calls the 'universe of discourse' (which is symbolized by *one* or *unity*) in this manner:

$$1 = x + x'$$

$$1 = xy + xy' + x'y + x'y'$$

$$1 = xyz + xyz' + xy'z + xy'z' + x'yz + x'yz' + x'y'z + x'y'z'$$

In the example provided by faculty psychology, if we expand the universe of discourse of mental faculties (unity), we can combine intellect, feeling, and will, and any act of mind can share the properties of all three (or more) attributes. To see how the addition of y to x, and z to y and x, is analogous to the introduction of a factor at right angles to the previous analysis (here we are expounding our own ideas and not Boole's), let us represent the situation in terms of Cartesian coördinates:

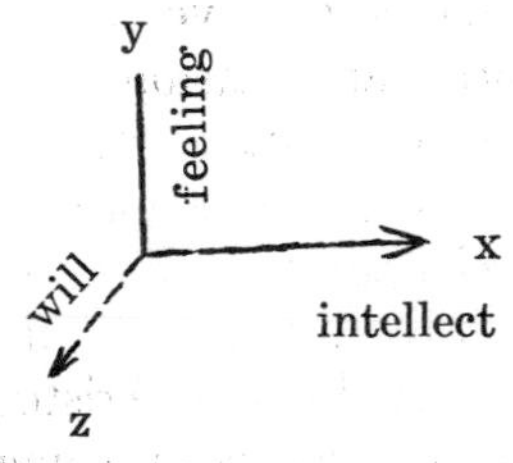

y
feeling
x
intellect
will
z

Now if — remembering that nature produces new emergent realities in a temporal order, — we think of the supplementation of x with y, to produce this 'emergence' as analogous to adding a new dimension to human nature, we can represent this emergence as a rotation of the x-axis in a plane at right angles (orthogonal) to itself, in this manner:

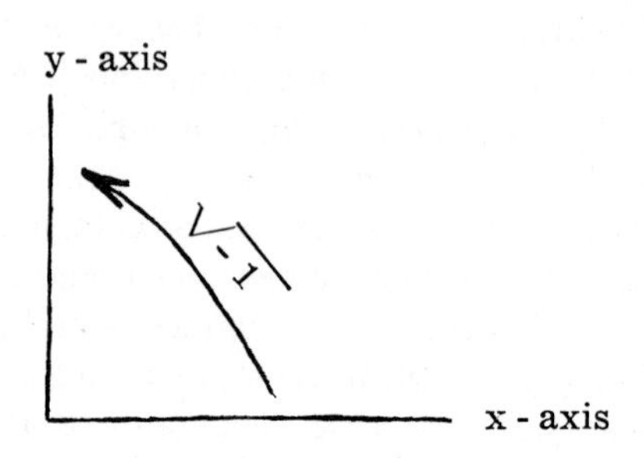

This, in a non-Euclidian and non-Aristotelian universe of emergent evolution, calls for a hyper-dimensional manifold: rotations in the domain of complex numbers. However, before continuing the exposition of hyperdimensionality, let us retrace the historical steps by means of which modern mathematics and science attained the purview which makes possible this new vision of reality.

III. The Evolution of Electromagnetic Concepts

Our fundamental idea is that the modern world is developing into an electromagnetic culture. All typically modern inventions are fundamentally an exemplification of electrical conceptions. The many inventions which have transformed society are such inventions as the automobile, the radio, the airplane, the telephone, television, radar, nuclear energy developments, and so forth. But the important thing here is that these practical achievements could not have been introduced without the prior articulation of theoretical ideas in such an apparently useless field as pure mathematics. Following Alfred Korzybski's argument in *Science and Sanity*, we realize that any machine that depends upon principles of electromagnetic induction could not have been constructed, and cannot now be operated, upon the principles of the traditional Aristotelian-Euclidian-Newtonian system of nature. When electricity came in, the old orientation of classical physics had to go.

The reason electricity brings in new concepts arises out of the fact that the understanding of electrical phenomena calls for the use of imaginary numbers, something of which the Greeks had no comprehension. Imaginary numbers, such as the square root of minus one, $\sqrt{-1}$, which are invaluable in the representation of electromagnetic processes, involve the use of a non-Euclidian geometry of rotations —

something inconceivable to those who were thinking in terms of the mental habits of traditional logic and science.

It is not at all strange that these mathematical developments behind the growth of the electrical industry should also provide the tools necessary to create the recent ideas in physics, such as are found in relativity theory and quantum mechanics. Expounders of relativity theory, who are familiar with the role of $\sqrt{-1}$ in the electrical industry, also know that this same 'imaginary' number enters into the mathematics of relativity theory. The thing that makes it possible to transform the three-dimensional geometry of Cartesian coördinates (which is in essence the Euclidian geometry of Newtonian physics) into the non-Euclidian geometry of the four-dimensional space-time continuum is this square root of minus one; therefore it represents not only the relation between the electric and magnetic vectors of a moving current of electricity, but it also has the property of turning mathematical time into space.

In the same way, as we believe, the ethical-social problems of our new civilization can be dealt with only when we learn to apply new concepts to the solution of our geographical-political relationships. In tracing the course of this argument, we shall try to show that the next step in social evolution involves the use of global thinking on a planetary scale. In exhibiting the full meaning of this, we develop an analogy between geometry and ethics based on a contrast between two types of orientation, designated as *planal thinking* and *global thinking*.

IV. Planal Thinking Versus Global Thinking

Planal thinking is illustrated by the old belief that the world is flat. It expresses the presuppositions and implications of the Euclidian frame of reference. The older classical physics, the Newtonian-Laplacian particle-picture of nature, treats 'time,' 'space,' and 'matter' as absolutes, as independently existing realities. The objection which some have made to our statement that the Euclidian-Newtonian world-picture is an unfolding of the idea that the world is flat is based on the ground that Newton (and some of the ancient Greeks, for that matter) believed that the world is round. They will also urge that Newton brought the Copernican cosmology to its perfection, and this surely surrenders the medieval layman's idea of the flatness of the earth. In reply we reaffirm our statement. Newton's world-view is based on the supposed uniqueness of Euclidian geometry, and his thinking in terms of physical absolutes and the 'straight lines' of Euclid's parallel postulate is fundamentally *planal* rather than *global*.

That Newton's views at many points were strongly influenced by the habits of thought engendered by the Euclidian theory of three-dimensional space is illustrated by Newton's definition of time and space as absolutes. Newton says, "Absolute, True and Mathematical time, of itself, and from its own nature flows equably and without regard to anything external, and by another name is called duration." But if, in those earlier times, men could have covered large distances in short times, as we now do in trains and airplanes, the correlativity of space and time would have been evident to them. When a ship, sailing over the surface of the earth, crosses the 'international date line,' it goes into 'tomorrow,' as reckoned by calendar time. Under these circumstances we see that our measures of time are relative to our frames of reference. In such situations it becomes clear that the entire Newtonian physics of absolutes, — 'space,' 'time,' 'matter,' 'force,' and 'motion,' all the concepts of classical mechanics, — betray an inadequacy as a framework for nature.

The several developments that have discredited Newtonian physics are these: (1) the appearance of the electromagnetic theory of matter, and (2) the advent of the physical theory of relativity. The first development has shown that 'matter' or 'substance' is relative: electromagnetic mass is not an absolute of physics, since mass is a function of velocity. In the second place, and not independently of the formulation of the electrical theory of matter, Einstein's theory of relativity did much to undermine the older Euclidian-Newtonian orientation, and to establish the need for a new system of science. The older system of thought is a $3 + 1$ language, a language of 'space' *and* 'time.' The language of the new physics is, at the very least, a language of a four-dimensional structure, the language of a space-time continuum. It is because the physics of Newton is based on the first language, the elementalistic language of absolute and independent realities, while the physics of Einstein is based on the language of the space-time matrix, that we picture the contrast between the old and the new science as a contrast between planal and global thinking.

In the flat universe of Euclid, parallel lines go off to infinity, they never meet, and they never return to their point of origin. But in the curvilinear (Riemannian) universe of relativity, the universe of modern astronomy, the lines of the universe are not straight in Euclid's sense. Now just as geometry, or earth measurements, and astronomy, or star measurements, have been compelled to adjust their ideas to the notion of curvature, so humanity in its social orientations must realize that it is time to think politically and economically in global terms. And here is where our analogy between geometry and ethics comes into the picture. The force of the analogy is to suggest that just as geometry and astronomy have adjusted their ideas to the notion of curvature, so humanity in its social and cultural orientations must learn to think in terms of curvature. We must learn to grasp realities in global terms not only geographically, but politically and spiritually.

I seriously propose that this connection between changes in our geometrical notions and the necessary changes in our ethical insights is something more than metaphorical. Nations and peoples must learn that they live on a round earth, rather than a flat earth, in the sense that the consequences of what they do sooner or later return to them. In astronomy and geography the shortest distance between two points is the arc of a great circle, a 'geodesic,' and either of these prolonged sufficiently returns to its point of origin. In the same way, the consequences of our acts, like the proverbial bread on water, returns to the doer to plague or bless him. This 'social Karma' is the modern Western world equivalent of the ancient Oriental doctrine of *samsara*.

Of course the ethical-social applications of global thinking had to wait upon the antecedent development of ideas in mathematics. It is time to survey the high peaks in this intellectual revolution, and here is the summary of what this survey reveals.

V. The Role of Imaginary Numbers

We have seen that modern society is based on electricity. This, we have found, implies a non-Euclidian geometry of rotations, represented mathematically through the use of imaginary numbers, such as $\sqrt{-1}$. All this, — the new physics of electromagnetic theory and relativity theory, — rests to a considerable extent on the introduction of the Cartesian coördinates of three-dimensional space *and the subsequent developments which then freed mathematics from this traditional limitation.*

Why is it that the procedure which produced generalized coördinate geometry, implicitly contained within the earlier structure of number language, required three thousand years to discover? The answer to this question, as given by Tobias Dantzig in his fascinating book on *Number, the Language of Science* (p. 199) is to be found "in the tremendous influence which Greek opinion exercised upon European thought. The emancipation of number from the inhibitions imposed on it by the Greeks was not so easy a task as it may appear to us today." According to Dantzig, the principal inhibition was their fear of irrational numbers and infinity. That this idea of a limitless (infinite) process was foreign to Greek thought, that "in Greek physics the dynamic is missing," is also pointed out by Irwin Schrödinger in his book, *Science and the Human Temperament.* Then here Professor Schrödinger points out that "in the case of Greek science the idea of the infinite is scarcely understood. The concept of a limitless process frightened the Greek, as is evidenced in the well-known paradox of Achilles and the tortoise. The Hellenic mind could not have interested itself in the Dedekind definition of irrational number, although the idea of the irrational was already present in the synoptic form of the diagonal of the square or of the cube." While referring to the mathematical deficiencies of the Greeks, we may also recall that they did not possess the concepts of zero and the negative numbers.

The honor of discovering imaginary numbers belongs to the Italians of the Renaissance. Cardan in 1545 developed a formula which gave negative numbers (less than zero, and therefore called 'absurd') as the roots of equations; but Cardan considered these as impossible solutions, even though he did denote the 'meaningless' by a symbol. Somewhat later, another Italian, Bombelli, in his work on algebra published in 1572, makes explicit use of imaginary numbers. He discovered that these 'impossible' and 'imaginary' numbers, when subjected to the operations of ordinary arithmetic, were useful in solving real problems, and thus encouraged, he created the domain of *complex numbers*, which supersedes the domain of 'real' numbers in the same manner that these supersede the 'rational' numbers.

Following these courageous beginnings by the Italians, a Norwegian mathematician named Wessel, toward the end of the eighteenth century, (1797), developed a method for the representation of complex numbers in a plane, a geometrical interpretation of complex quantities which is still commonly used. This contribution remained unnoticed for some time, and it remained for a German, Gauss, to demonstrate the mathematical interpretation of the domain of complex numbers in terms of plain Cartesian geometry.

While previous mathematicians had declared that such expressions as $\sqrt{-1}$, $\sqrt{-2}$, being neither nothing, nor greater than nothing, nor less than nothing, were impossible or imaginary, Gauss went ahead to show (in 1831) that such complex expressions as $a + ib$ (where i is the modern substitute for Bombelli's $\sqrt{-1}$) can be represented in terms of Cartesian coördinates in a diagram which has a for the abscissa and b for the ordinate. If these quantities are interpreted as *vectors* in the now familiar parallelogram of force, the operation of multiplying by i (or $\sqrt{-1}$) means a right-angle rotation in a counter-clockwise direction.

The next step in this evolution of imaginary and complex numbers, so far as the mathematical development is concerned, was taken when Sir William R. Hamilton created the algebra of *quaternions*. The aim of Hamilton was to interpret algebra as the 'science of pure time or order in progression'; that is, to arithmetize mathematics, — give a geometric representation of the imaginary in a plane by emphasizing the notion of succession. These quaternions, or vectors in space, contain a double infinity of imaginaries, any one of which, with real numbers, constitutes the ordinary complex number domain. This may seem very abstract and unreal, but it all turns out to be of utmost 'practical' importance. For just as the phantom creatures of Cardan and Bombelli in a remarkable way describe the characteristic features of alternating currents and electromotive forces (in Steinmetz's representation), so Hamilton's investigations of rotations in three-dimensional space are generalized to include the higher complex algebras of multi-dimensional manifolds of non-Euclidian geometry and the space-time continuum of Einstein's relativity theory. That is to say, the geometrical manifolds of Riemann and Minkowski, the theory of matrices, the 'odd' numbers of Dirac, quantum mechanics, relativity theory, and the like, are the flesh and blood incarnations of the queer ghosts and impossible entities of imaginary numbers and their geometrical interpretations.

All this has taught us to think of nature as consisting of (at least) a four-fold manifold, the space-time continuum. The observer appears on the scene and separates the continuum of space-time in a direction at right angles to the path along which he himself is traveling, and this sectioning gives the three-dimensional space at that moment, as well as the perpendicular time-dimension. This difference between time and space is indicated mathematically by assigning the minus sign to time which the geometry of relativity requires. This means that while the geometry of space (Cartesian-Newtonian space) is Euclidian, the geometry of space-time is hyperbolic or non-Euclidian. In other words, Euclidian geometry is identical with non-Euclidian geometry of a sphere of radius $\sqrt{-1}$, and this symbol, $\sqrt{-1}$, therefore has the property of turning time into space. Or in still other terms, in a multi-dimensional geometry where time plays the rôle of the next highest dimension, $\sqrt{-1}$ represents the rotation of an axis of time, and this enables us to translate the dynamic into the static. This is the meaning of the popular statement that time is the fourth dimension of space.

The moral of this most interesting movement of thought is this: Our whole modern civilization, in so far as it is based on the science of electrical engineering, — and that includes automobiles, airplanes, radio, telephone, television, and other devices that employ magnetos and the principles of electromagnetic induction, — would be impossible in fact if the corresponding theoretical developments successively freeing mathematics from the narrow preconceptions of Greek mathematics had not occurred. And just as our industrial civilization is possible because we have broken away from the ancients, so our social advances will call for a similar breaking with the past. That is, if our machine civilization is non-Euclidian and non-Newtonian, so likewise our social framework must become non-Aristotelian, non-Euclidian, and non-Newtonian — if we desire to make a similar progress in the ethical-social domain.

VI. The Role of Non-Aristotelian Logic

Here and there, in the preceding pages, we have reiterated that the logical foundations of modern science will have to be expanded. When, several decades ago,[1] the author advanced the idea that modern physics requires a non-Aristotelian logic because, among other things, the 'law of identity' is rendered non-true by the wave-particle opposition, several critics of the writer objected to this conclusion. The two most searching criticisms of my arguments were presented by Dr. L. O. Kattsoff[2] and Dr. Ernest Nagel[3]. I replied to Kattsoff's criticisms in an article[4] published subsequently.

My own views on these matters have not undergone any great changes as a result of these criticisms. The strange thing (to me) is that both Dr. Kattsoff and Dr. Nagel have overlooked the main idea that is proposed as the basis for a non-Aristotelian logic. I refer to the idea of the emergent dimension, which carries such a heavy burden in the earlier argument, and which still constitutes a major concept in the present scheme. At the risk of repetition, I shall retrace the course of the argument, and then bring it into line with the more recent phases of our presentation.

By now the reader will realize that, for us, the necessity for a non-Aristotelian logic is tied in conceptually with the belief in creative evolution through the emergence of hyperspace dimensions which stand in isomorphic relation to their material bases somewhat as an $n + 1$ dimension can be put into homomorphic relation to its lower counterpart. But in addition it must be kept in mind that over the years our rejection of the law of excluded middle is linked with our rejection of what we have termed the *fallacy of the absolute individuality of substance,* the 'subject' of predication in the Aristotelian logic.

In our *monism of action* we look upon emergent evolution as the progressive elaboration of ever-more intricate patterns of *behavior-stuffs.* This *universal behaviorism,* as we have termed it, is connected with the notion of an historically new or emergent dimension, a concept deliberately framed to provide a reconciliation of the *relativity* of motion (as Einstein treats it) and the *absolutivity* of motion as nature achieves it. Here is the manner in which this synthesis is attained.

We recognize that the type of motion in which the science of mechanics is primarily interested is subject to Einstein's relativity principles. But growth and evolution (physical and biological), types of motion or change in which physics has hitherto not been interested, are *not* relative. These are forms of change (motion) to which present relativity considerations do not apply. Motion as it is conventionally represented by a fourth coördinate of the space-time continuum is relative; but evolution calls for a new kind or dimension of time, a unique form of temporal organization. This historically new dimension of growth is the $n + 1$ dimension, where n is any lower spatial dimension of 'materiality' out of which the higher organization emerges. Thus in our conception emergence adds a new degree of reality to any lower plane of being.

Whenever we refer to a system as a whole, with its spatial coördinates and its own 'local' time, this time is transposable across the inner parts of that whole. If now this system (K_1) enters into dynamical interaction with another system (K_2),—as, for example, atoms may combine, — the several systems may form a new and more inclusive system, — a molecule, in our selected case, — and this new system, so long as it is treated as a whole, will have its own (phenomenal) time transposable across the whole. *This new ('public') time is what we mean by the emergent dimension.*

The 'social' order which brings an emergent public time out of the 'local' times of the constituent parts may even have its own 'emergent mass,' as George H. Mead termed it, and this, for us, represents the *field* or *gestalt* property of the family of subordinate systems. The significant thing here is that this permits us to utilize the notion of a trans-spatial time in what can be shown to be organismic or non-elementalistic situations. That is, in such cases we can determine whether one event is 'simultaneous' with another when they can be 'experienced' together by the 'consciousness' of the organism (even atoms are organisms, as Whitehead taught us) that spans the local times of its own elementary constituents.

Now let us indicate still more explicitly how this notion of an 'organic' time as the emergent coördinate associated with the unique (absolute) dimension of evolution fits in with our non-Aristotelian approach. The process of evolution whereby a thing ceases to be what it was (as an isolated element) and becomes what it is, as a constituent of a higher behavior-stuff, defies the laws of Aristotelian logic in the sense that it is unintelligible in terms of the traditional principles. This 'unintelligibility' is curiously reminiscent of the difficulties inherent in Zeno's paradoxes of motion. To see this, let us turn to the ancient Greek philosopher for a moment.

In order to demonstrate that Zeno's paradoxes of motion are characteristic of the mode of thinking which later was stabilized into the 'laws' of traditional logic, let us note first of all that the law of excluded middle would be applicable in a static universe, or in a universe of discontinuous change and movement. But this 'law' creates difficulties when we are face to face with a temporally continuous process. This point can be made clear by reference to the first premise of one of Zeno's paradoxes. The premise states: *a thing must either move where it is or where it isn't.* This is the law of excluded middle (or *tertium non datur), that A is either B or non-B, but not both.* Zeno then continues: but a thing cannot move where it is; neither can it move where it isn't; therefore, motion is impossible! Putting the argument in symbolic form:

$$m < w + w'$$
$$m \nless w$$
$$m \nless w'$$
$$\therefore m = 0$$

Now the difficulty here is that *motion is precisely the process whereby a thing gets from where it is to where it wasn't*, — a third possibility that was overlooked in Zeno's argument. In reality, therefore, we find: $m = w + w' + (w \rightarrow w')$. In this criticism of the 'excluded middle' analysis we agree with Brouwer that Aristotelian logic was derived as an abstraction from a mathematics of finite classes which was then universalized. Brouwer goes on to argue that the law of excluded middle is not applicable to (cannot be shown to hold for) the domain of the *transfinite.* But the idea of *infinity*, along with that of *continuity*, underlies the mathematical analysis of *motion* (e.g., in differential calculus). And so Brouwer, like Hegel, must reject the modern handling of the problem of motion and change, and like Hegel, — though for a different reason, — must surrender one of the classical laws of thought of Aristotelian logic.

Those versed in the technical details of philosophy will note that Brouwer agrees with Bergson's view that continuity cannot be handled in the classical manner as a completed aggregate of points. We repeat, therefore, that Brouwer's intuitionism seems to support our view: we do not reject infinity, continuity, and motion; we merely reject the unrestricted application of the 'law of excluded middle,' an application which makes motion impossible. The fundamental intuition of life is the experience of duration, of a continuity in time which unites past and present. As Arnold Dresden put it, "thus intuitionism, upon which not only mathematical thinking, but all intellectual activity is held to be based, is found in the abstract substratum of all observation of change, a 'fusion of continuous and discrete,' a possibility of conceiving simultaneously several units connected by a *between* that can not be exhausted by interpolation of new units."[5]

In our own conception, we try to bring these several views (Hegel, Bergson, Brouwer) together. We hold that our foregoing symbol $(w \rightarrow w')$ represents neither *logical addition* nor *logical multiplication*, nor any other operation of traditional logic. This is what in mathematics introduces continuity and infinity into the analysis of motion and change; but it is also what (for us) symbolizes the passage from the 'is' to the 'is not' in any evolving entity. In this case '→' symbolizes the growth whereby the new time-dimension emerges. At this point the particle-aspect associated with identity is lost in the emergence of the phenomenally new whole, with its own public time transposable across the parts, like any other gestalt or field property. This viewpoint applies likewise to the emergence of the waterwave in a fluid medium, which forms a convenient hydrodynamic example.

It should now be clear that we are irrevocably committed to the thesis that all philosophy from Aristotle down to the year 1894 is misleading, because it is based on partially erroneous ideas about space and time. This date is picked because, so far as I know, it affords the earliest suggestion we have that the ether provides the continuum of space-time as the formative field of influence for physical events. In this year G. F. Fitzgerald (in his *Scientific Writings*, 1894, p. 313) set forth the idea that Einstein was later to unfold into what is now termed *field physics*. This development is profoundly significant, heralding as it does a revolutionary conception of nature and promising ultimately a new mode of social relatedness.

The intimate connection between relativity theory, isomorphism, and topology, is clearly indicated by Hermann Weyl in his very revealing article on "The Mathematical Way of Thinking" (*Loc. cit.*), where he points out that the most general form of the principle of relativity is found in the fact that the study of the worldlines and causal structure of the universe is a study of continuous deformations of the world relative to the observer. As Weyl notes, these one-to-one continuous transformations are based on pictures that are isomorphic between observed facts and symbolic representations. This, of course, is the great power of topology as a study of the qualitative space relations: the theorems of topology are unaltered by any continuous point-to-point transformations, and thus reveal properties which are *invariant*. Indeed, according to Lefschetz[6], topology may be defined as "the study of properties of space or their configurations invariant under continuous transformations."

To the electrical engineer, the ideas we have been working with come as old friends, — as we have previously noted. To be sure, the applications of harmonic analysis to social systems has not proceeded far, but when the higher electrical-social system has attained its emergent existence, electrodynamics will find its proper applications.

VII. The Topology of Humanity

The philosophy for this coming electromagnetic society may be described as *Planetism.* As a form of orientation, Planetism means that we are becoming more global in our thinking. Global thinking envisages situations as wholes, as totalities. Elementalistic approaches, — such as science, religion, and art, — concentrate on what might be called the line-elements of human nature, — 'intellect,' 'volition,' the 'emotions,' and the like, — whereas global orientations represent the volume-element, the most inclusive of wholistic orientations.

Wholistic orientations represent the progressively expanding vision of the earth-organism; they recognize this planet as the environment within which the human race moves on to the fulfillment of its biological goal: the fabrication of a spiral of history which not only unites space-separated areas, but which also bends the arc of time into the curve of a higher matrix, a planetary space-time synthesis. This is what we mean when we say that global thinking represents the transfer of ideas useful in the science of electrodynamics and relativity theory and gestalt theory to the domain of geo-political relations. Our topology of humanity, as it is termed, is the study of the developing embryo-organism moving toward the maturation of a world sensorium.

In our recent book on *World Philosophy*, we surmised that this coming electromagnetic civilization will represent a unification of the subjective intuitions of the East (India primarily) and the objective science and technology of the West. Thus the Oriental and Occidental hemispheres would appear as the two halves of an earth-armature that is spinning out patterns or images over the proliferating ganglia of a giant planetary brain. These pictures that are being scanned are the patterns of a planetary humanism. Scientific humanism is thus searching for the overall patterns for an earth-society, creating the *guiding fields* for the emergence of an electromagnetic society of the future.

From this point on, the job calls for the special knowledge of social engineers, as Dr. John Q. Stewart points out.[7] The social engineer, dissatisfied with the failure of political leadership to make adequate use of the marvelous powers created by technology, thus finds that he has many problems to consider. For example, should the maximizing of demographic energy, by increasing the number of human interactions, be set as a proper social goal? What part would the freedom of the individual play in this, or must human relations be channeled through a chain of social command? Can the individual by taking thought add a cubit to his demographic stature? Or were the prophets right in insisting that every increase comes as a gift of spiritual grace from a Power above mankind? These are some of the questions that are raised by social physics.

It is not possible at the present time to give completely acceptable answers to all questions in this field. But it certainly looks as if the kind of society we designate as a planetary civilization can only arise out of a democratic kind of society. Forms of totalitarianism which impose order from above through a chain of authoritarian controls choke down the potentials of individuals, and in that case the electromagnetic society can generate enough voltage only through voluntary coöperation on the part of individuals who have the maximum of freedom consistent with a progressively integrating society. Perhaps a scientific analysis of this situation will turn into a problem of determining maxima and minima in the calculus of variations.

Up to the present, we have not had a powerful urge toward such a world society because we are not mentally prepared to take the next step in the direction of a planetary way of living. This is because we have not been able to derive the principles of a one-world society simply and directly from the dominant characteristics of our present organizations and ideologies. It is hoped that social physics and cybernetics, suitably combined with a cultural semantography, may supply the formative energy and guiding field for the spiraling movement toward the planetarily polarized objective, — the creation of a world sensorium.

VIII. Intuitionism, Non-Aristotelian Logic, and Emergence

In the present and the preceding chapters we have been concerned with the evolution of mathematical thinking. We have surveyed the various philosophies of mathematics and examined the issues that are inherent in the area. We finally have decided to adopt a modified form of the intuitionist program: our analysis leads to intuitionism in the sense that we begin with the consciousness of temporal passage as the irreducible minimum of experience. This primary intuition of time as a continuum can be 'spatialized' into a linear aggregate of points; but this is an abstraction from an experience of time which *flows*, and in that respect our philosophy, like that of Bergson and Whitehead, is one of *process*.

From this point forward our investigation may advance in two somewhat independent directions. On the one hand, we may follow the tide of becoming into the logic of multi-valued calculi which recent investigations have disclosed. On the other hand, we may explore the mathematical developments which culminate in the analysis of higher manifolds of space.

If we follow the mathematical developments, we retrace the story of the arithmetization of geometry, the rise of imaginary numbers and their representation in the domain of complex numbers, and the flight from Euclidian space into the hyperspaces of non-Euclidian manifolds. Here, as in so many other cases, the mathematical developments call for innovations in logic, for while the commutative law holds for ordinary algebra, when Caley introduced *matrices* and Hamilton developed *quaternions* the commutative law of logic was set aside. This paved the way for more abstract algebras dealing with *groups* and *fields*, — and the end is not yet.

One of those who understood some of the implications of what was happening was the American mathematician, Benjamin Peirce (father of Charles S.). Benjamin Peirce saw deeply into the significance of Hamilton's quaternions, for in connection with imaginary numbers he pointed out that $\sqrt{-1}$ doubles the actual universe and by means of 'curious connecting fibers' forms with it an organic whole.[8] Just how 'curious' this connection can become is illustrated by what George D. Birkhoff[9] terms the 'mystical equation' of special relativity theory:

$$186{,}300 \text{ miles} = \sqrt{-1} \text{ seconds}$$

Here Dr. Birkhoff has in mind the fact that in an electromagnetic universe with a three-dimensional space and a one-dimensional time, the velocity of light gives the 'time' component of the space-time manifold. And, indeed, light does occupy a unique place in relativity theory, for in the equation $E = m \cdot C^2$, C^2 indicates the square of the velocity of light as the fundamental constant of an electromagnetic energy. Thus we get the Einsteinian revolution of the non-Euclidian universe of relativity theory.

As we have already noted, this record of steady progress in scientific thinking is indeed inspiring, and the mathematicians might well take pride in their cumulative achievements, — were it not for the fact that a distressing obstacle has appeared on the scene to halt the advance. The problem that baffled the Greeks and disturbed Bishop Berkeley, — the ineluctable question of infinity, — has appeared once again to plague the mathematician. The Dutch mathematician, Brouwer, has raised questions the answers to which must be found before a resumption of progress is possible. The simple fact is that the acceptance of the extreme intuitionism which stems from Brouwer's argument would rob the mathematician of some of his most beautiful creations, the theory of transfinite numbers, for example, and would make even ordinary analysis very difficult. Our own solution to this problem has come by way of an abandonment of the law of excluded middle, — and this brings us to the advances in logic which the modern synthesis has built upon.

As pointed out in the preceding chapter, Brouwer's formulations have deprived us of the benefits of the completed infinite, but we still retain the concept of the infinite as a non-terminating process: the dynamic infinite of a becoming process. In taking this stand, we agree with Bergson and Brouwer that continuity cannot be handled in the conventional manner as a completed aggregate of points. But this does no violence to our philosophy. The law of excluded middle assumes that the objects of which it is predicated are determinate in nature, but in our view there is an inherent indeterminateness of entities as related to their enclosing fields, and these entities lose a measure of their individuality as they participate in the formation of more inclusive integrations.

From our point of view, the symbol previously suggested ($w \longrightarrow w'$), represents neither logical addition nor logical multiplication; it is the process which introduces continuity and extension into the dynamics of motion; on the level of empirical reality it also represents the process of growth whereby the particle-aspect, associated with 'identity,' is lost in the emergence of a phenomenally new whole with its field properties transposable across the whole. In the present chapter we have sought to show how this ladder of emergent evolution has culminated in our present human social system and how the next level will constitute a world organism, — the electromagnetic society of the future.

IX. Summary: The Postulates of Dimensional Analysis

In bringing this chapter to a termination, it should prove helpful to summarize the presuppositions of knowledge which our investigation seems to have revealed. I shall group these postulates into two classes, though the dividing line is not so easily established. Roughly, however, the Epistemological Postulates have less reference to empirical reality, while the Scientific Principles appear to be a posteriori, — for all one knows, nature does not have to be this way rather than some other way.

A. Epistemological Postulates:

1. *Independent existence of the external world.* This postulate of the existence of a physical world rules out any form of Berkeleyan idealism, — that reality is nothing but a system of ideas in the mind of God.
2. *Reliability of sense perception.* It is true that men have illusions and hallucinations, but this implies that there is a real world which can be perceived by way of sensory experience.
3. *Causality and predictive uniformity.* This is frequently termed the 'principle of the uniformity of nature,' and is now associated with the 'cosmological postulate.' The justification for this principle is that it works, at least most of the time. The entire body of laws of nature bears witness to the fact of uniformity of behavior under constant conditions. The facts of emergent evolution and the uncertainty principle offer no challenge to nature's relatively stable regularities.
4. *The possibility of matching concepts (ideas) and percepts according to a principle of epistemic correlations.* An example of this is provided by the process of matching the properties of the number series (i.e., serial order) and the entities of the empirical world which can be enumerated.

   In general, abstract systems of mathematics (arithmetics, algebras, geometries) are constructed according to the procedures of dimensional theory.

B. Scientific Principles:

1. *The basic space-time continuum of the manifest world.* This ubiquitous manifold is the seat of serial order relations in nature.
2. *The relativity theory of motion for all types of behavior, except rotational motion.*
3. *Einstein's principle of the equivalence of energy and matter.* The manner in which this appears in the cyclic-creative

cosmology has already been indicated, but this matter will come up again later.

4. *Planck's quantum theory of energy and Pauli's exclusion principle for matter-energy relationships within the manifest universe.*
5. *Heisenberg's uncertainty principle as a relative limitation upon the accuracy of measurements.*
6. *The first and second laws of energetics or thermodynamics;* that is, the principle of least action and the principle of the degradation of energy (maximum entropy) for ideally isolated systems.
7. *Orthogonal emergent dimensionality in a hierarchy of evolutionary stages.* This is the principle of levels of organization which display their wholeness in gestalt, non-additive properties publicly transposable across the emergent wholes. Here a function of the sum is not a sum of the functions.
8. *Homomorphic images or similarity of logical structures holding between levels of organizations of behavior-stuffs.* This principle replaces Bertrand Russell's postulate of analogy and Keynes's principle of limited variety.
9. *The spiral action of time.* It may be that this 'spin' principle is implicitly contained in the previous principles. In any case it deserves emphasis. I shall return to this topic in the last section of this chapter.

In reviewing what we have done, we discover that mathematics deals with manifolds which can be ordered according to dimensions. For example, the serial ordering of points on a line constitutes a linear manifold of one dimension; and this becomes a geometric manifold (area) when we have a range of two variables. Thus we may pass from points to lines, from lines to planes, on to solids and polyhedra, in a hierarchy of ordered aggregates until we reach up into the geometry of n-dimensional spaces and the generalized topology of function-spaces.

In reviewing this, we see that the entire dimensional theory of thought-systems rests on the foundation of number theory as the basic mathematical discipline. In turn, we have observed how Brouwer has sought to derive the properties of number series from the *ur-intuition* of time. In this respect, the present theory follows the intuitionist approach. But this experience of the flow of time also introduces us to a form of empiricism, for the unidirectionality of experienced time (and serial order) is related to the irreversibility of the biochemical reactions of the living organism. This has been shown by the work of Hudson Hoagland.

This survey of dimensional analysis leads naturally into the study of spirals and their place in nature. There are two kinds of spiral curves of interest to students of nature. One is the 'spiral of Archimedes,' a spiral with a constant radius of curvature, and the logarithmic spiral, discovered by Descartes, and illustrated in nature by the spiral nebulæ (galaxies) and the siren whistle, whose mathematical equations represent an increase of distance between radii. In such cases the cycle is never a circle but an expanding curve.

In our cosmology the logarithmic spiral is so common in the manifest world because it represents the response of the visible world to the archetypal forms of the invisible universe. Quite probably the unidirectionality of experienced time as represented mathematically is not a straight line, but a spiral, especially as illustrated by the hierarchy of mental functions. We have surmised that this represents the increase of angular momentum with time as this reflects the interaction of the field-plenum of consciousness and the matter of the brain.

We are facing a difficulty here: we have said that communication of knowledge in the physical world is limited by the finite velocity of radiation influences, so that time-lag is an inescapable feature of all information transfer. On the other hand, there is a kind of instantaneousness of events in consciousness, an interpenetration of content, which illustrates the near-infinite velocity of a super-dispersive medium. In the psychic field point-to-point transmission gives way to something like action-at-a-distance. In the evolutionary scheme, however, it required millions of years to get the cells of the brain elaborated and functionally orchestrated. But what we need here is some sort of theorem, analogous to Fourier's theorem about the synthesis of harmonics, which shows how the behaviors of microscopic constituents can be compounded in an overall rotation which is our 'macroscopic rhythm.' The 'spiral action of time' designates this creative synthesis, but it does not explain it. Here, presumably, the 'guiding field' does the work, — but what feature of the influence of the unmanifest world is responsible for the spiral effect poses a question to which we have not yet provided the answer. Let us see what can be done to formulate an answer.

X. Preview: Angular Momentum and Spiral Structures

For the scientist the most valuable principles are those that hold within several areas of nature, such as atomic physics and astrophysics. Such a principle is found in the principle of the constant quantity of angular momentum in an isolated system. The *angular momentum* of a revolving body, whether it be a planet revolving about the sun or a particle of a rotating globe of gas, is the product of the mass, the square of the radius, and the rate of angular motion. The principle of the conservation of angular momentum asserts that the sum-total angular momentum of an isolated system always remains the same. In the case of the rotating globe of gas, the total angular momentum is found to be the product of the mass, the square of the distance from the axis of rotation, and the angular velocity for all the molecules of the gas. But since the distances of the molecules from the axis are diminished, the angular velocity must increase to maintain the same total angular momentum. Thus the shrinking of a rotating globe causes it to rotate at a faster rate.

This principle is widely employed in astronomical theory. Without it, such a theory as the nebular hypothesis (Kant, Laplace) and the recent cosmological hypotheses of Fred Hoyle and George Gamow would not be possible. This phenomenon of rotation is of special interest to us for it calls attention to the importance of 'spin' in nature. We have come up against this problem at various stages in the present investigation. Here is our problem in its most general form.

How do microscopic spins of particles of ensembles get organized into macroscopic systems having their own angular momenta? In our philosophy, particle-spin and the angular momenta of physical systems (e.g., atoms, spiral nebulæ) are phenomena in a three-dimensional space which have their isomorphic images in the rotations in the emergent dimensionalities whereby the higher rungs of the ladder of emergence, from *matter* → *life* → *mind* → *world sensorium*, are brought into being. This step-wise emergence has a symbolism in mathematics in terms of *operators* which rise in a corresponding hierarchy. Thus *energy* corresponds to a *scalar* quantity in mathematics, in the sense that it is non-directed and therefore added arithmetically, while *force* is a directed quantity, a *vector*, which is added trigonometrically. Upon the basis of vector analysis analogues, it is possible to proceed step by step from *vectors* → *versors* → *tensors* → *spinors* to some higher operation of a cosmic *lensor* which functions through a circumambient

Cosmic Field and supplies the archetypal pattern for all rotational phenomena. This final step would involve the establishment of a nexus or bond between the hierarchical spiral and the partial differential equations of Einstein's non-linear field theory.

All this is difficult business. But I trust the reader will bear in mind that some of the difficulty in following the argument arises from the fact that, here and there, I am of necessity presupposing some theses I have stated in previous volumes. It would be a poor form of 'time-binding' which did not build upon the achievements of the past, and in that sense I hope I do not fall short of the 'energy integrated through time' form of philosophical synthesis.

These tangential remarks are relevant to the problem of time. In my previous book, *The Promise of Scientific Humanism* (pp. 215–216), I pointed out that there are three types of relativity: (1) *physical relativity*, (2) *biological relativity*, and (3) *psychological relativity*. We there argued, and here reaffirm, that the upper levels of relativity represent a kind of hysteresis of the next lower level, which provides the structural or physical basis of that relativity. Thus psychological relativity is conditioned by biological constitution, while biological relativity is a special case of history as recorded in physical structures that have preserved a residuum of past environmental influence. Therefore, except for the ultimate elementary particles of the manifest world, structure on all levels is crystallized function, behavior in accordance with 'habits' that are preserved in time. Accordingly, spiral structures are ingrained in nature because the Cosmic Imagination creates and guides the manifest universe through spiral arrangements (galaxies, protoplasmic systems, and the spiral hierarchy of neuropsychic functions), *which spirals are the manifestation of the increase of the radius of angular momentum with age as this expresses the pressure of the field-plenum on matter.* That is to say, the tempo of emergent evolution is an index of the inertial response of the manifest world to the world of archetypal influences: Platonic solids, circles, spirals, and the higher patterns of spherical harmonics.

It may be that we have here an important principle. The phenomenon which appears as the effect of distance in space, for example, the 'tiring' effect of light as it comes to us from the external galaxies, is known to us in near-at-hand phenomena as the tribute levied by history on the evolution of systems from physics through biology to psychology. In the first case, the penetration of cosmic space (or matter in space) slows down the frequency of radiation, and this is due to the inertia of the intervening matter; in the second case, the inertia is recorded as time-lapse of geological eras required for biological evolution. There may be a logarithmic spiral action in both cases, representing an accumulation of angular momentum, except that in the case of cosmic time the observation of the spiral action is denied us because we observe the system from within, whereas, sitting as we do at the top of the ladder of evolution, we are in a sense outside the system of physical-chemical-biological evolution, i.e., the lapsed time of evolution is 'behind' us in a way in which it is not when we view the 'receding' galaxies.

In biological evolution archetypal fields of influence must struggle against the inertia of previous deposits to create new and higher integrations. Inertia here is resistance to transformation, as the 'tiredness' of light represents the relatively slight resistance of cosmic space to penetration by radiation. However, this time-lag on the level of manifest reality is compensated for in the Cosmic Imagination's knowledge of the physical world through an information system which operates without time-lag. This means that the Cosmic Imagination knows what is being done before it is done in the manifest world because the 'doing' is simply the sequence of 'images' as these are observed in the space-time of the perceptual world. That is to say, the Cosmic Imagination transfers spin from the sub-ether to the ether of events in such a manner that the *inner thoughts* appear as the *outer signals* telling the scientist, the philosopher, and devotees of poetry and religion, that behind the life-history of the celestial cinerama there is a veiled meaning still to be penetrated. What this meaning is I shall try to predict in the last chapter of this volume.

FOOTNOTES CHAPTER VII

[1]Cf. "Physics and the Laws of Thought," *Psyche* (London), 1931, vol. 11, 70-80.

[2]Cf. "La logique non-aristotelicienne et la crise en science," by L. O. Kattsoff, *Scientia,* 1938, Vol. LXIV, 49-52.

[3]See the long and rather careful review of my book, *The Promise of Scientific Humanism,* by Ernest Nagel, *Scripta Mathematica,* 1943, Vol. IX, 49-54.

[4]Cf. "Physics, Probability, and Multi-valued Logic," *Philosophical Review,* 1940, Vol. XLIX, 662-672.

[5]*Bulletin of the American Mathematical Society,* 1942, Vol. 30, p. 32.

[6]Cf. "Topology," by Solomon Lefschetz, *American Mathematical Society Collected Publications,* Vol. XII, 1930.

[7]Cf. "The Lawyer as a Social Engineer," *The Princeton Engineer,* March, 1951.

[8]On this matter see R. E. Moritz, *Memorabilia Mathematica,* 1914, p. 282.

[9]Cf. "The Principle of Sufficient Reason," by George David Birkhoff, *Rice Institute Pamphlet,* 1941, No. 1.

8

SCIENTIFIC METHODS IN PHYSICS AND IN PSYCHOLOGY

"This search and re-search for integrated concepts has gone on through all the ages since men learned to use words. The theologians have tried to integrate the universe around two concepts: God and anti-God. Aristotle proposed ten basic categories. Kant proposed four (quality, quantity, relation, and modality) each with three subcategories. Adler is developing his "Syntopicon" as an encyclopedia of the 102 great ideas drawn from the "great books." These and many other proposals are based on the best experience and thinking of the past; they do not, however, use the scientific method of controlled experiments which can generate better thinking for the future."

— Stuart C. Dodd

I. The Unity of Science

Among the important problems in the philosophy of science is the question of whether scientific method is the same in all the natural sciences, or whether, as some students believe, there are many 'scientific methods.' If, for example, the methods of the social sciences are not the same as those used in the physical sciences there would then be a plurality of scientific methods.

The argument that the methods in the physical sciences and those employed in the social sciences are not the same usually rests upon the assumed existence of two differentiating characteristics: (a) that physical science rules out the subjective elements in scientific data, and (b) that physical science is ethically neutral, whereas the social sciences, either deliberately or covertly, introduce into social studies evaluational elements which are not present in the objectively orientated investigation in the physical sciences.

As we have tried to show, the present viewpoint concerning this problem is that scientific method is substantially the same in all the sciences, even though we concede that it is more difficult to apply scientific methodology in some fields than in others. By the time we have completed our survey of the sciences, we shall have disposed of both of the two alleged distinctions. In the present chapter, I shall deal with (a), the idea that physical science rules out the 'subjective' elements. The second distinction (b), that science has no room for ethical considerations, raises a question I shall deal with at length in a later section of this study. But the overall conclusion we arrive at is that scientific method is one and the same in all branches of science, and does not undergo metamorphosis as we pass from one pillar to the next in our 'temple of knowledge.'

It seems surprising that there should be any doubt about this matter. That at least a minimal nucleus of methodology is shared by all the sciences is certainly obvious when one considers the importance of such common ingredients as 'love of truth,' 'objectivity,' 'freedom from bias,' 'careful observation of facts,' 'cautiousness of generalization,' and the like. All these regulative ideals, plus other general principles of logic and scientific method, such as rules of definition and principles of classification, are surely the common property of methodology wherever it is employed. In order to recall specifically what we mean when we state that science has a common logical structure, we refer back to our earlier Diagram VI of the 'logical structure of science.'

However, the statement that scientific method is the same in all the sciences, means more than the fact that this method can be analyzed into a common logical structure. All the sciences begin with the same empirical data or 'raw material,' and thus the experiential point of departure is the same. It is not true that physics is completely objective and free of anthropomorphism, whereas psychology and the social sciences are tainted with a subjectivism that is not present in the sciences dealing with the non-human, external world. Since this is an important conclusion, if correct, for science and philosophy, it is necessary to state the argument as cogently as possible. Thus we return to the problem of perception.

II. The Problem of Perception

In his forceful statement of the position of positivistic phenomenalism, Karl Pearson argues in Chapter III of his classic, *The Grammar of Science* that science deals with the 'reality of things.' Starting with an 'external object', — such as the blackboard the scientist writes upon, — Pearson insists that our knowledge of this object is first of all in terms of our sensations of it, — its shape, its color, its texture, and so on. The blackboard has a smooth, hard surface, has weight, resistance to fragmentation, a temperature, and the like. All these, it will be noted, are clusters of conscious *sensations*, or rather, *perceptions*, since inferences are added to the bare sensations of the blackboard.

Some decades later, and in a somewhat similar manner, Professor Arthur S. Eddington begins his celebrated book, *The Nature of the Physical World*, by calling the reader's attention to the table on which he is writing. The immediately perceived table has weight, color, hardness, — pretty much the qualities that Pearson's blackboard has; but the 'scientific table' is composed of molecules, atoms, electrons, and the rest, all in rapid agitations and bombardments.

This shows that physics does not exclude immediate experience; the sense data which are given in consciousness are dependent upon an observer, the scientist himself, and physics does not rule out this observer. It merely standardizes the rôle of the observer. Though the procedure begins with subjective experience, it does not end in subjectivism. In truth, the very theory of relativity is but a device for stating the laws of nature (i.e., the observed uniformities of relations given in groups of sense-data) in such a way that they are independent of any special frame of reference. Such 'properties' as masses, lengths, times, velocities, and the like, are relative; not relative to the 'mind' of the observer, but relative to the frame of reference from which they are measured. However, 'properties' are not 'laws'. The laws of nature remain invariant.

In contrast to physics, psychology is (or ought to be) interested in 'consciousness as such.' Physics leaves consciousness to the psychologist, and psychology, if it wishes, can study immediate experience independently of the physical (external) conditions for such experience. The introspective method of psychology need not concern itself with the objective cause of subjective states. However, there is a branch of psychology called 'psychophysics' which does investigate the correlations between physical stimuli and conscious sensations.

It will be apparent to those who are familiar with recent discussions in the field that my approach follows closely the views of the gestalt psychologists rather than the earlier psychophysics of Weber, Fechner,

Wundt, and Titchener. Indeed, we have already employed the concept of *isomorphism* as a key concept in understanding the relation between the external physical world and the inner or subjective world. This is our equivalent concept for what George P. Conger has termed 'epitomization.'

III. Man's Place in Nature

In order to see more clearly how science does get started, and also to place everything in proper perspective, let us for a moment consider man's position in the universe in order to determine what the function of perception may be.

In broadest terms, the universe may be described as a three-level arrangement. These three levels may be visualized in the following manner:

Level I Supra-Universe:
- Galaxies and Meta-galaxies
- Island Universes (toward the "infinitely big")

↓

Level II Middle-Scale Universe:
- Macro-universe of man
- Earth and earth's observable objects
- (This is the engineer's universe of Euclidian-Newtonian science).

↑

Level III Micro-Universe:
- Infra-world or micro-universe
- Molecules, atoms, electrons, protons, neutrons, photons, mesons, etc.
- Sub-universe of wave mechanics (toward the "infinitely little").

Accordingly, Level II is constituted of materials that genetically arise (exist) on Level I. It is believed that the middle-scale entities of Level II (non-living bodies and living organisms) were evolved from the substances of Level III; for example, organisms, chairs, buildings, and the like, are enormously complex configurations of molecular aggregates which, in turn, break down into atomic patterns or complexes.

That man, in his perceptual world of engineering science, literally does stand mid-way between the supra- universes and the infra-universes, that he is in a sense at the cross-roads of the universe, is indicated by calculations which show that while about 10^{27} atoms make a man's body, 10^{28} human bodies constitute enough material to build a star. Man lives his life in a middle-scale universe, suspended between two infinities, and he appears to possess characteristics derived from both domains.

This three-level arrangement of the physical world gives rise to an interesting situation, which Hans Reichenbach describes in his book on *Atom and Cosmos*. Professor Reichenbach points out that both the minute and the cosmic worlds have essentially different appearances from the world of medium dimensions we perceive directly, and our concepts are appropriate to these moderate dimensions only. He informs us that the old ideas of *space* and *time* for the large-scale world, and those of *substance* and *laws* for the small-scale one, are only approximations. This recognition that "the old basic concepts of natural science apply only to medium-sized portions of space constitutes the Copernican crisis in our time." According to Reichenbach, the mapping out of a natural science which comprises the small, the moderate-sized, and the large alike requires first the creation of more general, deeper fundamental concepts.

It may be that the synthesis of the three sets of laws into one type of law will come, not through seeking to evolve macroscopic behavior from microscopic phenomena, but from regarding the laws of the middle-scale universe as a compromise, the product of an interaction. (That, in fact, is the purpose of the arrows pointing from Levels III and I toward the intermediate Level II of our diagram. To my knowledge, no one has worked out a theory of how galaxies could be related to the evolution of matter, life, and mind although the writer has made a beginning in his studies on 'Cosmecology.')

IV. The Structure of the Physical World

The actual starting point for human experience is of course on Level II, the level of human organisms and the earth-environment. Looking out upon nature from this level, — up toward the stars and down toward the atoms, — we theorize about the structures that we see, or believe that we see. We don't actually see the stars and galaxies of stars and we don't actually see atoms. In both cases we see blobs of light, and the blobs of light we see in the heavens we interpret as coming from the stars, and the blobs of light we see flitting across a Wilson cloud chamber we interpret as being made by electrons and like particles.

Laws are possible in both these domains because the scientist is able to establish a correspondence between the structure of conscious experience and the structure we seem to discover in physical events, which, on a causal theory of perception, we say produces these experiences in us.

In the present chapter we are not primarily concerned with the physicist's theories about the nature of 'matter.' But it is necessary to point out that we can no longer start from the naive position that 'matter' (i.e., particles or aggregates of particles) is a primary datum. What we start with has been well stated by Eddington when he points out that "The occurrence of identical, or closely related, structures of sensations in different consciousnesses provides the logical starting-point of physical science." This sentence, quoted from Eddington's book on *The Philosophy of Physical Science* (p. 215), restates Eddington's earlier position as set forth in his book on *The Nature of the Physical World*.

The view that knowledge in physical science is always knowledge of the group structure of sets of sensations in consciousness has also been set forth by Gustaf Stromberg . According to Stromberg, "The epistemological error that has crept into our conception of matter is due to the false idea that we observe external particles and configurations of particles (matter), whereas the things we directly observe with the aid of our sense of vision are 'shadows' in consciousness." In support of this view, Stromberg quotes Max Planck, as follows: "I regard consciousness as fundamental. I regard matter as derivative from consciousness. We cannot get behind consciousness."

Without, for the present, taking a stand on whether we can or cannot 'get behind consciousness,' we may at least say that this is where our analysis must make its beginning. But when we take the next step and try to pass from conscious states to the brain states to which 'immediate experience' is somehow attached, we get into deep water. The 'brain-mind relation' has been described as the "no-man's land on which the theologian, the psychologist, and the physiologist meet face to face." Perhaps the difficulty in this area is increased by the fact that in passing from the mind to the brain we are reversing what seems to be the genetic (evolutionary) steps which nature followed. Accordingly, let us begin as nature appears to have begun: by retracing our path, starting with the physical world as a structure of events.

The occasion for a mental percept is provided by a stimulus pattern in the external world. This pattern is transmitted to, and affects, a sense organ such as the eye, or ear, or one of the other exteroceptors (receptors that receive stimuli from the outer world). There is considerable evidence to indicate that the pattern of stimulation on the retina (in the case of a visual response) bears a definite relation to the objective stimulus pattern.

The cortical pattern has roughly a one-to-one correspondence with the retinal pattern: the physiological pattern is a kind of mirror image of the external pattern in space. And if time is an element of the pattern (as in a melody, which one hears), the temporal sequence corresponds roughly in a one-to-one fashion. However, if we refrain from thinking in terms of the elementalistic separation of space and time intervals, we may say that, if the percipient and the pattern he perceives are in the same reference system, the spatio-temporal attributes of the external physical pattern have their corresponding features in the spatio-temporal pattern on the physiological level. As we have already seen, this similarity of pattern is designated as *isomorphism* — a similarity of logical structure in the two patterns or gestalten.

V. Isomorphism in Brain-Mind Relations

It needs to be observed that the correspondence (isomorphism) we are dealing with is not perfect. There is some evidence to show that the *duration* of stimuli is related to the temporal pattern of the nerve impulses arriving in the cortex. There is also evidence showing that *brightness* discrimination (in visual experience) may be a function of the thalamus and the midbrain; while perception of *form* and *color* are localized in the cerebral cortex where higher accuracy and discrimination are achieved. However, these simple instances of correlation of sensory and neural events must also be weighed in the light of Dr. Harry Helson's discovery that the 'space' and 'time' phases of experience are interdependent and may influence each other in a kind of psychological 'relativity,' thus complicating the 'isomorphism' of inner and outer events.

These considerations indicate that not every attribute in the external world has its parallel features in physiology. And, still higher in the series, not every physiological pattern has its corresponding conscious attributes. As Hermann Weyl points out in his book on *Mind and Nature* (p. 7), the retina suppresses, reduces, and even distorts some of the properties of the external physical manifold. *This is analogous to a situation in projective geometry in which a manifold of a higher num-*

ber of dimensions is impoverished by projection on a two-dimensional manifold. However, the analogy is not complete, for when man is involved, his nature refuses to be denied the richness and variety of the external world as it is recorded on the receptor level. The cortex re-creates some of the qualities which were suppressed and, in the case of illusions and hallucinations, ingredients are even added which have no analogues in the external mosaic.

Therefore, although the correspondence between the three levels, — physical, physiological, and psychological, — is not perfect (not a one-to-one correlation), there is an approximate isomorphism between the three manifolds, and it is this correspondence which makes it possible for conscious man to adjust himself successfully to the external world *via* the physiological bridge which spans the gap between psychology and physics, mind and matter.

The foregoing analysis leads us into our main thesis, which may be stated as follows: *Evolution has produced the brain-eye structuring, which acts as a kind of step-up transformer, generating in consciousness the similarity of logical structure called isomorphism.* That is to say that in addition to the assumption that the nerve impulse preserves something analogous to the properties of the external frequencies and foreshadows most of the characteristics of the cortical process, the assumption is made that in the brain there is reinstated a form of field phenomenon somehow corresponding to the original wave frequencies which acted as the stimulus. This hypothesis was first set forth in my little book on *The Alchemy of Light and Color* (1928) and subsequently in other volumes.

VI. Mechanism Not Sufficient

It is important to observe, however, that even though we subscribe to a type of 'parallelism' between brain events and mental events, this does not commit us to the mechanistic theory that the mental series is merely the sequence of primary brain processes seen from the inside. The inadequacy of such a simple 'identification' is quite evident, but it must not be overlooked.

For one thing, we know, — as the gestalt theorists have pointed out, — that a tune is recognized even when it is played in a different key; just as we know that the same shape can be recognized whatever part of the retina its image may fall upon. It is not the precise stimulation of definite nerve cells in the brain which underlies this 'recognition' of melodies and shapes. *There must be some abstract pattern (concept) which the cortex (or mind) extracts from the receptor pattern.* It is this property of the brain-mind of responding to abstract patterns which lifts man above the calculating machines which man has invented to imitate his own brain processes. This, of course, brings us back to the important development known to the public by the name of 'cybernetics,' and we must pause to restate how this development fits into our scheme of analysis.

VII. Cybernetics and Brain Mechanics

Cybernetics, the science which studies the common elements in the human nervous system and the electrical circuits of mechanical brains and calculating machines, promises to rival relativity theory in its dramatic implications. The basic concept in automatic control devices (such as the steering mechanism of a ship) is that of a *feed-back mechanism* (a 'circular reaction-arc' was the older biological concept for this), which operates in response to information fed back to it as the system continues to function. It is claimed that this revolutionary conception will make possible a new philosophical approach to the old argument of 'mechanism or purpose,' and can be used as the basis for studying the relation of "ideological man to the scientifically known natural man," as Professor Northrop puts it.

The most obvious comment that can be made of this unifying theory is that it is too 'mechanistic' (materialistic), since it reduces the psychological phenomena of sane and insane man to purely physical formulations. Perhaps to some extent the force of the objection will be reduced by Norbert Wiener's flight into higher dimensions. Cybernetics pulls out all the stops; it uses every arrow in the scientist's quiver of concepts: it is by no means confined to a space of three dimensions, for in studying groups of transformations, operations which form multi-dimensional configurations in *n*-space can also be handled (*Cybernetics*, pp. 160–161). Interestingly enough, this conception fits in nicely with our formula of 'consciousness as a new dimension,' but in our theory this was specifically made an integral part of a more general theory of emergent evolution, whereas in Wiener's theory this seems not to be the case. Therefore, until we do get the cosmic background of this latest form of 'physicalism,' we must suspend judgment on the question of whether Wiener's theory of cybernetics is a mechanistic-materialistic formulation.

Another, and more valid criticism is that *such electronic devices cannot deal with (duplicate) the creative element in human thought.* ENIAC, MANIAC, UNIVAC, ORDVAC, ERA, EDSAC, and BINAC (names for the electronic calculating machines) can do problems in mathematics, but mathematics, like all deductive thinking, is automatic in the sense that nothing comes out in the conclusions which was not put into the reasoning machine at the beginning. If, as Leibniz proposed, all thought processes could be reduced to the symbols and operations of mathematics, the electronic brain might indeed duplicate every characteristic of the human brain except consciousness itself. But creative thinking brings in elements of novelty which no machine can duplicate.

Both Dr. Wiener's 'cybernetics' formulations and Dr. N. Rashevsky's theories about the "mathematical biophysics of the central nervous system" face the same difficulty. The electronic machine of Dr. Wiener works on the principle of a set of choices between alternatives, each set depending on earlier choices, and the machine orders its operations through a clocking device which times the sequence. Hence the need, in the human animal, of a central or master clock, such as Hudson Hoagland has been searching for in the organisms. These choices we speak of are, as Wiener points out (*Cybernetics*, p. 140), based on a dichotomy of 'yes' and 'no,' regulated by relays that are 'on' and 'off.' This two-valued choice corresponds to the 'zero' and 'one' of the Boolean algebra of logic. Of course, another kind of logic (not the two-valued logic of 'yes' and 'no') would call for a more complicated machine; but should such a machine be constructed, we would still be up against that fact that in organismic situations it is not true that a neurone (vacuum tube, in the electronic brain) is either active ('on') or passive ('off') in any absolute sense. The same neurone may be 'active' with respect to one brain-area and 'passive' with respect to another. We have here a non-elementalistic situation which calls for a non-linear mathematics, a new pattern of causation, and a new logic of relations that still remains to be created.

Although our approach definitely renounces mechanism and materialism, it does not suggest a return to any older forms of dualism. In the face of the difficulties we have mentioned, it would seem to be the part of wisdom to explore the possibilities of a relative dualism, such as may be derived from the theory of emergent evolution.

Applied to the problem of perception, the concept of isomorphism would present the following levels of emergence:

SPACE-TIME PATTERNS

Physical	Retinal	Cortical	Conscious
△	a	1	△
□	b	2	□
○	c	3	○

For each space-time organization of matter in the external world to which the organism responds visually there would be a corresponding retinal, cortical, and conscious pattern. If this were all that could occur, according to a monistic theory, one might (in terms of current theories of wave mechanics) suppose that the relation between the brain-mind and the physical world is analogous to the relation between particles and the field, where the brain structure represents the particle-aspect and consciousness represents the field-aspect (the sub-ether, in our theory).

One difficulty in working out a satisfactory theory of the relation of consciousness and its neural concomitants is that in the matter of the electrical processes involved in brain events, several types of manifestation seem to be implicated. There are the action currents that traverse the individual neurons, which are synchronized into cell-group action-patterns; there is the scanning operation in the brain, as a gross interpretation of alpha-rhythm pictures for single brain lobes; and then, finally, as Professor Wolfgang Köhler has insisted, there are events in the brain which are mediated by continuous field action. Thus brain activity is at least in part a matter of field physics, even though the electrochemical phenomena of individual nerve impulses are also a part of the total picture.

In spite of these complexities, it is possible to work out a theory of visual perception of an object in the external (physical) world in terms of what might be called *homomorphic resonance images* between the above four levels of reality, from the sub-universe of the 'matter' of the outer environment, through the eye-brain system, into the domain of consciousness. Such a theory would naturally culminate in the theory known as panpsychism: the theory that the universe is ensouled.

Dr. Gustaf Stromberg seems to be moving toward such a theory in his book, *The Soul of the Universe.* The great virtue of such a theory is that it makes possible an 'epistemological monism,' free from the difficulties of the 'copy' theory of knowledge as expounded by John Locke.

In our own theory, based on a relative dualism of 'matter' and the 'field,' we are left with a dualism of the 'observer' and the 'observed,' of an external world of *perceptible particles* and a subjectively experienced *field-plenum* which the older psychologists termed the realm of 'mental states.' Accordingly, in true perception, — as opposed to illusory and hallucinatory experiences, — these subjective perceptions stand in isomorphic relation to their objective counterparts. However, it seems that the mental gestalt occurs in a higher (emergent) dimension than the underlying physiological gestalt out of which it developed. This takes us back to the emergent time-dimension, a concept which provides the avenue of escape from a mechanistic theory of the brain-mind nexus.

VIII. The Emergent Time-Dimension

Our fundamental idea grows out of an analogy, the stages in the argument being these. Physics treats 'time' as a one-dimensional component of a space-time manifold in such a fashion that, — as Minkowski puts it, — three-dimensional dynamics can be viewed as four-dimensional statics. In our physical world it is the consciousness of the observer which stratifies the four-fold continuum into a *three-plus-one manifold* (three dimensions of space and one dimension of time or motion). Time, in a general way, plays the role of a higher dimension when it stratifies the perceived universe into the static and dynamic aspects.

Let us therefore think of consciousness as the highest dimension, the irreversible time-axis, which emerges to add a new degree of reality in the universe. This temporal dimension, as the sense of experienced change, incorporates within itself the inner aspects of the objective space-time patterns as these are transposed from physiological patterns into conscious patterns. Consciousness *is* the experience of temporal passage (duration) as aroused in us by the reception of stimuli-patterns while they are being supplemented by, and integrated into, the subjective discriminations. Not only is the sense of time-passage related to the body temperature, as Hudson Hoagland has shown; not only is there a general synchronism between different parts of the cortex, related perhaps to the alpha rhythm of the electroencephalogram, and clocked by some deeper center which may involve the hypothalamus; but to make the situation even more complex, the experience of time, as Koffka points out, is a field-conditioned property related to factors which apparently have little to do with it.

By this time the reader will have observed that our theory is not only a theory of the 'structure of knowledge', but also a theory of the 'structure of reality.' It serves as a proposed solution to the traditional mind-body problem. We hold that there is no rift between the physical and the psychical, because we find the homologue of the dualism of consciousness and the nervous system on all levels of nature where emergent evolution is at work.

Alternative cosmological theories have attempted a similar task, and to clarify the present view, I shall first compare it briefly with the solution proposed by Whitehead's 'method of extensive abstraction,' and then point out similarities between this view and the cosmology of A. E. Milne.

IX. Comparison With the Whitehead-Northrop Cosmology

Writing on the occasion of the death of Professor Whitehead, F. S. C. Northrop[1] pointed out that Whitehead had the great insight to discover that the basic difficulties in contemporary philosophy have their origin in errors made at the beginning of modern thought and that, as a consequence, contemporary problems can be solved only by going back to the origins of such theories to remove the initial errors.

These errors, Whitehead claimed, were first made by Galileo and then repeated by Newton. The distinction which threw modern thought into confusion is the distinction between (*a*) apparent sensed qualities in apparent relative sensed space and time, and (*b*) public or 'real' scientific objects in 'true, real, and mathematical' space and time. This distinction, Northrop points out, involves two different assumptions: (1) the thesis that (a) scientifically conceived, indirectly observed, experimentally verified nature is not identical with (b) directly observed and sensed nature, and (2) the theory that (a) is related to (b) by a three-termed relation of appearance in which the observer is the mediating term between (a) and (b).

Northrop argues that this distinction (ordinarily described as the dualism of primary and secondary qualities) results in the identification of the observer with Locke's 'mental substance.' Whitehead's solution was to get rid of the 'bifurcation of nature' by rejecting the first of the two assumptions of Galileo and Newton. This forced Whitehead to derive the concepts of mathematical physics from sensed nature, and this Whitehead achieved by inventing a new scientific method — the *method of extensive abstraction.*

To the detached onlooker, one of the curious things about the evolution of scientific thought is the manner in which the correctors of the mistakes of predecessors are in turn subjected to correction. Thus we find Martin Johnson developing the thought, in his important work on *Time, Knowledge, and the Nebulae* (1947), that Whitehead's advances, good as they were, are now out of date because Whitehead was making use of relativity theory at the stage reached by Einstein, which is prior to Milne's reconstruction of the physical foundations on a basis of temporal experience of communicating observers. Whitehead's attempt to bridge the gap between mental and physical time (which was developed by Galileo, Descartes, Newton, and Locke) loses its validity through not starting, as Milne does, with communicable knowledge as it arises through equivalence of observers.

The fact is that while Whitehead and Northrop start from the foundations of field physics and agree that there is no bifurcation in nature (except as Northrop's later distinction between the *theoretic* and *esthetic components* restores a dualism), they are unable to pass in any clear manner from physical fields to biological fields to the mental space-time of the 'percipient event' which, in Whitehead's language, somehow then gets into 'cogredience' with the extra-organismic universe in which the scientist makes his observations. What we need is something more than 'prehension into unity' and the 'best average cogredience' between the passage of nature and the passage of mind; what we need is an 'isomorphism' or similarity of structure between physical, biological, and mental levels.

X. Comparison With Milne's Theory and Brouwer's Theory

Since the present theory of the emergent time-axis has points in common with the cosmological speculations advanced by A. E. Milne, it is desirable to compare the two theories briefly.

Dr. Milne's theory, first presented about fifteen years ago, gives a meaning to uniform time. His formulation starts with the individual's awareness of the passage of time and arrives at a system of agreeing time-keeping for different places in the universe. Commenting on this development, J. B. S. Haldane has remarked that it provides a beautiful illustration of the Hegelian dialectic: Einstein negated the notion of simultaneity, but an extension of relativity ideas has brought back the idea of 'cosmical time', — and thus Einstein's negation has been negated!

Some writers consider Milne's cosmological theory to be a milestone in the philosophy of science. As Martin Johnson interprets it, one of the outstanding features of this new approach is that it culminates in a formulation of a *principle of communicability* as a basis for all science. In this conception, the relativity transformations in the time scales of Milne make it possible to communicate experience (i.e., the laws of physics) from one observer to another. This is an absolute requirement of any physical theory, for the very possibility of science presupposes communicable, publicly verifiable knowledge.

Milne achieves this synthesis by introducing two kinds of time: in the *dynamical* representation of the universe the past is infinite and is the same for all observers; while in the *kinematical* time we are representing time as measured by atomic vibrations and radioactive clocks. Accordingly, it may be said that matter keeps dynamical time and radiation keeps kinematical time. Thus two systems of equations are produced, both equally valid, and the one can be obtained from the other by 'regraduation' of the clocks that are used.

To the student of philosophy this is an important development. To me this is especially interesting because it appears that the distinction that Professor Milne establishes between the two kinds of time is in some measure analogous to the distinction I have set up[2] between the local times (statistical, and therefore in a sense kinematical) and the dynamical time of any macroscopic body wherein the 'local times' of the constituent entities of a statistical ensemble are integrated into a phenomenal whole, with a 'public time' transposable across the parts. We have described such a gestalt with its emergent time axis as a 'macroscopic rhythm' of microscopic entities, and we have tried to show that emergent evolution is simply the ladder of emergent time-axes of organismic wholes from atoms → molecules → unicellular organisms → multicellular organisms → world psychosomatic creature.

At least one point of difference distinguishes my theory from Milne's. Since the orthogonal time-axis is, for us, an emergent (whether it is the dimension which emerges, or new phenomena which require a new dimension for their description, is a problem we shall deal with later), it would appear to be impossible to translate the one kind of time into the other (*dynamical* into *kinematical* time) by any 'regraduation' of the clocks, as Milne proposes. For us, the 'clocks' on any two given levels of emergence are functioning in two different dimensions, even though the one (later one) emerged out of the earlier one.

As some advocates of the theory of 'emergent evolution' present the argument, consciousness appears as a kind of epi-phenomenon attached to biological organisms at the upper end of the scale of evolution. But in the present theory the entire pyramid of emergence is erected on what Milne terms the *substratum* (I shall call it the *harmonic base* of reality). This 'substratum' for Milne resembles Mach's view that the mechanics of a single body is determined by all the other bodies in the universe; or as Johnson puts it, it refers to the smoothed-out pull of the whole system of bodies to which the particle's motion belongs. Upon this substratum or harmonic base, nature builds organic wholes which have an isomorphic structure reflected in the time-axis of the emergent dimensions. Nature could not possibly be a system, were it not for the harmonic base which is epitomized in the projective geometry of higher (emergent) time-like spaces.

The idea that time plays the rôle of the next higher dimension is the basis for the idea that emergent evolution is always adding new dimensions to reality, — 'times' which are later turned into 'spaces.' Thus the distinction between *static* and *dynamic*, *substance* and *function*, is but another way of viewing the distinction between *space* and *time*, for when the particles of a lower level (e.g., atoms) are organized into a new behavioral unity or macroscopic rhythm (e.g., molecules), we have a new time introduced. Space is not an antecedent vessel or container into which things are put, — it is a serially ordered relationship between coexistent things on the same level of complexity which provides the basis for a new simplicity as ever-new space-times are brought into being.

The relativists have said that the distinction between space and time is relative, because what is a space-interval from one point of view will appear as a time-interval from another viewpoint. This is only a half truth. In the transition from atoms → molecules → living cells → multicellular organisms, and so on, *the time-direction of evolution is not relative.* This view is in harmony with S. Alexander's theory as expounded in his *Space, Time, and Deity*, where he argues that *the order-*

ing of points in space is due to the 'betweenness' of instants of time. For us, the time that emerges rises in an absolute scale because the test of growth and evolution is in terms of complexity of structure and unity of function, *and this cannot be 'relativized.'* This does not seem to contradict Brouwer's notion of the primacy of time in living experience and in thought system. At the same time it is clear that such a conception of the primordiality of time fits in nicely with the remainder of Alexander's theory, namely, that time is the moving principle of space, while space is the body of time.

As one thinks over Brouwer's theory and the modifications he has welded into the Kantian form of intuitionism, one can't help feeling that in ruling out the space-form from human experience something was lost. One suspects, too, that Brouwer smuggles space back into the original intuition. Brouwer's view is associated with a temporal outlook in which visual perceptions are regarded as separating into two parts (in relation to before and after), and from this experience comes the intuition of 'two-oneness', — the intuition of a whole capable of division into two parts, which are in turn capable of division into two parts, and so on. This illustration really suggests a spatial representation, unless we think of the eye movements which are necessary to survey a field in a succession-process.

At this point, it seems that the theory developed in my book, *Philosophy and the Concepts of Modern Science*, comes closer to the psychology of this intuition. Our illustration of 'two-oneness' is based on the distinction between an *instant* and the synthetic unity of the specious present. The distinction between a mathematical *instant* and the psychological *present* or *now* is that the mathematical present is a dimensionless cut in a linear continuum, whereas the psychical present, while dividing the one-dimensional time-line into past and future, does endure, — sometimes for as much as several seconds. In this book (p. 115), is shown how the 'specious present' of conscious experience is time-spanning, as follows:

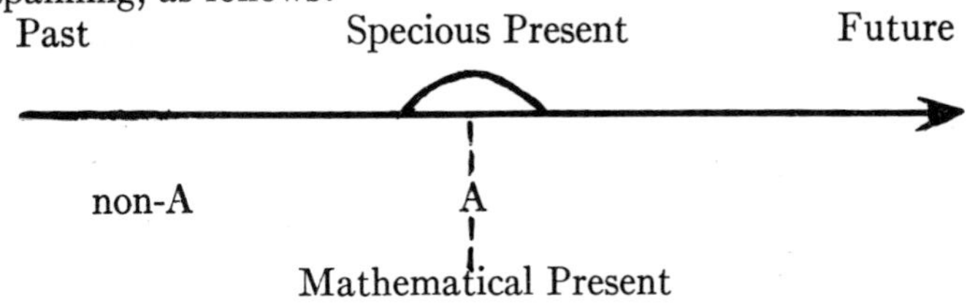

Past Specious Present Future

non-A A

Mathematical Present

This transtemporal power of consciousness to transcend the figure-ground (of gestalt theory), incorporating the *thesis-antithesis* (or 'two-oneness') in a higher synthesis, seems to provide the psychological basis for Brouwer's claim that mathematics rests on an intuitive principle which is synthetic in character, i.e., is not deducible from tautologies.

Thus do we bring Milne and Brouwer together, — even though the one is working in the field of physics and the other in the field of mathematics. Nevertheless, we have juxtaposed them in the foregoing manner precisely because we want to get from mathematics to physics. The bridge between them is provided by time and the subsequent spatialization of times (or the structuralization of functions) through successive emergences of time-axes. But these are pyramided on a basic and ubiquitous foundation which apparently has to be spatio-temporal in order to be temporal! Thus Brouwer's philosophy has to be emended somewhat to fit this 'organic' view of nature.

Now let us summarize the argument up to this point, bringing together as best as we can all this new and astounding knowledge which current physics and cybernetics have placed at our disposal.

XI. The Resolution of the Mind-Body Problem

Physics, as we have seen, starts with the sensory continuum, the manifold of sense-data, and then investigates this perceptual world as an ordering of phenomena in the space and time of an external world. In Newton's conception, the structure of this space had nothing to do with the presence of matter; whereas in Ernst Mach's view the structure of space is related to the presence of matter. The contemporary view starts from Mach's position, so that space is now thought of as being permeated by an invisible field containing a definite structure or metrics, and it is therefore called the *metrical field*.

A correspondence of some sort must relate this objective field and consciousness if the organism is to 'understand' and make adjustments to the external world. The determination of this correspondence is made the explicit problem of psychology. The task of psychophysics is to establish a congruence between the metrics of the space-time continuum of external events and the structure of the conscious experience of it. One of the more promising approaches along these lines has been presented by James T. Culbertson.[3]

The next step in this program brings us to what goes on inside the organism: the so-called mind-body problem. In the present volume we have portrayed the nexus between consciousness and the brain as a one-one relation, brought into existence by some projection process whereby the three-dimensional mapping of brain-events serves as the geometrical basis for an emergent dimension of conscious events which sustain an isomorphic relation to the lower plane of being. Mental events, accordingly, have an organization in space-time which in a general way is parallel with the ordering of brain events. The suggestion now frequently put forth is that the bioelectric basis of consciousness is provided by the alpha rhythm, which represents a scanning operation in the cortex. This theory would not be out of harmony with our own hypothesis, especially in view of the fact that scanning exchanges one dimension in space for time, and this, properly generalized from an n to an $n + 1$ dimensionality, provides us with the basis for the emergent passage to the level of psychic events.

Of course, the physiological substratum of conscious life is more complex than the above passage indicates. For one thing, consciousness is not merely a matter of perceptual pictures (images) in consciousness; concepts also arise; and emotional overtones frequently are present in human experience, occasionally very intense in nature. Fortunately, it is now possible to explore some of the physiological bases of such concomitants, and we find that our statement that man needs a 'cortico-thalamic integration' turns out to be good neurophysiology as well as good psychology and ethics.

The evidence indicating that these reverberating circuits of activity involve conduction between the thalamus (possibly even the hypothalamus) and the cortex and back again was confirmed by Bishop and Bartley.[4] This generalization was further substantiated by the later research of Duser De Barenne and McCulloch,[5] which supported the conclusion that the alpha rhythm depends on circular feed-back resonant activity between the cortex and the thalamus. This also seems to confirm the view that these brain waves represent the sweep of cortical scanning circuits.

However, it must be noted that while cortico-thalamic circuits serve to set the tempo for the rhythms of cortical events, spontaneous electrical activity of the cortex also occurs. This appears to be compatible with the hypothesis that brain waves represent a 'tonic background' for activity anywhere. Nonetheless, the central integrating center of conscious life (attention, awareness) appears not to lie in the cortex itself, but in the thalamic system which exercises control over the stream of consciousness.

The fascinating lines of speculation thus opened up in no way contradict the theory of 'consciousness as a new dimension', — unless the problem turns into the fundamental question of whether the brain is a machine or a teleological vehicle of conscious experience. Our own attitude is that while the electronic devices which man makes are the product of human imagination, they nevertheless lack the creative aspect of human intelligence. The human thinking organ, the brain, has a kind of spirit that lifts it above the particle-physics and classical science.

Many cyberneticists, of course, regard this view as 'mysticism.' To the criticism that machine logic is Aristotelian logic, which is not adequate as the brain-substratum of human thinking, the defender of the electronic-thinking-machine theory may reply as follows: We cyberneticists believe that the mind is a function of the brain, and the brain, so far as we can discover, is a binary digital type computer. But how can an infinite-valued logic, which is perfectly suited to an analog type computer, actually be used by a digital type computer?[6] If a digital computer is fed analog-computer-type material, and given the instruction, 'the answer must be computed on an analog basis, and no infinite-valued logic employed,' this will only produce confusion. This is like feeding a logical machine the problem: "solve for your own operating mechanism, but include in the problem data the postulate, 'the method of operation is illogical'," which automatically excludes the possibility of a solution.

The human thinking 'machine' *can* shift from the one to the other (digital to analog and back again), while a machine cannot (by the above admission), and in that sense the human brain-mind is superior to the electronic machine. It is true that any effort to induce the mind to solve the problems of mind must include the postulate that the mind thinks logically, and thus it appears that the mind's mistakes come from being fed false data. But this still allows for the possibility that the mind can change its ideas about what being 'logical' is, — and that is something no machine can do!

Finally, we come to the supreme problem of all science: What is the basic reality of the universe in virtue of which nature is ordered from top to bottom, from galaxies to atoms, from island universes to the human cortex, — and everything in between? The answer to this, in

DIAGRAM XVII

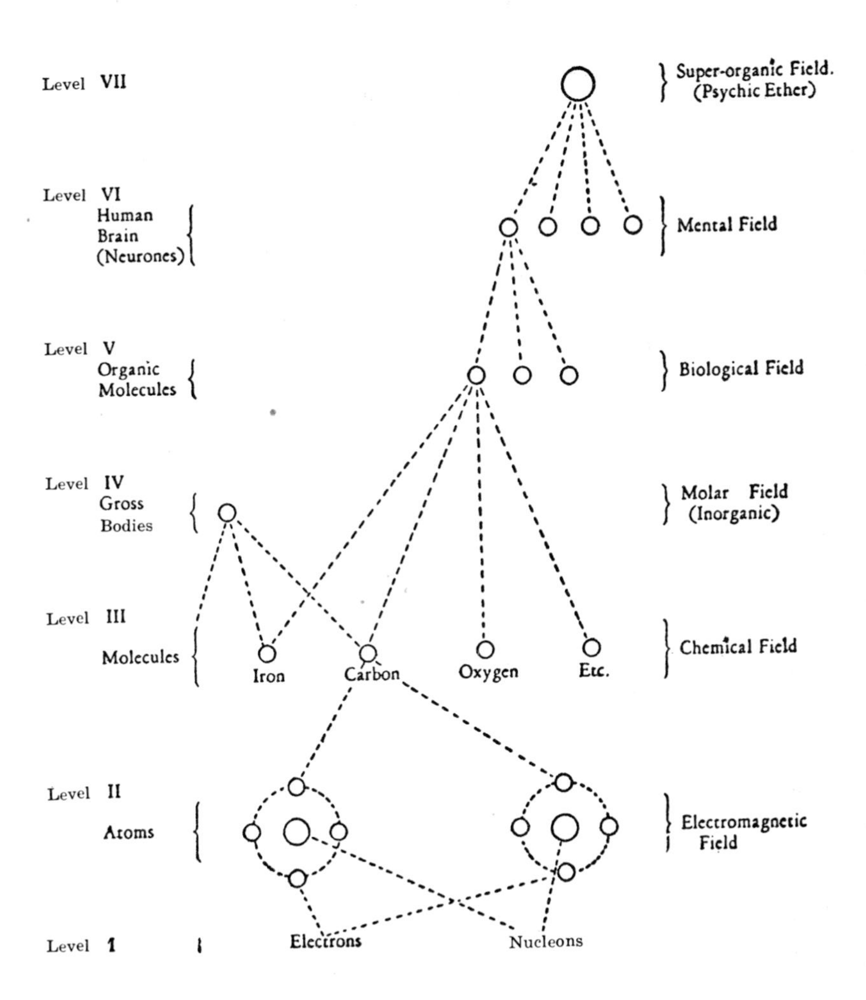

The Levels of Emergent Evolution

the present scheme, is contained in our Diagram II. Here it will be observed that new dimensions, with orthogonal time-axes ($n + 1$ dimensions which cannot be visually represented in the Diagram), are pyramided on the foundational matrix, the four-dimensional space-time manifold. In the unidirectional course of emergent evolution isomorphically related aggregates arise out of the interactions of microscopic 'behavior-stuffs,' integrated into historically new macroscopic wholes with their own transposable properties fabricating novel time-axes, in the manner indicated in the preceding chapters.

The reader will observe that Diagram XVII (p. 271) focuses attention on the successive levels of integration, including their *guiding fields*, whereas in Diagram II (p. 35) the Cosmic Field is emphasized as providing the background agency of cosmic integration. Here is where the Pantheistic part of the cosmology becomes conspicuous. This part of the conception was worked out in collaboration with my friend, Mr. B. G. H. Vanderjagt, a Dutch engineer who now resides in, and is a citizen of, the United States. The reader will observe that in this cosmology God is thought of as the Archetypal Guiding Field (or Cosmic Imagination) impressing the form of unity upon the emerging realities of nature as they progress from the lowest physical entities through the biological level into the highest social integrations. The confirmation of this scheme through the marshaling of evidence gleaned from the diverse fields of the natural sciences is the main task of this venture into the integration of knowledge.

XII. Cybernetics and the Spiral Action of Time

The preceding chapters have dealt with the significance of cybernetics for modern science and philosophy. We have noted how the understanding of the relations between consciousness and the brain has been facilitated by the study of electroencephalograms, — the records of the 'brain waves' which are associated with various phases of conscious experience. It appears that the wave-like rise and fall of the electrical potentials on the surface of the cortex have a complex structure which is functionally correlated with the conscious state of the subject on whose brain the electrodes are placed.

One investigator who has done much with the hypothesis of the alpha-rhythm sweep of the bioelectric potentials up and down through the cortex, — thus providing the scanning mechanism for the recognition of *forms*, — is Dr. Warren S. McCulloch. Following through on Norbert Wiener's suggestion that some sort of scanning by planes through the layers of the cortex may provide the underpinning for form vision, McCulloch and Pitts proposed that a plane of scansion could move through the layers of the cortex and thus transmit information concerning the visual world. McCulloch argued therefore that form vision has its physiological basis in the sweep of scansion of the so-called alpha rhythm of the brain.

Criticisms of this ingenious hypothesis were soon forthcoming, but after facing up to these criticisms, McCulloch (as late as 1953) still held to the thesis that these objections were not fatal. Indeed, instead of abandoning the theory, McCulloch[7] later extended the idea to include the notion that a similar scansion, with a frequency of about ten per second in the auditory cortex, could account for the appreciation of music and syllabic speech, while other sensory modulations (smell, etc.) were similarly conditioned by brain processes. This view presupposed that the impulses coming over the afferent (sensory) nerve channels were pulse-interval modulated, and thus the various aspects of the sensory experience were coded into the spatio-temporal configurations of the pattern of nerve impulses.

However, it appears that McCulloch has recently discarded this theory, or at least modified its original form. For one thing, there was too much emphasis on the cortical aspect, to the neglect of the subcortical contributions. The feed-backs of reverberating circuits certainly involve the brain stem, as Dr. W. Penfield and others have observed. Moreover, there were always those who were skeptical of the hypothesis of the alpha rhythm scanning mechanism *when this was combined with the theory of an 'isomorphism' between brain patterns and conscious patterns.*

Especially critical of the theory of 'psychoneural isomorphism' was Professor R. W. Sperry[8], who pointed out that the electronic methods of recording and analyzing nerve potentials have failed to reveal anything like the qualitative diversities of 'specific nerve energies' that could be correlated with the manifold aspects of conscious experience. Moreover, — Professor Sperry argued, — the hypothesis of the gestalt theorists that this isomorphism involves the secondary electrical fields which the neural excitations create in the brain runs up against the difficulty that there is insufficient evidence of the influence of postulated field forces in cerebral processes.

Having rejected all forms of isomorphism, Professor Sperry then sets forth an 'alternative' in terms of a 'motor theory of thought,' which he regards as a behavioristic extension of the pragmatism of Charles S. Peirce. Basing his idea on the proposition that topographic projection of the retina upon the cerebral cortex fails to reveal a similarity of form between the patterns of perceptual experience and brain excitations, Sperry concludes that the patterning of perceptual process is as much determined by the organization of motor patterns as by stimulus patterns.

For my part, I must confess that it does not seem that Professor Sperry's analysis provides a solution. For one thing, I do not admit that this 'motor' theory necessarily excludes the type of theory Sperry rejects. Moreover, the theory of *homomorphic images* (a better term than 'psychoneural parallelism') still seems plausible. For me, however, the field forces are not in three-dimensional space (though the lower-level brain-correlates are). The field of conscious experience is in the orthogonal (off-at-right-angles) space of an emergent dimension. However, a parallelism exists in the sense that there is a functional correlation: the similarity of structure (*isomorphism*) is as arbitrary as any 'symbol' and its 'referent,' and the decoding involves finding the key to the cipher of nerve messages which will provide the semantic bridge between the language of neuro-cortical behavior and the transposed symbols in the emergent dimensionality of consciousness. If the reader will refer back to our Diagram XIII, he will see how structurally dissimilar two isomorphic patterns may be, though functionally the two patterns are conjugate.

The inherent potentialities for such perceptual-conceptual correlations reside in the brain. Just how such inherited potentialities of experience are sustained is something of a mystery. Among those who have considered this problem is Professor D. M. Mackay.[9] Dr. Mackay has proposed that the Kantian categories, as illustrated by man's organization of experience (space, time, causality, etc.), "find their physical embodiment not in the nature of a set of built-in *filters*, but in the characteristics of the possible modes of *response*, partly built-in, partly evolved. . . ." As Mackay puts it, "my world (as known) is structured by me in terms of my basic modes of matching myself to it." This shows a better balance than Sperry's view exhibits.

In summary comment on this view, I would say that the organization of experience according to the sense of time-passage (Brouwer's intuitionism) is 'built-in,' as is also the retinal response to the two-dimensionality of space, and that higher spatio-temporal patterns (three-dimensionality of perceptual space and the multi-dimensionality of 'imaginary' constructs) are a result of ontogenetic developments. Individual memory also plays an important rôle in our perceptions. Of course, the physiological basis of memory is still obscure, but we know a little more about possible bases from an understanding of how electronic machines 'remember.' Electronic machines have several types of memories, the slowest machines (with the fewest number of operations per second) employ the magnetic drum, while the electrostatic memory of the cathode ray tube is faster and increases the number of operations per second by something like powers of ten. In the case of the human memory, the 'drum' or 'tube' is probably the individual protein molecule.

But how is imagination interpolated into the perception-memory-conception cycle to produce the unity of purposive behavior, — especially at its highest level of creative activity? If the mind is an emergent from the brain, *how can an 'emergent' change the pattern of causality in the matrix from which it emerges?* The solution to this riddle may be found in the concept of the *self-field*. Physicists are now considering the possibility that particles and fields, *and their interactions*, must be treated as equal partners. Thus, even empty space is no longer vacuous, but is the creative repository of archetypal forms. Guiding waves are called into being by the interactions of inner and outer circumstances. The macroscopic field of consciousness emerges out of its microscopic constituents, but in turn it lives to dominate the subordinate rhythms through an electromagnetic bond of fealty which unites body and mind.

It will be apparent that our theory goes beyond current cybernetics in at least one direction. As already noted, the main idea of cybernetics is that of feed-back mechanisms. The great virtue of this concept is that it enables the scientist to handle the problem of 'purposive behavior' without resorting to extra-scientific notions. Cybernetics, according to Anatol Rapoport, is a teleological or goal-directed system in which the behavior of the system is controlled by a negative feedback over the goal; that is, purposive behavior is regulated by signals which indicate the discrepancy between the actual and the desired state of affairs.

As we have constantly insisted, however, the human organism exhibits time-binding properties, and so a spiral theory of time and integration is required if we are to represent correctly the progressive organization of mental functions. Therefore, the above cycles (of reverberating circuits) of momentary purposes are really parts of a more inclusive spiral, with the orthogonal time coördinates designating the higher levels of synthesis whereby lower-level purposes and concepts are woven into higher-level goals of life. In terms of logical patterns, the relation here is similar to the transition from propositional functions to system functions. Corresponding to the cerebral cybernetics of the individual organism, there can be a social cybernetics which curves the sweep of human history into the spiral of a time-binding synthesis on a planetary level. Accordingly, there should be 'planetary encephalograms' for a giant earth-organism, — as we shall see later. Thus the spiral theory of levels is at once a theory of knowledge (the *dimensional theory of thought-systems*), a theory of reality (the theory of *archetypal synthesis*), and a theory of emergent social evolution, — the *cybernetic spiral of a planetary time-binding synthesis.*

XIII. Summary: The Harmonics of Integration

According to the present philosophy, our universe is one of *action.* Action is energy integrated through time. Planck's constant 'h' is the indivisible unit of action. In atomic processes this constant is a kind of instantaneous 'jerk.' In a monism of action, however, the concept of *action* will have to be generalized: just as the product of *length* and *breadth* represents a new dimension, an *area,* so the product of *energy* and *rate-of-action* will yield a new dimension of action. It then appears that 'mass' can be regarded as a result of field-integrated units of inertia, wherein 'particles' are replaced by a frequency form-of-action with chemical combinations appearing in the form of a dimensional binder of spiral or whorl unities and the atoms themselves constituting *spiraloids of energy.* Thus action means rhythms in time, in octaves. 'Planck's constants,' on various levels of complexity, are thus stuck together by units of frequency, something like Korzybski's time-binding. But in all cases we combine world-rate and expanding-rate to create a new spiraloid. In other words, cosmic integration expresses, step by step, the hierarchy of dimensions as the product of spinning and radiation, thus giving us a sequence of four primary dimensions plus a secondary set of four dimensions which can be pyramided on the base. Living organisms and mental organizations may therefore be regarded as higher cycles using primary cycles of the harmonic timing-and-spacing of whorl-rates of energy. That is:

$$(\textit{Quivering}) \times (\textit{Radiation})$$
or
$$(\textit{N frequencies}) \times (4/3\pi c^2)$$
$$= \textit{a New Dimension}$$

In this dynamic geometry of space, frequency times expansion of energy yields the definition of a *field*, and we get dimensions in space as radiating components of spinning energy fields. To build a universe then requires three fundamental units: (1) *Infinity*, (2) *Nothing* or *Zero*, and (3) the product of the two, a *New Unity*, which is off-at-right-angles. This would be illustrated by a point's spinning in relation to expansion. That is: (1) instantaneousness or infinity-of-quickness-angular time-rate, (2) mathematical point, and (3) number of balanced units (balanced in time), all united in a concept of growth (expansion and radiation), proceeding off at right angles to yield a *New Unity* of atoms, where 'atoms' represents a higher level of emergence, — the product of a dimensional binder. As we have frequently pointed out, the mathematical description for this harmonic progression is given in Bombelli's operations on the square root of minus one, $\sqrt{-1}$.

In the harmonic scheme we make a directional change from radius to volume when we note that light fills a succession of concentric spheres of $(4/3\pi c^3) \times (189{,}264)^3$. The idea is that we may pass from a linear-change ratio to a volume-change ratio by a unit of action instead of a Euclidian static or 'spatial' dimension. In other words, the dimensional relation which exists between point, line, plane, cube, is matched by thinking of a velocity in each new dimension reaching an 'infinity-of-quickness' action which is instantaneousness. (This is brought out in the table of the "Constants of Nature" on page 278.) This monism of action makes it possible to assert that the two inseparable components of the 'timing-and-spacing of energy' are tied together by their geometrical relation: they are at right angles to each other. The relation of frequency to radiation is dimensional. Therefore we may write:

$$(\textit{N frequency}) \times (4/3\pi h^3) = e^4 = (\textit{N whorls}) \times (4/3\pi h^3)$$

This cosmology explains nature's combining 1840 units of energy in the nucleus of the hydrogen atom by way of a shell of action in the medium of time (or 'inside' space), with a degree of quickness beyond the linear speed of light.

The Constants of Nature

e = *the charge of an electron*
h = *Planck's constant (of action)*
m = *mass of the electron*
c = *velocity of light in vacuo*
v = *linear velocity up to c*
t = *a quantum instant*
w = *angular velocity to t*
G = *gravitational constant*

Axioms of Euclidian or Static Space

1. — *An infinity of instants equals time.*
(An instant is a point in time)
2. — *An infinity of points equals a line.*
(This is supposed to be the photon's path)
3. — *An infinity of lines equals a plane.*
(or polarized light)
4. — *An infinity of planes equals three-dimensional figures.*
(cubes, spheres, etc.)

Translating Static Geometry into Kinematic Analysis

1. — *Energy as point-charge*, with angular velocity for *e* as rate of angular action. This is whorl-rate for energy, represented as $\sqrt{-1}$.
2. — *Linear velocity*, which is photon's path, or photonic *c*, represented as $\sqrt{-1^2}$, a one-dimensional space.
3. — *Velocity in a plane*, which is polarized light, $\sqrt{-1^3}$, a two-dimensional space.
4. — *Velocity in a field*, a three-dimensional space, $\sqrt{-1^4}$. This means frequencies of *e*, multiplied by speed in space, radiating concentrically outward.

This at least constitutes a beginning. It provides a basis for the 'mysterious truth' revealed by Rydberg's constant. But much more remains to be done. In this cosmology we have reality as a hierarchy of spirals, built upon the rhyming of energy from patterns of periodicity. It is obvious, however, that the notion of angular momentum and 'particle' spin as phenomena of three-dimensional space having hyperspace analogues (homomorphic images) in the macroscopic rotations of emergent dimensions is consistent with our general viewpoint. In our monism of action we proceed from *vectors* → *versors* → *tensors* → *spinors* → *whorl-elements*, thus finding the basis for the indwelling logarithmic spirals in the time-trading whereby the unmanifest world struggles against the inertia of past achievements in the manifest world to create higher organizations. This provides a basis for the coming emergence of a world sensorium, as we shall see later. Here the space-time-energy relations of person-to-person interactions yield to a higher order of individual-to-universal-consciousness-to-individual relations, with the extra-sensory wholistic properties which are studied in parapsychology.

The idea that the organization of consciousness is a spiral organization, — the reverberating circuits forming part of a helix which is superimposed on the unidirectionality of experienced time, — does not introduce any non-scientific terms into our vocabulary. If a 'self-field' is created by the interaction of matter and radiation, why shouldn't the neural patterns involved in the interactions of inner and outer factors generate a brain-field as an emergent with its own orthogonal existence, having transposable properties on its own level standing in homomorphic relation to the lower-level brain processes from which consciousness has emerged? Such is the hypothesis here proposed.

FOOTNOTES CHAPTER VIII

[1]"Alfred North Whitehead," by F. S. C. Northrop, *Science*, March 12, 1948 (Vol. 107).

[2]Cf. "Probability, Natural Law, and Emergence," *Journal of Philosophy*, 1926, Vol. 23, p. 430. See also my book, *Philosophy and the Concepts of Modern Science*, Introduction and Chapter VII.

[3]See James T. Cullbertson's article, "Distance and Qualities in Perceptual Space," *Journal of Psychology*, 1945, Vol. 19, 109-132.

[4]Cf. "A Functional Study of the Nerve Elements of the Optic Pathway by Means of the Record of Action Currents," by Bishop, G. H., and Bartley, S. H., *American Journal of Ophthalmology*, 1934, Vol. 17, 995-1007.

[5]Cf. "Functional Inter-dependence of Sensory Cortex and Thalamus," Duser De Barenne, J. G., and McCulloch, W. S., *Journal of Neurophysiology*, 1941, Vol. 4, 304-310.

[6]The *digital computer* (such as an adding machine) operates in terms of units; all values fed into it must be represented by whole numbers. Here everything is done by arithmetic. Data are fed into such a machine in terms of digits, for example, punches in tape, which either *are* or *are not* present. Graph curves, therefore, cannot be used. An *analog computer*, on the other hand, does nothing by way of arithmetic, but does everything by geometrical methods. The simplest examples of an analog computer are the slide rule, the planimeter used by architects, surveyors, and map-makers, who measure irregular areas.

[7]Cf. "Information in the Head," by Warren S. McCulloch, *Synthese*, Vol. IX, Issue 3, Nos. 3-5.

[8]Cf. "Neurology and the Mind-Body Problem," *American Scientist*, Vol. 40, 1952, 291-312.

[9]Cf. "Operational Aspects of Some Fundamental Concepts of Human Communication," by D. M. Mackay, *Synthese*, Vol. IX, Issue 3, Nos. 3-5, p. 192.

9

CAUSALITY, PREDICTION, AND EMERGENCE IN NATURE

"Time and the heavens came into being at the same instant in order that, if they were ever to dissolve, they might dissolve together. Such was the mind and thought of God in the creation of time."

— Plato

I. The Scandal of Induction

The philosophy of science has two major tasks: in the first place, it is concerned with the examination of the formal foundations of all science; and secondly, it aims at the integration of the more significant generalizations of science into a body of wisdom for the purposes of social guidance. As part of the first task, the philosophy of science must work out satisfactory definitions of the fundamental concepts of all science, such as *causality*, *law*, *uniformity*, and the like. These concepts, along with the theoretical presuppositions of scientific investigation, are a part of the basis on which the empirical sciences are built.

In the present chapter we are concerned with the problems of inductive procedure. This is a part of any complete and unitary theory of knowledge for science. The problem of causality is concerned with discovering the grounds for the feeling of certainty about our predictions. The empirical sciences aim at generalizations of the form, *ALL A is B*, which are called 'laws of nature.' If we can attain such generalizations, it is then possible to move on to the next goals of natural knowledge: *prediction* and *explanation within the areas of experience* wherein such spatio-temporal connections are found to hold. In cases where causal laws have been established, it is sometimes possible to *control* what happens, — produce such effects as are desirable and eliminate the undesirable. Thus knowledge is power, as Francis Bacon said. To those who understand the causes of things is given control over the future.

Unfortunately, all is not well in the domain of inductive reasoning. Ever since the time of David Hume's attack upon the idea of necessary causal connection, this problem has occupied a crucial position in the philosophy of science. Some writers have described the status of empirical logic, or inductive inference, as a 'scandal.' Accordingly, logicians since Hume's day have been seeking ways to escape the 'intellectual suicide' of Humean skepticism by creating a logic of induction that can restore our confidence in a methodology for the natural sciences. If propositions which are anticipations of future experience cannot be validated, the very existence of natural science is an anomaly.

The great French thinker, Henri Poincaré, pointed out in his *Science and Hypothesis* (1905, p. 145) that every generalization presupposes a belief in the unity and simplicity of nature. But since that time, so much of a 'revolutionary' nature has appeared, — Heisenberg's *uncertainty principle* is the most obvious, — that the faith in the orderliness of nature has been shaken. For example, Professor G. N. Lewis[1] tells us that we have not the slightest idea of whether the belief in the simplicity of natural law (uniformity of nature) is due to the structure of the objective world, or to some hitherto unanalyzed trait of human psychology.

If we are not to get lost in the tangle of problems in the field of inductive logic, it will be necessary to isolate the issues. After that we may be able to offer some solutions. Several of the major problems in this area have been pointed out by G. H. von Wright in his *Treatise on Induction and Probability* (1952). Here Professor von Wright lists the following problems: (1) the psychological problem of the origin of inductive inference; (2) the philosophical problem of the justification of induction; and (3) the logical problem of analyzing the inferential mechanism of induction.

To this list of problems, I shall add four more questions, as follows: (4) What does causality mean or imply in a deterministic world? (5) Can the theory of emergent evolution, which we have embraced, be brought within the scope of scientific methodology, and what shall be its implications for causal analysis? (6) Can the acceptance of Heisenberg's uncertainty principle be used to justify indeterminism? And if this is so, can causality ever be restored to science and rest on a firm foundation? (7) Can the feeling of human freedom in making choices be reconciled with the objectives of social science? If such a reconciliation of freedom and predictability is not possible, where does this leave the problem of induction in social science? What status can causality have in psychology, if man's behavior is free and unpredictable?

No one doubts the practical necessity for a confidence in the uniformity of nature. For that reason anyone who follows Hume does so reluctantly while a number of logicians are trying to provide a theoretical justification for the working confidence in causality in answer to Hume's skepticism. The chaotic state of affairs is indicated by Professor A. N. Whitehead who declares in *Science and the Modern World* (p. 35) that "the problem of Induction is the despair of philosophy — and yet all our actions are based on it." Bertrand Russell, adopting the same attitude in his book, *Philosophy* (p. 14), states, "Induction raises perhaps the most difficult problems in the whole theory of knowledge. Every scientific law is established by its means, and yet it is difficult to see why we believe it to be a valid process."

The question of finding a rational ground for induction has called forth so much study that one is tempted to say that contemporary philosophers have developed an induction complex. Just why should this be such a stubborn problem? Is there some unusually profound mystery about the 'necessity' inherent in inductive generalizations? Or is it possible that the uniformity of nature is a pseudo-problem, — perhaps even a meaningless question?

One reason sometimes given for the view that the principle of uniformity cannot be used as the foundation for the causal laws is that this principle is itself the result of induction. The only basis we have for assuming it to be true is that experience has shown it to be true. But the proper comment is that you cannot take as certain or necessary a principle that can at best only attain a high degree of probability. As a matter of fact, you cannot assert that nature will behave uniformly in the future simply because of past behavior. For nature never does repeat herself and no two instances of anything are ever exactly alike. Statements about uniformities and repetitions of experiments presuppose ideal conditions that in fact are never realized. In other words, the principle, to be true in all cases, must carry us beyond past and present experience; but empirical science has no right to go beyond experience, the actual. Natural laws are descriptive, — not legislative.

The situation is somewhat analogous to the status of the 'laws' of probability for which physicists have assumed that the mathematicians have proved the 'laws,' while mathematicians have assumed that the physicists have accomplished this. In reality, neither has proved them. Similarly, the scientists assume that there must be some philosophical justification for the faith in uniformity; and philosophers hope that empirical science can justify it, — if it is justifiable at all.

This way of stating the matter brings us to a more general type of situation with which we should know how to deal. Where this type of problem arises, the only way to avoid circularity is to rest the case (it may be to justify an 'axiom,' or a definition, or a principle) on postulation, or self-evidence, or the pragmatic usefulness of the concept or proposition. In mathematics the justification for an assumption is intuition or postulation while in empirical science, it is its fruitfulness or practical usefulness.

Where does this leave us with respect to the problem of induction? For one thing, it places our faith in the uniformity of nature in that class of concepts and propositions which are *primitive*, in the sense that they cannot be derived from anything which is logically prior. But there are many such concepts and propositions, which suggests that induction has no unique status as a special problem. It is therefore doubtful whether the problem of induction is more difficult than any other phase of the problem of knowledge.

Does this undermine the utility of the doctrine? Not at all! No matter what happens to the theory of the uniformity of nature, in actual practice we will always be forced to employ something that amounts to the same thing. In the present view, uniformity, — as we shall see in more detail, — is grounded in the Cosmic Field, and on empirical evidence we conclude that this is the way the universe is built. Behind such an ultimate fact we shall never be able to penetrate in theory. And indeed, this conclusion is supported by Hume himself.

II. Hume Refutes Himself

David Hume's *Treatise on Human Nature* was a two-edged sword that cut through the cherished doctrines of science no less than the dogmas of religion. His reasoning is like the logic behind Zeno's paradoxes of motion: no one believes the argument, and yet it is very hard to refute. But if one looks carefully into Hume's analysis, one begins to realize that perhaps the best refutation of Hume is given us by Hume himself.

Notice what Hume is doing: having destroyed the basis for belief in causal connection, *Hume seeks to find the reason why human beings ever came to believe in causality in the first place!* If Hume believed his own argument, he would not look for, let alone be able to find, a reason why we should expect that because *A* has preceded *B* in the past, the two should be associated together as antecedent and consequent in future experience. Of course, as students know, Hume derived this conjunction from the associationist psychology current in his day. These psychological 'laws' supposedly made possible a science of psychology, — thus Hume gave away his cake, and ate it too.

Those who follow in the tradition of Humean empiricism, — the logical positivists, for example, — admit that Hume's epistemological theories are a bit outmoded. As Professor Northrop[2] has pointed out, Herbert Feigl and other positivists are now in a mood to accept modification of empiristic psychology, and this brings a more satisfactory theory of knowledge within shooting range.

At present the inheritors of the Humean tradition are deeply involved in the development of probabilistic theories of induction. Historically the frequency theories were first seriously studied by Venn and Peirce, and their work has been extended, most recently by Keynes, von Mises, Reichenbach, Carnap, and others. But their mathematical approach, good as it is, does not go to the root of the problem, — the cosmological ('metaphysical') basis for induction and even a reform of Humean psychology is not sufficient. A more adequate science of mind, the gestalt theory, will certainly make the psychology of induction less difficult to understand, for we employ a field-physics approach, with 'closure' as the plenum basis for the logical and physical 'requiredness' (to use Köhler's term) which causality implies. But even beyond this, in our philosophy, nature's processes occur within a space-time-matter universe, and this, in turn, is the manifest world that emerges from the unmanifest Cosmic Field. Order, uniformity, and causality, are therefore grounded in field-plenum levels which provide the space-time networks of relations, the binding forces of causality. But more of that later on.

Having thus discussed somewhat the psychological-philosophical problems, we come next to those which have to do with the inferential mechanisms of induction. The problems here are difficult, but unavoidable. It is the general impression that the statisticians have something of importance to contribute, so we cannot bypass their equity in the matter, even though we keep this at a minimum.

III. Induction, Probability, and Statistics

In the early days of modern inductive logic considerable confidence was placed in Mill's methods of induction. It is usually stated that these methods are still useful in the experimental sciences. The residual confidence in induction is therefore due to the fact that while the social sciences, which admittedly are non-experimental, were and are relatively undeveloped, the logicians could always go to the physical sciences for their illustrations of inductive procedure. Here controlled experimentation, — leaving out and introducing at will the variables, — was and is a standard procedure of laboratory experimentation.

But now the social sciences find that Mill's methods are not suitable for social investigations. The non-experimental nature of social research and criticism which Moreno has made of the sterility of Mill's methods in spontaneous social phenomena add to the realization that social causation is highly intricate, due to interactions of non-repeatable patterns of events. The statement that data can be regathered by the repetition of situations is no longer regarded as true in the social sciences. Since no two samples of some supposedly homogeneous population or/and situation are ever identical, there does not seem to be any possibility of exact verification of alleged 'social causation.'

At first the recognition of this dilemma disturbed the social scientists and led them to take greater pains in making their cases as nearly the same as possible. But more recently the emphasis, even the interest, has changed. Now the social researcher realizes that there is no such thing as constancy of results except as this may be achieved through *statistical control*, — a concept introduced within the last quarter century. Today it is possible to measure the failure to maintain constant conditions, and also it is possible to express the order of magnitude of error in terms of 'probable error.'

Here, apparently, we have a promising technique for estimates of the future. Based on probability estimates of observational error, plus estimates of the adequacy of the sampling procedure, the social scientist is in a position to calculate future probabilities. Thus, making a virtue of necessity, the social scientist may actually prefer statistical control of conditions over exact (experimental) control. Society is still the 'laboratory', but in a new sense of the term in that authoritarian controls over the variables are not required.

Statistical control is preferred over exact control because the standardization sought by experimental control always carries with it the disadvantage that the information yielded by such a set-up is true only within the narrow range of conditions within which it was observed. That is, standardization of conditions may weaken rather than strengthen the grounds for inference. As R. A. Fisher points out, any conclusion has a wider inductive basis when (on the human level) it is inferred from an experiment in which considerable variation has existed as compared with an experiment in which the conditions are kept as constant as possible.

This is especially important for biological science, including sociology. Consider for a moment an experiment dealing with a living subject. One might wish to control the temperature, the humidity, the illumination, and the rest, along with the amounts of all dietary factors save one. From this one could make some inference about the effect of varying amounts of that one dietary factor. If the inference were limited to animals that live at that one temperature, humidity, etc., it would seem quite valid. But the typical investigator extends his conclusion to cover the effect of that factor on all animals in the natural environment, ignoring the fact that in the natural environment conditions are never constant. Moreover, the interactions between these factors are also exerting their own peculiar effects on the organism. Yet this sort of reasoning from the controlled particular to the widely varying general situation does go on. With statistical control of the situation, one may deliberately vary some of the conditions of the experiment and thereby more nearly approach the natural conditions. Granted that one cannot duplicate exactly the natural situation in any laboratory, we can, by introducing the several varying factors, gain a wider basis for inferences. This suggests the desirability of conducting experiments not in the laboratory at all, but in the natural environment. Untold amounts of time and money have been expended by scientists in their efforts to build machines, chambers, tanks that would duplicate the natural environment of an animal, and yet allow the scientist to control conditions. Surely a paradox, since upon introducing constant conditions the scientists have thrown away their efforts. It is only recently that investigators have dared to go out to the environment with their experiments; only lately have a few realized that if a way can be found to measure the natural environment, and measure also the reactions of life to that environment, here would be the widest basis for inference. This study of the interaction between life and its environment is called *ecology*, — a field still subject to lively criticism on the part of laboratory experimentalists. Yet what could be more ideal than to study living things in their natural habitats?

Experiments in which several factors are allowed to vary simultaneously, or experiments conducted in the natural environment wherein all factors vary, are criticized because 'they lack sufficient control.' If many factors are changing at one time, how can the effects of any one factor be distinguished from the effects due to other factors? How can one determine which factors exert significant effects unless one factor alone is permitted to vary at one time? It is at this point, — the designing of the experiment, — that statistics comes to the aid of the investigator. Let us therefore consider some of the principles of statistics and discover how these operations affect the pattern of scientific inquiry.

Among the basic concepts of statistics is that of 'population.' A population is any group of events. The size of the population is the number one obtains by an enumeration of each event of the collection. Frequently, however, to measure the entire population of a class of events would be impossible and, therefore, the observer takes only a sample of the population. The relation between the sample and the whole population is a much discussed topic. Let us first examine the characteristics of a population that we may better decide what the characteristics of the sample must be if it is to be a reliable representation of the population.

In examining any population of entities or events, one finds that the majority of the events tend to cluster around one point, the remainder being dispersed more or less symmetrically about the center of the dispersion. If such a point exists, it describes the *mean* of the population, or the average observation. The amount of the dispersion is measured by a parameter called the *standard deviation* from the mean. If, therefore, we know the number of events in the population, and the mean value of the events, and the average deviation from this mean, we can characterize the population. To the extent that this is an orderly world in which we live, we find that events tend to follow some coherent pattern in their occurrence, and this pattern can be described mathematically.

The pattern to which many events in this world adhere is the so-called 'normal' distribution, characterized by a high peak in the middle (the mean), with a symmetrical tapering off on both sides of the mean. Among the properties of the normal curve of distribution are these:

1. The curve is unimodal.
2. Half the instances are included on either side of the mean.
3. The arithmetic mean, the median, and the mode coincide.

By virtue of the 'simplicity' of the curve, one might wish that nature's processes were all so arranged as to conform to the normal curve; but since wishful thinking has no place in science, one must let the facts inform us what kind of pattern is exemplified. Accordingly, the pattern may be altered so that the curve is flattened or more highly peaked (kurtosis), or the distribution about the mean may not be symmetric, falling off more rapidly on one side than on the other (skewness); but the altered pattern can still be submitted to critical analysis. Among such possibilities is the J-shaped or Poisson distribution which occurs with a low frequency, but in a sufficient number of observations to imply that the product of the probability of occurrence times the number of observations still remains finite. A third type of distribution is the binomial. This is characterized by a condition in which the probability of occurrence (p) equals the probability of non-occurrence (q), whereas in the normal curve p does not equal q.

We see, therefore, that a population of events tends to fall into a pattern which can be described if we know the mean (m), the number of observations (n), and the average or standard deviation (s). These three, — m, n, and s, — are the parameters of the curve of distribution. For any *sample* of the population one can work out a similar set of parameters. The question is, will the parameters of the sample be the same as the parameters of the population? Such exact agreement among living populations is unlikely, since variation is the first order of things here. At best the sample is only an approximation. By taking a number of samples from a known population, the parameters of which have been worked out, statisticians are able to ascertain the relationship between the sample parameters and the population parameters. Of course, as the sample size increases the sample parameters more nearly approach the population parameters.

Now let us consider briefly the nature of the dispersion of events around their mean. We noted that this dispersion is measured by the standard deviation, usually symbolized by the lower case Greek *sigma*.

This is indicated in the following example.

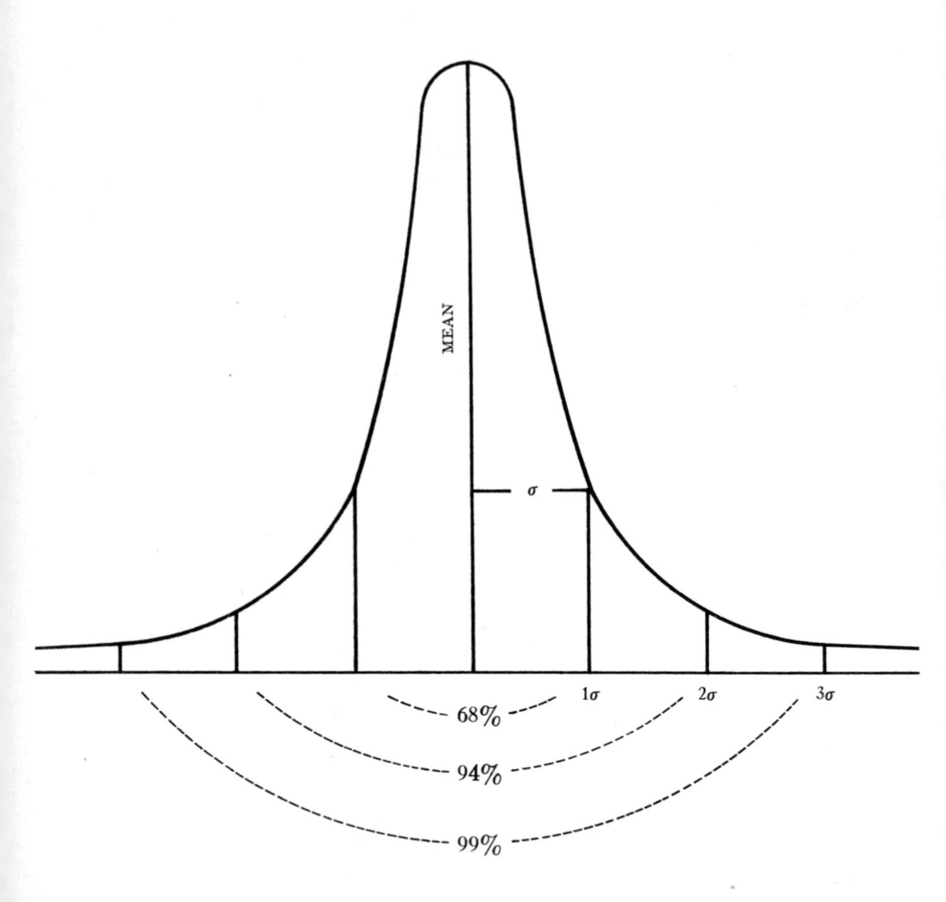

Thus we see that sigma equals the number of units measured from the mean to the point of inflection of the curve. It is known that 68% of the events of a population fall one sigma on either side of the mean. In terms of probability this means that the probability of finding an observation belonging to a given population and deviating from the mean by more than one sigma is .32. Within two sigma on either side of the mean are included 94% of the events, while within three sigma are included 99% of the events. Therefore an observation, the deviation of which places it three sigma away from the mean, has a probability of only .01 of belonging to that population. Accordingly, it is fairly safe to consider all the events of the population as included between the three sigma on either side of the mean.

We are now in a better position to consider how statistical methods affect the pattern of scientific inquiry. We cannot hope to make a series of observations all of which are exactly alike. Yet we wish to make some statement about the population based on the observations made, with some assurance that the statement is true. Subjecting a series of observations (the sample) to statistical analysis, we can determine the mean value and the average deviation (sigma). Since we know that 99% of the observations lie within three sigma on either side of the mean, we can state that any observation made in the future from this population will have a value equal to the mean plus and minus three sigma, and we would be correct in this statement 99 times out of each 100 trials.

This is one example of the utility of statistics in scientific inquiry. A second example is given in the use of the *null hypothesis*, where the hypothesis is that the variations in the results of the experiment are due to chance. This hypothesis can be disproved, but never proved. If the hypothesis is disproved, the experimental variations are not just the sum of the random natural variabilities of the organism but include an additional variation induced in the subject by some environment factor.

The foregoing considerations, briefly stated, outline the basis of the analysis of variance, a statistical method which allows the experimenter to evaluate the effects not only of a number of parameters, but of their interactions as well. In situations where individual phenomena cannot be dealt with as such, it is possible, by means of 'partial correlations,' to 'isolate' the variables concerned and arrive at quantitative correlations as measures of causal influence. More complex methods of analysis, such as multiple regression and covariance, enable the investigator to design more intricate experiments. Thus the social scientist may analyze the masses of data from measurements of the natural environment.

With such methods at his command, and basing his predictions on experiments designed to exhibit concomitant variations with the natural environment, the social scientist is in a position to generalize about the future, expressing even his uncertainties in rigorous terms.

Thus it becomes evident that the inapplicability of Mill's canons of induction does not render impossible the establishment of causal relations.

The theory that any entity represents a statistical constant of high stability (or an ensemble of such constancies which has its own higher-order central tendency) implies that whether any *thing* (a macroscopic swirl of micro-events) is to be treated as an 'individual' or a 'population' remains merely a matter of the level of analysis. It is not surprising in statistics that as the size of the sample of a population increases the sample parameters more nearly approach the population parameters, and that the distribution of the means of all samples have a normal distribution with a 'mean' of the means and a correlative standard deviation of the standard deviations. Thus the mean and the standard deviation are close in value to the population mean and standard deviation as one would expect wherever the individuals of a population are in turn populations of individuals.

These broad but fundamental considerations, which are discussed at greater length in such volumes as Donald Statler Villars' *Statistical Design and Analysis of Experiments for Development Research* (1951), bring us to a realization that Mill's methods, based on experimental control over the individual variables, are themselves statistical methods where the 'control' that is exercised is simply the control made possible by statistical constants of high stability. Thus the unity of any *continuant* (any stable individual as a statistical ensemble with a strong central tendency) is like the unity of a vortex, — a functional synthesis of constituent entities.

This in a measure takes care of the problem of methodology for social science. The philosophical problem, however, remains where it was at the beginning of this excursion into statistical methods: the comprehensive basis for induction still lies ahead of us, and if there is any philosophical justification for it, this is yet to be discovered and formulated.

IV. Causality in a Mechanistic World

At various points throughout this volume we have referred to the 'mechanistic' theory. The time has come to make this idea more precise, — to determine what causality means in a mechanical system, — in order to understand what is implied when we say that contemporary science makes mechanism an untenable doctrine.

A classical statement of this has been given by Laplace, and we can do no better than use his summary as a point of departure. According to Laplace[3]:

> "We ought to regard the present state of the universe as the effect of its anterior state and the cause of the one which is to follow. Given for one instant an intelligence which could comprehend all the forces by which nature is animated and the respective situation of the beings who compose it, — an intelligence sufficiently vast to submit these data to an analysis, — it would embrace in the same formulas the movements of the greatest bodies of the universe and those of the lightest atom; for it nothing would be uncertain and the future, as the past, would be present to its eyes."

Because of his attainment in mathematics and science, Laplace was peculiarly fitted to summarize the essentials of this doctrine. Now let us examine the presuppositions and general implications of this conception.

Science, in so far as it is reducible to mathematical formulae, is the study of the functional relationships among the variables of natural phenomena. In general such functional relationships are symbolized thus: $y = f(x)$; $y = f(x, z)$; and so on. That is, a certain phenomenon y (e.g., weather) is a function of (or dependent upon) another independent variable x, or two variables x, z, as for example temperature and humidity, and so on. Here y is the dependent variable, for it gets its value from the independent variable x.

In its most abstract form, science is concerned with the descriptions of the motions or behaviors of nature and the intercorrelations of the various types of behaviors described. *Motion* is a phenomenon involving *space* and *time;* for example, we may want to know the velocity of an automobile in order to calculate the time it will take to travel from one place to another. Here velocity, the simplest measure of the rate of change, is a ratio; that is, $v = s/t$. One of the most important types of motion is that illustrated by a body acted upon by a 'force.' For Aristotle, and the ancients generally (except the Greek materialists), motion was not natural. It required a 'force' or 'energy' to explain it. The great achievement of Galileo and Newton was to show that motion is 'natural', — that it does not require an active cause. But *inertia*, which is resistance to change of state, does require explanation by forces. Thus inertia as resistance to change of state is the property of remaining at rest, or remaining in motion, depending upon the previous state. Thus, only when a body undergoes a change (rest to motion, or uniform motion to accelerated or decelerated motion) is it acted upon by a force. Einstein later on got rid of this last vestige of animism through a relativization of motion, — with the possible exception of rotation, which may still be absolute, — but Newton could not foresee how physics was to be de-anthropomorphized.

In the cases where there is accelerated motion, a change in the velocity of the moving body, this acceleration a is represented by the differential equation:

$$a = \frac{d^2s}{dt^2}$$

The science of bodies acted upon by forces is called *dynamics*, and dynamics is concerned with conservative systems in which there is a conservation of motion. As indicated, such systems are subject to treatment in terms of the infinitesimal calculus, — linear differential equations, as they are called. To discover the reason for this, we must go back a bit. The principle of *inertia*, originally introduced by Galileo and later embodied in Newton's first law of motion, means that the laws of physics governing the behavior of particles are based on *accelerated* motion rather than *uniform* motion. The definition of *force as mass times acceleration* means that *force* = $mxv \cdot v$, which is velocity squared or acceleration. Thus, as Galileo showed, a freely falling body 'attracted' to the earth by the 'force' of gravitation, falls faster and faster through successive intervals of time, and this behavior is expressed in the formula, $S = \frac{1}{2}gt^2$, where t^2 is velocity per second per second. In technical language this is summarized in the statement that acceleration is the second differential of position with respect to time. Thus the fact of inertia requires that the causal laws of physics must be stated in terms of differential equations of the second order, for here the description contains no explicit reference to time and nothing new appears in the future distributions which were not present in the parts as observed in the past, as Laplace pointed out. In other words, a mechanistic universe is a conservative system without any elements of novelty or unpredictability, — determinism rules throughout. This point has been made by Professor P. W. Bridgman in his book on *The Logic of Modern Physics*, where he informs us that those properties of a system which can be described in terms of linear differential equations have the property of *additivity*: the effects of a number of elements is the sum of the effects separately, and no new properties appear in the aggregate which are not present in the individual elements. That is, a function of the sum is a sum of the functions: $f(x + y) = f(x) + f(y)$, as when 'the integral of the sum is the sum of the integrals,' and so on.

To summarize: the statement of the laws of nature in terms of differential equations enables the scientist to assimilate the notion of causality to that of functional dependence by eliminating the importance of the temporal interval, while at the same time reducing to a minimum the possibility that qualitative novelties will appear in the processes of change to introduce non-linear (or non-additive) properties.

The question of whether relativity theory strengthens or weakens the case for mechanism is not so easily decided. From one point of view, relativity theory strengthens the mechanical-causal view, since in the four-dimensional manifold of relativity physics the space coordinates are tied up with time in one equation, and analytically such equations are dealt with in the same manner as those of three dimensional dynamics; indeed, time can be turned into space merely by giving it a minus sign. This is what Minkowski meant when he noted that 3-dimensional dynamics becomes 4-dimensional statics. But it must also be remembered that the equations of general relativity are non-linear equations wherein the theorem concerning the addition of vectors (ompounding of velocities of light) is rejected. For our present purposes, however, this is not an important matter, since we find reason for accepting relativity theory as only half the truth.

Thus in rejecting the mechanistic conception of the universe we are forced also to modify relativity theory so as to bring emergence into the picture. Even in so elementary a matter as the persistence of ultimate particles something more than relativity must be recognized, for as de Broglie points out, the persistence of elementary particles requires an asymmetry of time that the Minkowski-Riemann continuum does not provide. One cannot construct a physical universe out of 'event-particles,' or intersecting 'world-lines,' if there is only the space-time manifold *with a symmetrical time*, a time which is the 'phantom of space.' And on higher levels of organization, the particles that do persist and participate in the formation of more complex patterns, such as atoms and molecules, require *spin*, and this 'spin' is not deducible from relativity theory. As Professor A. N. Whitehead notes in his book, *The Concept of Nature* (1920, pages 138 and 194), rotation (including 'spin') is absolute. Thus we come to emergent evolution and the meaning of causality in the theory of levels.

V. The Duality of Natural Law

We have previously had occasion to point out that our own theory of nature recognizes two types of 'laws' in the universe. This duality of natural law is stated in terms of a contrast between dynamical laws and statistical laws. The first type, dynamical laws, are causal laws, giving determinism and predictability; whereas the second type, statistical laws, are based on probabilities and introduce a measure of uncertainty into the calculations.

A dynamical or causal law eliminates contingency and implies the ability to visualize the elements of the mechanism in operation. But in statistical laws, concerned with the calculation of mean values, the individual elements of the statistical ensemble are not studied as elements. Let us set down the contrasts between these two types of laws, as follows:

Dynamical Laws	*Statistical Laws*
1. Illustrated by the principle of least action (including the first law of energetics).	1. Illustrated by the second law of energetics (or thermodynamics).
2. Causal (or necessary).	2. Probable (or contingent).
3. Microscopic processes are visualized.	3. Macroscopic states (or averaged results).
4. Real mechanisms.	4. Phenomenal viewpoint.
5. Reversible processes.	5. Irreversible processes.
6. Independent of history (or hysteresis).	6. Cumulative mnemic effects.

As illustrations of these two laws, let us note that the atomic processes of microscopic mechanisms (e.g., the rectilinear motions of molecules) are reversible and subject to necessary causal laws of attraction (inversely as the square of the distance for atoms and inversely as the fourth power for molecules), whereas the macroscopic states (e.g., the gas laws) represent the mean value of a large number of individual processes of a statistical aggregate.

It is sometimes supposed that since the mechanical processes are reversible, for reasons already noted, the second law of thermodynamics, expressing as it does the irreversible character of familiar natural processes of entropy-increase or degradation of energy, is therefore a non-mechanical law. It must be noted, however, that the second law of thermodynamics does not contradict a dynamical law, such as the principle of the conservation of energy, but is supplementary to it. The second law of thermodynamics, or energetics, which gives the *arrow* to time, as Eddington says, does not disturb the foundations of classical kinetic theory. Classical statistical mechanics, in fact, rests upon the conception of the kinetic theory, the theory of mass particles in motion. The real difference in the two types of laws lies in the point of view one adopts in studying the two levels of behavior. As Max Planck indicated in his book, *Survey of Physics* (p. 103), the dualism of reversible and irreversible is associated with the dualism of the atomistic and the phenomenal points of view.

It is interesting to recall that my argument[4] that it is the second law of thermodynamics which describes the emergence of macroscopic or phenomenal states preceded Eddington's statement in his volume, *The Nature of the Physical World* (1928), where he favors a dualism parallel to my own distinction between dynamical and statistical laws. These he terms *primary* and *secondary laws* (*op. cit.*, p. 75). Eddington states primary law holds for the behavior of individuals and is indifferent to time direction; whereas secondary laws for aggregates, rather than individuals, express probable rather than necessary results, and therefore introduce 'chance' into nature. The second law of thermodynamics, illustrating a secondary law, gives time the irreversibility of the arrow. Analogous is my own supposition that the unidirectionality (irreversibility) of experienced time of the biochemical reactions proceed in accordance with the second law of thermodynamics. Some experimental confirmation of this idea was later provided by Professor Hudson Hoagland.

While Professor Eddington accepts the second law of thermodynamics as an illustration of a secondary law, he does not explicitly regard it as a basis for the production of what, in the present view, is termed a macroscopic or phenomenal pattern. And yet this assimilation is easily accomplished. Eddington tells us that the external world has become a shadow world, and that the drama of familiar life is a shadowgraph performance. Therefore one wonders, why should we not identify this 'shadow world' with the phenomenal world of statistical ensembles which thereby *exhibit* themselves? And why shouldn't the second law of thermodynamics be generalized to provide the physical basis of macroscopic patterns, whether on the level of molecular or human societies? Eddington approaches this view when he tells us (p. 105) that *entropy* is to be placed alongside beauty and melody, because all three appear as features of *arrangement.*

Nature produces what I have termed new or *second order simplicities* out of *first order simplicities.* Except for the bottom-most level of the ladder of emergent evolution this distinction is relative. What is a simple simplicity from one point of view is a complex simplicity from another, just as a cell is an elementary unit of an organism but also a complex aggregate of the molecules of which it is constituted. Part of this thesis has always been that the gestalt properties of the phenomenal state are field properties, representing as they do the tendency of particles to lose some of their potential energy to the environment. This partition of energy makes possible the interaction of parts to produce the non-summative wholes of emergent evolution.

VI. Levels of Simplicity

Having dealt with the subject of simplicity and the relativity of simplicity in terms of the levels of analysis, it now seems advisable to consider one additional line of investigation as relevant.

The significance of the foregoing two levels of analysis has been studied by John Q. Stewart[5]. In his excellent survey he says:

> "In the study of matter, physicists have two valid points of view, the macroscopic and the microscopic. The macroscopic view presents a gas as a continuous medium, and describes its physical condition in terms of such 'field' quantities as density, pressure, temperature, gravitational potential. The microscopic view recognizes that a gas is made of a huge number of separate molecules. If observational attention could be focused on the rapid and intricate movements of a single molecule, bouncing against the others, there would be no hint to be gained, from its momentary velocity, momentum, or kinetic energy, as to the value of the temperature or pressure. And a physicist who insisted that a gas as a whole could be studied only by making a detailed point-to-point and instant-to-instant record of the paths of typical molecules would find his ill-chosen task impossibly laborious."

The characteristics of the two levels indicated here by Professor Stewart have a partial explication in an article by Dr. Warren Weaver[6] wherein he notes that in the search for simplicity there are three, instead of two, levels of 'complexity': those involving a few variables, solved by the classical physical approach before this century; problems of 'disorganized complexity,' solved by probability theory dealing with large numbers, after 1900; and problems of 'organized complexity,' where sizeable but limited numbers of variables interact as parts of an organic whole.

It seems to me that Dr. Weaver's analysis is not ultimate: his three levels are reducible to the two levels I have previously indicated. Certainly his second and third levels have much in common, the differences between them being of two sorts: (a) in the number of variables involved, and (b) in the number of individuals participating in the interactions. With respect to (b), this is only a quantitative distinction in numbers of individuals, — e.g., in the number of molecules of a gas or human individuals in a community. With respect to (a), we have the qualitative problem of the 'reducibility' of the new 'dimension' (e.g., 'intelligence' as the factor behind teleological planning on the human level) to the dimensions of the lower level complexity, such as the bioelectric activities of the nerve cells wherein 'intelligence' does not appear. In its most general form this is a problem that occurs at every level of emergent evolution where the transition from a lower rung of the ladder to a higher rung takes place. And once we know the *trans-ordinal law* (explained in the next section) according to which this emergence occurs, *one can apply probability calculations appropriate to the new level, provided a sufficient number of individuals are involved in the interaction to make statistical methods applicable.*

By way of illustration, one may note that statistical predictions about the number of births, deaths, suicides, marriages, and the like, are possible on the human level, and this does not deny the elements of intelligence and teleology in human nature which make man more than an electronic calculator machine. There is here a statistical constancy in the purposes of human beings. Statistical predictions deal with norms and deviations from the norms or means, and these appear on the atomic and molecular levels as well as the human level.

In general, one may say that small-scale deviations may upset macroscopic states, on all levels, at points of bifurcation, and the more variables there are, — on the human level, for example, — the greater the possible deviations from mean states. An electron's behavior is unpredictable (within limits) because it has only three dimensions within which it can exercise its freedom of motion; but a living animal has more degrees of freedom and therefore a greater range of possible deviations, including mutation into a new species; while man possesses a maximum number of degrees of freedom and consequent deviations from statistical norms, — but trends will still be observable. This is the reason, it seems to me, why the phenomena which Dr. Irving Langmuir[7] describes as *divergent phenomena* become more important on the higher levels of the ladder of emergent evolution. In contrast to *convergent phenomena* (in which the behavior of the system can be determined from the average behavior of the component parts), *divergent phenomena* arise out of a single event (depending sometimes on a single quantum change) which becomes magnified in its effects so that the behavior of the entire aggregate depends upon something that started from a small beginning, — like the origin of a new species, or germinal activity in the human brain. This does not contradict anything we have said, and it also remains true that phenomenological observations of human society will yield the gestalt-patterns of lawfulness (simplicity) analogous to the beauty of the flower or the macroscopic beauty of crystals based on space-lattice structures. It is a matter of the level of observation.

VII. Predictability and Emergent Levels

We see, therefore, that the theory of levels is not out of line with science's demand for uniformity, causality, and predictability. The situation has been well stated by C. D. Broad in his book, *The Mind and Its Place in Nature* (1925, p. 77), as follows:

> "On the emergent theory we have to reconcile ourselves to much less unity in the external world and a much less intimate connection between the various sciences. At best the external world and the various sciences that deal with it will form a kind of hierarchy. We might if we liked keep the view that there is only one kind of stuff. But we should have to recognize aggregates of various orders. And there would be two fundamentally different types of law, which might be called 'intra-ordinal' and 'trans-ordinal' respectively. A trans-ordinal law would be one that connects the properties of aggregates of adjacent orders. . . . An intra-ordinal law would be one which connects the properties of aggregates of the same order."

In this excellent statement we find all that we need for building a science, — or a hierarchy of sciences. Moreover, such a theory of nature provides a place for human freedom, for as E. G. Spaulding points out in *The New Realism*, the properties of the higher level are, at least some of them, new, and in this respect are a 'law unto themselves,' *and in this sense free.* This does not mean that they are lawless, but only that their specific principles of behavior are not identical with those of the parts.

In this view, as Spaulding observes (*op. cit.*, *passim*), *freedom* consists of actions in accordance with those characteristics at a certain level of organization but does not exist at lower levels, yet it is quite compatible with law and determination at this and other levels. An important point to keep in mind is that freedom of this sort appears at each level of reality, not only on the mental level but also on the physical level. But, the reader will ask, is such 'freedom' in harmony with the goal of social causation, — the establishment of predictive generalizations on the basis of which the social sciences may build?

VIII. Human Freedom and Social Causation

Among the problems bothering the social scientist is that of determining the meaning of human freedom in a scheme of causality. Do we humans have 'freedom'? If so, doesn't this disturb the predictability that psychology and sociology require if they are to formulate principles of lawful behavior? How can there be lawfulness, if freedom introduces indeterminism? Before answering these questions in more detail, let us retrace our steps a bit.

As we have seen, in the lower level of physical science the classical particle theory has given way to new developments in statistical mechanics, — and yet lawful behavior still emerges. The postulates of classical physics, — now considerably modified, — were based on the idea that the position of a particle can be determined at a precise instant of time by means of its coördinates. It was also supposed that as the time varied, it was possible to trace the path of a particle through space. The concept of causality came in when one wanted to investigate the effects of the actions of external forces on the motions of such particles. Here it was assumed that the phenomenon studied could be observed without disturbing it, so that, given the initial conditions, one could predict the subsequent behavior of the particle (or system of particles) by knowing the quantitative values of the variables disturbing the particle.

As we know, much later the Heisenberg uncertainty principle taught us that any small-scale phenomenon involves an interaction with the agency of the observation. The term that Heisenberg used to describe the resulting inexactitude was the German word *unbestimmtheit*, which can be translated as uncertainty or *indeterminacy*. According to those who interpreted this indefiniteness as 'indeterminacy,' the conclusion is that accurate causal analysis is not possible. To make the accurate predictions that causal relations demand, one must know both the position and velocity of the particles, but we see now that the more accurate the one variable becomes the less accurate the conjugate variable becomes, though the product of the two will remain the same.

Not only has this situation given rise to much philosophical argument; even logic has been scrutinized to see if it offers a way out of the puzzle. For example, Hans Reichenbach has sought to interpret quantum mechanics in terms of a polyvalent logic, a probability logic with a continuous scale of values having 'truth' and 'falsity' as limiting extremes. Those interested in keeping the record straight may wish to recall that Korzybski and the present writer (among others) have also explored the possibilities along this line. On the other hand, Bertrand Russell, Ernest Nagel, William Werkmeister, and Henry Margenau (to mention several) have rejected the attempts at interpreting quantum mechanics and the wave-particle dilemma in terms of a multi-valued or non-Aristotelian logic. In my own suggestions, however, this non-Aristotelian logic and ontology is related to a relaxation of the law of identity, and I think subsequent developments in the field have confirmed this modification of traditional principles of thought.

So far as the argument of *causality versus acausality* is concerned, it seems to me that a sensible compromise lies along the lines suggested by Max Born in his book, *Natural Philosophy of Cause and Effect* (1949). Here the idea is advanced that while quantum physics has not abandoned the causal postulate, it has modified rigid determinism sufficiently to bring physics and human experience closer together. Therefore we do not find the basis for human freedom in the alleged indeterminacy of key atoms in the microphysical phenomena in the brain, as Arthur Compton has supposed.[8] The interaction between a system and its ground, a particle and its field, the observed and the observer by way of the field, does give rise to mutual effects that require the concept of *complementarity*. It is true that the uncertainty principle places a limitation upon the amount of information which the observer can gain from a single experiment. But this, as we have already noted, does not exclude the possibility that statistical results give us more information than individual observations. This makes possible statistical generalizations, whatever may be the vagaries in behavior of the constituent 'particles' of the population.

Similar considerations seem to be transposable on the human level, except for one additional point. This complication arises out of the fact that in physics *the structure and behavior of elementary particles are independent of past history and external conditions.* Therefore hysteresis effects ('memory' influences) are ruled out in the physics of ultimate particles. But, as we have argued, when we pass in the sequence of emergent evolution to higher level unities (molecules, cells, multicellular organisms) memory effects become increasingly important, environmental influences more effective in modifying the increasingly flexible system, and as a result of the accumulation of mnemic effects mutations are necessary in order to open up new avenues of development. It is for this reason that probability is discontinuous, in the sense that the statistical expectations for events on any level must always be worked out empirically for that level, — they cannot be deduced from lower level probabilities. The curve of distribution in the representation of the behavior of molecules of an aggregate and the curve of variability of behavior of the human beings of a population may be the same curve, — let us say that they both follow an *S*-curve, — and yet this does not mean that humans are molecules, or that one can predict how human beings will behave in a group from the way molecules behave in a gas or a liquid.

The question as to which is more important in social causality, — the individual or the group, — is perhaps a false antithesis, an example of *either-or* reasoning misapplied. The 'great man' theory of history seems to assume that in principle *der Fuehrerprinzip* is correct. But this could be an example of the fallacious atomism of elementalistic thinking. Perhaps certain societies foster the personification of social forces in leader-individuals, who simply flow with the current. But even this is not exhaustive. Perhaps in the totalitarian societies the role of the individual is at a minimum, whereas in a democracy his role is maximized. But whether in social evolution a given society will go fascist, communistic, or democratic, may rest upon the presence or absence of the exceptional individual who may help decide which way the unstable society will develop. That is to say, at critical points of bifurcation (as the mathematician would say), the creative individual counts for more than he does when a society does not face a juncture. In Russia Lenin was there when the crisis came; and a decade later, in the United States, a Roosevelt was there when the crisis came. Both men had a plan, and so in large measure they determined the future of their respective countries. None the less, it remains true that Lenin could make the authoritarian stereotype work in Russia because of the tradition of Czarism; whereas in the United States an industrial-political democracy was possible because of an antecedent tradition of individualism.

All in all, it looks as if history casts its shadows before, and the freedom of the individual is nothing other than the freedom of the Cosmic Imagination to use the existent forms to build new levels of reality upon the pyramid of past achievements. In this respect man's freedom is the freedom of the god-like quality of creativity in man; and such a view is quite in harmony with the teachings of social physics as set forth by John Q. Stewart in the following lines[9]:

> "Perhaps the crass materialism of this treatment of human beings can be relieved by taking to heart Leibniz's philosophy of the monads. The monads, you will remember, are units of life which are characterized by possession of a soul. They do not push one another about as molecules do, but act through inner sympathy. When social physics advances to the quantum level, it may appear that the separating effect of distance is only external and statistical, and that one person can come into contact with another through impulses which make nothing of space and perhaps of time also."

Professor Stewart may have other things in mind, but to me his statement means that the opposition of 'mechanism' and 'teleology' is today a false antithesis. Certainly the old Newtonian-Laplacian mechanism is as dead as the atomism of old Democritus, and yet predictability and the feeling of human freedom still remain, — and both now appear to be compatible. What more can one ask?

I do not see that such a philosophy limits the possibilities of social reform, at least not any more than they were restricted by tradition, vested interests, and the general inertia of social hysteresis. No one today can believe in absolute and unlimited freedom, nor can the Cosmic Imagination work 'miracles', — which imply an absolute discontinuity with the foundational uniformity of the Cosmic Field.

IX. Field Theory, Matter, and Anti-Matter

In the present volume we have occasionally touched upon the problems of cosmology. At this point, therefore, it is appropriate that we relate our theory of uniformity and induction to the more general philosophy of Pantheism. Here we go beyond current astrophysics. Cosmogony as our astronomers have developed it, — at least until quite recently, — seems to have taken the matter of the universe as something given; that is, the astronomers have separated the *content*, stars and galaxies, from the *container*, space and time, apparently feeling little compulsion to discover *how* matter as content (hydrogen atoms) comes from the container which is the cosmic field of energy. They have failed to observe the principle that the two cannot be separated. They have not recognized that the particle universe is not ultimate but is derived from the field-plenum. The problem of Pantheism, therefore, is to provide an explanation of the origin of atomic hydrogen, the simplest atoms of matter out of which the cosmos is constructed.

The hydrogen atom, the mother substance of the cosmos, consists of one proton in the nucleus and one planetary electron in the first orbit, plus the organizing field which maintains this atom as a stable entity. From an overall point of view, there seem to be two possibilities for the creation of such atoms: (a) the creation of hydrogen through the integration of antecedently existent parts, and (b) the creation of hydrogen atoms in toto, which then degenerate into what later appear to be the 'parts', — elementary particles, — out of which the atoms seem to have been constructed. The first possibility starts with 'particles' as data, — which were what we were trying to explain in the first place, — so this really is not very promising. However that may be, let us treat each of these theories seriously, to see what can be said in its favor.

The first hypothesis (a) concerning the creation of matter might take its first step by way of a theory of the creation of neutrons. Unfortunately for the hypothesis, even the neutron is not ultimate (simple) for, as the work of Felix Block indicated, it has a complex distribution of positive and negative charges. It is therefore not surprising that the neutrons, with their half life of fifteen minutes, can decompose into protons and electrons, thus:

$$\textit{Neutron} \rightarrow \textit{proton} + \textit{electron}$$

Contrariwise, the proton-electron combinations constitute hydrogen atoms. The nucleus of the ordinary hydrogen atom is a single proton, so all one needs is a neutron archetypal field, plus an electron, and the hydrogen atom exists! The energy equivalent of a neutron is of the order of a billion electron volts, and this is a tremendous amount of energy to concentrate in one spot. It has been suggested that the conditions for this may occur in the vicinity of a collapsed star, where the gravitational potential would be so high that radiation could not escape into space. But whether the energy density here is sufficient to make possible the conversion of energy into matter presents a difficult question.

This elementalistic mode of explanation, — concerning which we have recorded our suspicions, — would attempt to synthesize the hydrogen atoms out of antecedent particles (neutrons). But gestalt principles would follow a different path. Here the proper way to bring matter into existence is to begin with complex wave-patterns of energy with nodal points which somehow produce electrons and protons as the 'parts' out of which the whole was previously assumed to have been made. This is our second (b) type of theory. Let us turn to this possibility.

Since in our conception the world of matter is dependent upon the unmanifest field, — or more fundamental still, a *sub-ether* supporting the visible physical world, — particles will appear as regions of reinforcement where *constituent waves* overtake each other at nodal points to produce *group waves* or matter. This is a somewhat more precise statement of what we mean by the more general conjecture that matter is composed of energy-knots or boundary-singularities in the field. The mechanism for the emergence of so-called ultimate particles (which in fact are emergents along an orthogonal time-line where gestalt-unity is present, and in another language is ascribed to *spin effect*) is difficult to conceive, and that is why we have said that the process governing the interconvertibility of matter and energy is not intelligible by present modes of thought. The *Cosmic Lens* is our name for this process, for as the Supreme Imagination pursues its career it guarantees the balance between matter and energy which constitutes the dualism of the manifest and the unmanifest universes.

Here, then, we propose our supreme effort at explaining the birth of atoms in space and time, — the genesis of the matter out of which galaxies are built. Instead of trying to visualize how isolated particles like electrons and protons could be born in the depths of space, we have supposed that hydrogen atoms may emerge from the unmanifest Cosmic Field somewhat as the goddess Minerva sprang into being, — full-grown and complete and lovely to look at. From the primordial hydrogen atoms the so-called 'ultimate particles' (electrons, protons, positrons, etc.) which we study in our laboratories are supposedly derived.

That is to say, once the particles are differentiated out from the organismic atoms, they are free to roam about, torn loose from the infinite bosom of the Cosmic Field and wandering through interstellar spaces like orphans in the storm, — until in aggregate a motherly nebula gathers them in to start a cycle of astral evolution. Their subsequent dissolution may be taken care of by the several mechanisms whereby the annihilation of particles is accomplished, — as for example through the mutual destruction of electrons and protons in the interior of stars, with the subsequent radiation of the equivalent energy into outer space.

According to this conception, the universe on the level of atoms is not so much a self-integrating multiplicity of antecedent parts as it is the consequence of a self-differentiating unity. On such a view the wholeness of the hydrogen atom is not a puzzle of unrelated parts that get assembled by a miracle of improbability: the radius of the electron and the mass of the proton are not elementalistic items of knowledge; the diameter of the innermost orbit of the planetary electron (to return to the Bohr theory), Rydberg's constant, and the rest, are what they are because of the gestalt-unity of the atom, if the atom is to exist in the space, and survive in the time, and specify the value of Planck's quantum unit of action, within the manifest world of the sense perceptible.

In order that hydrogen atoms can degenerate into elementary particles, we must conceive the atom as an organic whole, with something like polarity providing the basis for the duality of electrically charged particles. And here we come upon some interesting possibilities. The idea that positive and negative particles (protons and anti-protons, for example) represent oppositely modified vortices of the Cosmic Field, due perhaps to differences in the axes of rotation associated with an operator (*quaternion*) capable of double rotations in a hyperdimensional continuum, thereby creating mirror image (enantiomorphic) forms, provides a fertile line of theorizing. Thus every positively charged particle would have its negatively charged counterpart, as positrons match electrons and protons match anti-protons. There would then be a symmetry between particle and anti-particle, which could be created together ('pair production') and annihilated together. This symmetry of particles, and the interconversion of particles and field. once more confirms the Einstein relation between matter and energy.

Once we get the hydrogen atoms created, the story from that point forward is the record of how nature evolves the remaining chemical elements in a linear or octave sequence. What are the stages in nature's alchemy whereby the heavier and more complex elements come into being? The mechanism for this continuous synthesis of the heavy elements has been proposed by Dr. William A. Fowler: here fusion of the heavier elements from the light gases hydrogen and helium (as the 'carbon stove' reaction), and the ejection of this material into interstellar space, makes available the dust and gas of space for recondensation into stars. Of course this is still hypothetical.

Before leaving this matter, I wish to reiterate that the recent discovery of anti-matter (even the postulated existence of 'anti-galaxies') does not invalidate our cyclic-creative cosmology. The new found anti-matter fits in with our pantheism, provided we think of the complementarity which now appears as the *symmetry of particles,* — each particle having its oppositely charged counterpart, — as also a *complementarity of particles and archetypal fields*, the invisible field providing a kind of ethereal duplicate for each elementary particle. The complementarity of the manifest and the unmanifest realms is the ultimate symmetry of nature. We must not overlook the rôle of the guiding field in the creation of matter.

In this connection, it should be emphasized that on our theory the notion of *emergent dimension* and the notion of *spin* as explanatory concepts seem to serve the same purpose, for it is 'spin' which transforms time into space (gives asymmetry to the time component of the space-time continuum which is required for the *persistence* of particles), and this is but an alternative way of conceiving the emergent dimensions which rise upon each other in the ladder of emergent evolution. That is, when microscopic spins are taken up into a new macroscopic spin, there is a gestalt unity with the higher-level field properties transposable across the parts, plus a corresponding emergent polarity on this new level.

Everywhere in nature we see lower level conflicts (tensions due to polarity) reconciled in a higher synthesis. The modern electrical theory of matter gives us a picture of opposites kept apart and held together in a field of organization, a guiding field. But just as atoms have polarity, so molecules as new wholes also have their polarities, and living cells as aggregates of molecules have an emergent polarity, — and so on. The human society as a multicellular integration will acquire a similar (isomorphic) polarity or spin-property when it is unified into a world-organism. That is to say, a first-level polarity of a *North* and *South* dualism of elementary constituents is unified on the *n*th level, and the new (macroscopic) units thus produced are integrated into a new or $n + 1$ unity with a higher polarity. The property of 'spin' is but another name for the emergent dimension which turns function into structure. But on all levels certain isomorphic properties, — serial order, polarity, dominance-subordination patterns, and the like, — illustrate the transposable features of emergent evolution. All this has been catalogued for us by Professor G. P. Conger under the rubric of 'epitomization.'

X. Brouwer's Intuitionism and Causality-Induction

The theory that the Cosmic Continuum or Field provides the ground for the uniformity of nature yields a wider interpretation of the Bruno-Mach-Milne cosmological postulate: not only is the universe in its overall features the same from any point of view, but the hydrogen atoms out of which that universe (or a summitless hierarchy of universes) is built are the same everywhere in infinite space and time. Nature's transactions always occur within a space-time-matter universe; but these manifest universes (galaxies) emerge from the unmanifest field-plenum. Uniformity and continuity are therefore grounded in the Cosmic Field, and empirical inductions resulting in natural laws are possible because of the pervasive medium.

Now let us make an additional observation. Since time, wherever it is asymmetrical, gets its irreversibility from growth and emergence, this unidirectionality necessarily appears on the level of organic experience, and this *consciousness of time-passage* supplies the basic intuition for all thought, as Brouwer insists in his *intuitionism.* Accordingly, in a very real sense there is an underlying unity mediating the objective world and the subjective world, and this irreversibility of serial order reveals the common denominator for mathematical induction and empirical induction. Thus mathematics applies to nature because nature and mind have the kinship to a basic continuum with its generative powers.

So far as I can discover, only one investigator has explored the possibility of assimilating mathematical and physical induction. This individual is Father Gratry (1808–1872). In his book, *Logique* (translated by Dr. Milton Singer), Father Gratry seeks to show that mathematics and philosophy between them could explain the discovery of general laws and causes in nature. According to him, there are two major processes of reasoning, deduction and induction. Deduction proceeds by way of *identities*, — a middle term, as Aristotle noted. Here there is nothing new in the conclusion. Induction, on the other hand, rises above its point of departure. To infer a law or a universal from the particular is to go beyond identity and proceed through 'transcendence.' Attaining new information is the 'process of discovery par excellence.' This process of induction, — the same in mathematics, physics, biological science, and religion, says Gratry, — proceeds according to the 'irreplaceable law' that *what is true up to the limit may be said to be true at the limit.*

Gratry seeks to show that the principle of induction is also the principle of the infinitesimal calculus of Newton and Leibniz, and therefore we do not have two different processes, one for mathematics and one for physics; in both cases, given a continuous convergence toward a limit, one can conclude from the series to the limit. However, Gratry insists, between the finite and the infinite, between the series and its limit, between the polygon with the finite number of sides and the curve considered as a polygon with an infinite number of sides, there is a limitless 'abyss', — we reach the limit of the series, the infinite, by a process of *transcendence.*

How is this possible? We start from a few facts, from the particular, from the variable, and ascend to necessary general ideas marked with the character of the infinite by a 'miracle'; reason attains the power of ascendence by effacing the limits which confine it and achieves true, creative knowledge about the genus, the law, the cause, the end. Therefore, according to Gratry, *induction ultimately depends upon consciousness of the divine, which is felt rather than seen, because in man this feeling of transcendence, which is the basis of induction, is like prayer, the energy of movement, the feeling of divine awareness, — an implicit light which comes forth to explain.* This last idea reminds one of Bergson, who indeed was influenced by Gratry. It also gives us the key to George Boole's interest in Gratry, for Boole's theory, especially in the last chapter of his epoch-making *Laws of Thought*, that the human mind is led by powers greater than itself to the unity of thought, persuaded George Boole and his wife, Mary, to approve of Gratry's work.

The thing that seems to me to be most significant in Gratry's effort at reconciling the growing force of modern science with the age-old motives of religion is that the value of the theory does not rest upon the

Aristotelian-Thomistic tradition which Gratry accepts, but could easily be interpreted in terms of the pantheistic philosophy of our form of scientific humanism. We have here a means whereby physical induction may be regarded as an expression of the 'prayer' whereby we translate our faith in the uniformity of nature into a trust in the lawfulness of the universe's processes. *But this is no miracle in any supernaturalistic sense.*

The striving of the incomplete for completeness, the hunger for wholeness, is a natural principle of gestalt-closure. But for us the most interesting thing is the manner in which this idea hooks up with Brouwer's 'urintuition' of time. We have already studied the process of temporal transcendence which enables one to reconcile the thesis (the 'now') and the antithesis (the 'not-now') in a higher synthesis, and there is no need to go over this ground again. But the net result is that we can agree with Einstein when he says: "Certain it is that a conviction akin to religious feeling, of the rationality or intelligibility of the world, lies behind all scientific work of a high order." And this, we beg to observe, is what a pantheistic humanism requires in order to validate its program for a world philosophy growing out of the very data of science itself.

XI. Summary: The Postulates of Unified Science

1. In our monism of action we posit the existence of a Cosmic Continuum, an invisible ocean or field of electrical density, without mass, eternal, infinite, and omnipresent.

2. Empirical investigation reveals the existence within this cosmic field plenum of corpuscular units, — the particles of the perceptible physical world, possessing the material properties of mass, inertia, and discreteness. In relation to the Cosmic Continuum, these particles of electricity are variously referred to as 'energy-knots,' 'boundary-singularities,' and the like. But since, in a universal behaviorism, the unity of every entity (or *continuant,* to use a term we have sometimes employed) is analogous to the unity of a smoke ring or a whirl pool, — except that the relative strength of the forces of integration makes it easier or more difficult, as the case may be, to disrupt this unity, — we prefer to use the term *behavior-stuff* to designate these unitary or macroscopic modes of behavior. Every continuant is a macrorhythm of microrhythms of behavior-stuffs.

3. Physical science has established the principle of the interconverti-

bility of 'matter' and 'energy' on the floor-level of the cosmos (Einstein), and Bohr's principle of the *complementarity* of the wave description and particle description on higher levels is also on the road to acceptance. These wave-particle syntheses (or *continuants*) give us the *natural kinds* of various levels which are presupposed by the principle of *limited variety* (Keynes).

4. The emergent evolution of behavior-stuffs is pyramided on the basic physical level of space-time-matter and rises in a hierarchy of levels of orthogonal or 'off-at-right angles' time dimensions. It is this macroscopic spin effect (so to speak) which transforms the functional behavior of the continuants of an earlier level into the structural units of the next higher level. Mathematically the theory of quaternions (rotating vectors or *versors*) is one way of representing the orthogonal or emergent time-axes, and related to this is the theory of spin (*spinors*). But if we wish to represent what happens visually, the following will serve:

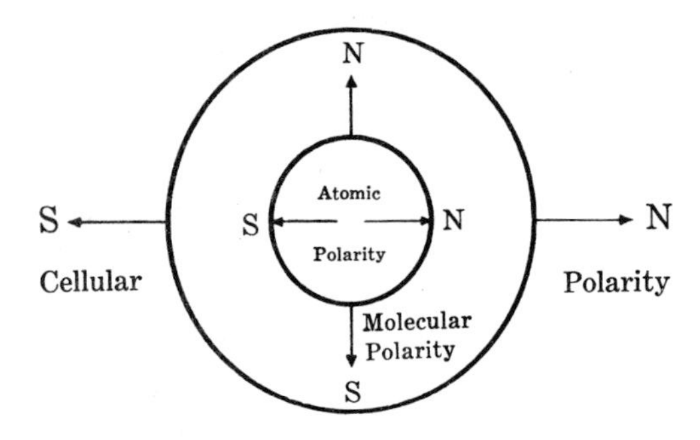

Here each higher polarity is in a new and higher dimension of reality.

5. The duality of causal laws yields (a) dynamic-deterministic predictability for the behavior of individuals, and (b) statistical generalizations permitting the passage from 'some' to 'all' members of a class or population of individuals when the cases are fair samples of the class, i.e., where the sample parameters and the population parameters approximate each other.

6. The potency of organizing fields of influence is required to bring the parts together in the right times and places if products are to emerge, and these force-fields provide the closure principles which operate in nature. The lowest organisms, such as atoms, have minds (field-unity) analogous to those of the higher organisms, such as man,

based on gestalt synthesis. The hunger for wholeness is the spiritual aspect of nature.

7. There appears to be an underlying basis for mathematical induction (based on Brouwer's primordial intuition of time) and empirical induction as the process whereby mind apprehends (or finds itself in resonance with) the passage of nature. This indissoluble unity and duality of the mental and the physical was first clearly enunciated by Giordano Bruno and Spinoza.

8. We find a relation of *isomorphism* holding between levels on the ladder of emergence, based on transposable principles of whole-part relations, entropy-trends, information-transfers, resonance-relations, polarity-gradients, dominance-subordination patterns, and other 'analogies' which are phenomenologically manifest.

9. The progressive accumulation of hysteresis effects and mnemic causation (Hering, Rignano, Russell) is responsible for the growth and evolution toward time-binding syntheses (Korzybski). In this onward movement there is a corresponding intensification of consciousness in the organism and a parallel increase in the span of attention and consciously purposive behavior.

The Cosmic Continuum is the everlasting repository of the archetypal forms which emerge in the manifest world. These forms are manifest to us on the floor-level of physical reality as universals, — world-lines, triangles, squares, circles, spirals, Platonic solids, and the like, — which emerge in the repeatable forms of electromagnetic societies: atoms, molecules, cells, organisms, and so forth. The higher universals of psycho-social integrations (love, justice, and the rest) are offspring of human interactions; but in a panpsychism the emotional concomitants of human aspirations have their precursors in so-called inorganic integrations.

10. If we reinterpret the Hegelian dialectic in terms of the theory of emergent evolution, we come out with the conception that physical reality, like the human mind, has the power of passing from the 'thesis' and the 'antithesis' to a synthesis that transcends the opposition. This phenomenon is illustrated in two ways: (a) on the one hand, by the electrical theory of matter, in the notion of opposites (positive and negative particles) kept apart and held together in a state of equilibrium by an organizing field of force; and (b) in the theory that the advance of knowledge is a process of overcoming the oppositions in thought, a process wherein human judgment appears as nature becom-

ing aware of its power of transcendence in reconciling oppositions.

Hegel's formula was (in theory) taken over by the Marxists, who in turn provided the ideological framework for Russian communism. The Marxists in Russia were willing to apply the dialectic to the past, up to the point that the Soviet Union reached in accepting the Lenin-Stalin formulations. But in theory the 'classless' society of Communism cannot be a final 'synthesis,' for by the logic of history it becomes the 'thesis' for a post-Communist continuation of the dialectic. Unfortunately, the present Soviet Union does not accept the doctrine of further developments. None the less, and whether one likes it or not, in the century that lies ahead the task is ours to rise above the present 'East-West conflict,' transcending the present antithesis in the next moment of becoming. This higher plateau of understanding is possible in the philosophy of Panhumanism, the electromagnetic version of the vision of Bruno, Spinoza, Einstein, and others. This cosmology has been referred to from time to time in the preceding chapters. Now these fragmentary suggestions must be gathered together into the form of unity. In doing this, I shall also relate the preceding conclusions about the 'uniformity of nature' to the 'cosmological postulate' as it has evolved from Bruno through Milne into what I have termed the *cyclic-creative universe.*

FOOTNOTES CHAPTER IX

[1]Cf. "Ultimate Rational Units and Dimensional Theory," by G. N. Lewis, *Philosophical Magazine*, Vol. 49, 1925, 739-750.

[2]Cf. "Criterion of Universal Ethical and Legal Norms," by F. S. C. Northrop, in the cooperative volume, *Moral Principles of Action*, (p. 138, 1952), edited by Ruth Nanda Anschen.

[3]Cf. *Theorie Analytique des Probabilities*, Eng. Trans., 1902, p. 3.

[4]Cf. "Probability, Natural Law, and Emergence," *Journal of Philosophy*, 1926, Vol. 23, 421-435. See also my article, "A Phenomenological Interpretation of Physico-Chemical Configurations and Conscious Structures," *Ibid*, 1927, Vol. 24, 373-385; 401-415.

[5]Cf. "Demographic Gravitation: Evidence and Application," by John Q. Stewart, *Sociometry*, 1948, Vol. 11, p. 31.

[6]Cf. "Science and Complexity," by Warren Weaver, *American Scientist*, 1948, Vol. 36, No. 4. This article appears in Dr. Weaver's book, *The Scientist Speaks*.

[7]Cf. "Science, Common Sense and Decency," by Irving Langmuir, *Science*, Vol. 97, 1943, p. 1.

[8]This whole problem is discussed by Ivan D. London in his article on "Psychology and Heisenberg's Principle of Indeterminacy," *Psychological Review*, Vol. 52, 1945, 162-168.

[9]Cf. "Concerning Social Physics," by John Q. Stewart, *Scientific American*, Vol. 178, 1948, p. 23.

[10]Cf. "Matter Anti-Matter and Cosmic Symmetry," by O. L. Reiser, *Philosophy of Science*, Vol. 24, #3, July, 1957.

10

THE FIELD THEORY OF MATTER

"It is evident that the past history of the universe and the future fate of man are involved in the issue of our studies. Hence we must be specifically careful to keep our judgments uninfected by the demands of theology and unswerved by human hopes and fears."
— Richard Tolman, *Relativity, Thermodynamics and Cosmology*

I. The Problems of Cosmology

To the scientists and the philosophers the existence of matter has always presented a problem. The question of why there is a physical world was solved for religion in our own (Western) tradition by the 'special creation' theory as it is recorded in *Genesis*. Over generations, however, most philosophers and scientists have not considered this Hebrew-Christian account a satisfactory solution to the problem. Accordingly, they have invented their own hypotheses about the origin and nature of the physical universe.

Among those who have pondered the problems of cosmogony was the German philosopher, Immanuel Kant. It is a tribute to his speculative genius that Kant not only sketched the essentials of the nebular hypothesis, but also outlined the alternatives in terms of which all future cosmologies must operate. In his epochal work, *Critique of Pure Reason,* Kant pointed to the contradictions in our ideas about the universe. He showed that, with equal cogency, we can prove the following propositions: (1) that the universe must have had a beginning in time, and that it could not have had a beginning in time; (2) that it must be limited in space, and that it cannot be limited in space; (3) that matter is infinitely divisible, and that it cannot be infinitely divisible. Kant, of course, gave us his own solution to these 'antinomies,' but most contemporary cosmologists are not satisfied with the manner in which Kant disposed of the problems. Cosmologists today are therefore still trying to discover a better resolution of the dilemmas. The 'exploding' universe of Abbé Georges Lemaitre and George Gamow, the 'expanding' universe of Eddington and Einstein, the steady-state universe of Fred Hoyle, Milne's dual-time cosmology, — these hypotheses have been developed in the hope that they would solve the problems posed by Kant's analysis.

In addition to the foregoing hypotheses, there has recently been advanced the conception termed the *cyclic-creative cosmology*. Developed by the present writer in collaboration with the Dutch thinker, B. G. H. Vanderjagt, this theory is a modernized (electro-magnetic) form of the pantheistic cosmology first enunciated by Giordano Bruno: the theory of the cosmos as infinite and eternal in time and space, with an endless number of worlds in varying stages of evolution. Whether this cyclic-creative theory of the universe provides a satisfactory solution to the problems remains to be seen. Before we decide that, we must look more carefully into the historical background of cosmology. We therefore begin with a brief statement of materialism as a philosophy of nature.

II. The Historical Background

In the history of Western thought only one philosophical tradition has taken the existence of matter as a datum, that is, as a reality not standing in need of explanation. The ancient Greek atomists, the first 'materialists' of our Western world, postulated matter and empty space (void) as eternally self-existent realities out of which the universe (or a succession of universes) was to be made. But this materialistic conception, like the special creation theory, has always presented difficulties. There were internal weaknesses as well as external difficulties. For one thing, there was the problem of the infinite divisibility of particles. Again, the idea of 'empty space' also created problems. How do these atoms attract each other? By 'action at a distance'? The universe we live in is a 'sticky' universe: the atoms cohere in rather stable configurations. The ancient atomists had crude ideas on how to explain what later was called 'chemical affinity,' and the idea that the 'void' is not empty but is really the vehicle of field-influences did not occur to them.

For these reasons, but more especially because materialism was out of line with the subsequent teleological explanation of religion, Greek materialism did not take firm hold — though, to be sure, in the form of the Epicurean philosophy it did enjoy a period of popularity, especially during the days of the pre-Christian Roman civilization.

With the spread of Christianity as the official religion of Europe, materialism as a philosophy dropped out of sight. It was not revived until the dawn of modern science, about 300 years ago. The enormous success of Galileo's efforts to fuse the two sciences of physics and astronomy, and the even greater achievements of Newtonian physics in describing in mathematical-mechanical terms the behavior of matter, encouraged a revival of materialism, first as a physical theory and then as a comprehensive philosophy of nature. In the first instance, Robert Boyle and John Dalton perfected the atomic theory as a physico-chemical doctrine, and their successes in this field added to the prestige of materialism.

Newton, as we know, was dualistic in his philosophy: he had God as the creator of matter, and, like Descartes, regarded the rational mind of man, with its 'secondary qualities,' as the super-material reality outside the scope of physical science. But others, — like Thomas Hobbes, Laplace, and La Mettrie, — rejected the dualistic features of Newton's thinking and consistently moved toward the conclusion that both God and the soul of man (seat of the secondary qualities) were superfluous adjuncts of materialism. Thus the second wave of materialism threatened to roll on like a tide sweeping all before it. The counter-movement was provided by the philosophy of Bishop Berkeley who held that the concomitant of materialism is atheism; therefore, partly because of religious motivations, he decided that it was necessary to stem for all time the wave of materialism.

As students of philosophy know, Berkeley's idealism attempts to show on the negative side that the notion of matter as a reality existing independently of all conscious experience is false and futile. Furthermore, he tried to show that the idea of 'matter' is self-contradictory. Galileo and Newton, in recognizing *inertia* as a fundamental property of matter, had created the notion of matter as passive, insentient, immutable particles acted upon by forces from without; thus the very definition of 'force' as *mass times acceleration* puts the concepts of *force* and *mass* at the very foundation of classical physics. On the other hand, as Berkeley pointed out, matter is said to be the *cause* of the perceptions we have of the external world. Thus we have the inconsistency of matter as the *passive recipient* of forces and as the *active cause* of sensations, — a fatal flaw in the materialistic theory, according to Berkeley. Of course, as we know today, the Newtonian idea of matter was destined to be replaced by a better theory. The modern electrical theory of matter seriously (but not fatally) wounded the particle-picture which was so much a part of the classical mechanical world view.

The third great wave of materialism is connected with the rise of the Marxist philosophy. This form of materialism, — Dialectical Materialism, — is now widely accepted in certain parts of the world, — to such an extent, indeed, that it threatens ultimately to engulf the planet. Marxism and atheistic communism are relatively free from the obvious defects of traditional materialisms. It is a mistake, therefore, to dismiss Dialectical Materialism as juvenile, as Hobbes's materialism may be so dismissed.

If one proposes to refute Dialectical Materialism as a theory, one must demonstrate not only that it is philosophically unsound, but one must show wherein its weaknesses reside and one must be prepared to correct these defects by designating the changes that must be made in order to produce a satisfying theory of matter. Thus, if there is to be a refutation of the latest form of materialism, it must come out of the very data of science. It is not sufficient to denounce Marxist-Leninist-Stalinist communism as 'godless,' as 'vile materialism,' and the like. For in truth the science of the Western democracies, as it has been interpreted thus far, contains little that demonstrably supports the claims of religion, — and that, it may be argued, is the reason some brilliant physicists have succumbed to communistic doctrine. If one is to deal with the philosophy of communism in a reasonable manner, it must be done by developing a world-view which refutes Marxism by data (facts, laws, and principles) rather than by vituperation. That is what a 'Cosmic Humanism' proposes to undertake.

With what I hope is a suitable sense of humility in the presence of great difficulties, I venture to present the outlines of a cosmology which offers an alternative to the endless and hopeless conflict of Christian supernaturalism *versus* atheistic communism.

When a philosopher enters upon the field of cosmology he feels as if he were an intruder in a territory alien to his proper interests, a domain now the exclusive province of scientists. And yet there was a time when the philosopher felt at home in this domain. Once, long ago, cosmologists like Pythagoras, Democritus, Plato, and Aristotle, were designers of universes, constructors of cosmological models. But with the increasing accumulation of knowledge in the now highly specialized fields of physics and astronomy the philosophers have progressively dropped out of the picture, and currently the realm of astrophysics is the closed corporation of experts who put up signs, "keep away, prying philosophers", — to quote Eddington.

Nevertheless, no matter how assiduously the modern astronomers try to escape their own shady past, the speculative phases of the subject, — the ghosts of astrology and alchemy, as it were, — return to haunt the cosmologists, and will not be exorcised. At least one shade still has a passport and is free to roam the wide domain of cosmology. I refer, of course, to Immanuel Kant, whose nebular hypothesis was recently rehabilitated by Karl von Weizsäcker. If, therefore, I have the temerity to present my own cosmology, it is because I am following in the footsteps of earlier explorers who groped their way through the wilderness of universes and tracked the paths for the rest of us to follow.

As indicated earlier, in Kant's discussion of the antinomies the following possibilities are provided:

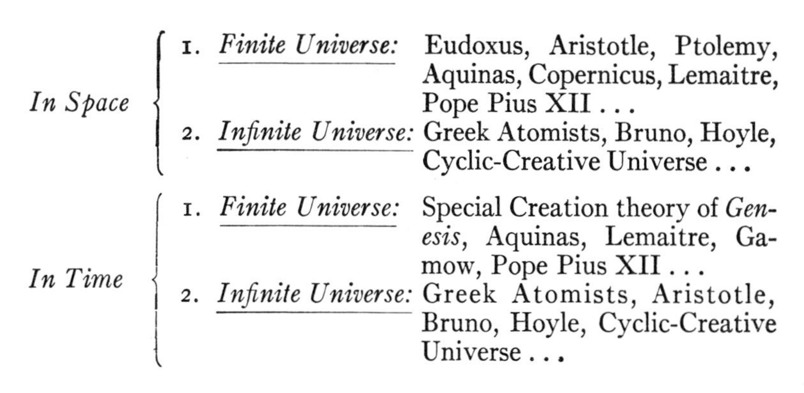

In Space	1. *Finite Universe:*	Eudoxus, Aristotle, Ptolemy, Aquinas, Copernicus, Lemaitre, Pope Pius XII . . .
	2. *Infinite Universe:*	Greek Atomists, Bruno, Hoyle, Cyclic-Creative Universe . . .
In Time	1. *Finite Universe:*	Special Creation theory of *Genesis*, Aquinas, Lemaitre, Gamow, Pope Pius XII . . .
	2. *Infinite Universe:*	Greek Atomists, Aristotle, Bruno, Hoyle, Cyclic-Creative Universe . . .

The universe listed above as the *cyclic-creative universe* is the viewpoint advanced in this book, and is a modernized form of the cosmology first outlined by Giordano Bruno: the theory of a cosmos infinite in space and time, filled with an endless number of worlds, all in varying stages of evolution.

III. The Cyclic-Creative Cosmology

The cyclic-creative cosmology presents us with a world-view in which creation is everlastingly taking place — and here we agree with Fred Hoyle's conception as based upon the Bondi-Gold notion of the continual creation of matter. *But this 'creation' is not ex nihilo; it is not making 'something out of nothing.'* As here conceived, creation is the process whereby, as the field-energy of an ocean of electrical density is converted into corpuscles, an equivalent amount of matter is dissolved into the ocean of cosmic energy. Thus nature preserves a balance between the 'matter' present in the *manifest universe* (particles in space-time which are actually or potentially perceptible) and the field-energy of the *unmanifest universe* which lies outside all space and time coördinates. That is to say, *Einstein's principle of the equivalence of matter and energy* ($E = mc^2$) *is here interpreted as a recognition of nature's proportionality between the manifest world in the space and time of the perceptible world and the invisible field-plenum from which matter emerges and into which it dissolves.* Accordingly, 'particles' emerge from the infinite and eternal Cosmic Field through a focalization, *via* the 'Cosmic Lens,' whereby nodal points are individuated into the manifest or sense-perceptible world. Thus the Cosmic Image-forming Influence (*Cosmic Lens*), which guides the processes of individuation and evolutionary integration, is defined as *that organizational factor in nature in virtue of which parts are made and put together in their right times and places to create products.* One virtue of this theory is that it gives us a unitary conception which applies not only in physics, but also on the level of economics and politics.

Because this cosmology is grounded in the fundamental thesis that energy is the basic reality of nature, we have described the resulting philosophy as a 'universal behaviorism' or a 'monism of action.' *Action,* — energy integrated through time, — is the pulse-beat of a cosmos which spirals upward in cycles of ever-evolving patterns, the cyclodrama of emergent evolution. Here, then, we have the idea of a Universal Field, the *Aether* of the Stoics, come to life again. But most of all, this cosmology resembles Bruno's conception.

One major idea that we take over from Giordano Bruno is the concept of the infinity of the universe. This brings us to the terrifyingly difficult problem of infinity, — with which we have already struggled, — and before dealing with Bruno's views we must return to a statement of the several types of infinity that are presently available.

IV. The Infinity of the Universe

In our philosophy we affirm that nature (the cosmos) is infinite. What does this mean?

In the history of mathematics the concept of infinity has many interpretations. Among the several different notions of it are the following: for one thing, there is the distinction between the *actual infinite* and the *potential infinite*. But since the latter term is used by Aristotle in his special metaphysical sense, — which is not here employed, — I shall substitute the term *dynamic* for potential. The *dynamic infinite* refers to a process, an endless chain of operations; whereas *actual infinity* refers to a set which, as the mathematicians say, can be put into one-to-one correspondence with a proper part of itself, and thus is treated as an 'entity.'

Dynamic infinity, therefore, is associated with the counting process, with the ordinal concept of number, and is indeterminate in the sense of being unfinished; whereas actual infinity is closely related to the cardinal concept, which suggests completeness and determinacy of being. In other words, cardinal number has reference to quantity and in a sense reflects a spatial notion; whereas the ordinal aspect of number brings in the idea of succession and implies a temporal notion.

With this as a background, let us now return to the question of whether the universe is infinite, and if so, in what sense.

The statement that the amount of matter in space, or the number of particles in the universe, is infinite may be interpreted in at least three ways, as follows:

1. The cardinality of the set of particles at a given time is infinite.

2. The number of particles countable in time is endless (infinite) because time is without limit (infinite).

3. From a strictly operational viewpoint, the number of particles is endless or non-terminating because we can never get through counting all the particles (ruling out the possibility that we may count some of them several times, due to our inability to attach identity to individual particles), either because they are created faster than we can count, or because they separate from each other in an expanding universe faster than we can count them, or for some other operationally conditioned reason.

With respect to the first possibility, it must be noted that to have cardinality the set of particles must be ordered, and it must be possible to tell each element from every other. The adoption of this notion of infinity seems to presuppose something like Laplace's Infinite Calculator, i.e., an intelligence that can count an infinity of particles without interacting with the entities being enumerated.

With regard to the second possibility, we have the problem of what is meant by the 'infinity of time.' If time is a measure of relations among particles, infinity is already presupposed in the statement. Most, — perhaps all, — measurements of time are of this sort: changes in any one system against a more inclusive and relatively changeless background.

In connection with the third possibility, it must be noted that a definition, to be significant, must be such that we can check to see whether or not a statement using the term is true. But this raises a broader problem of where empirical evidence enters into inquiry, — at the beginning when the axioms of physical science are constructed and from which the property of infinity is to be inferred, or after the system of science is established and can be examined. However, since the method of checking will rest on 'axioms' of some sort, it would be at least semi-deductive in any case.

Since on our theory we reject the completed or static infinite, the first alternative is eliminated. And since a strict or narrow operationalism is also rejected, we are forced to exclude the third possible meaning. This leaves us with the second possibility as the acceptable interpretation of the infinity of the universe. But since this ordinality of nature's particles is a dynamic infinite, this really means that we refuse to take the universe-as-a-whole as a fixed (static) object of thought. In other words, the principles governing statements of relationships within the cosmos cannot be extended to the cosmos, for there is nothing outside nature with which the cosmos may be compared. Thus the cosmos does not exist in space and time, although we measure relations among the parts of that cosmos in terms of space and time units. Therefore, to say that nature is 'infinite' in space and time does not mean that nature's qualities in these categories belong to the same series as the cases we observe but exceed them; it means that the terms themselves are inapplicable. Moreover, the statement that the Cosmic Field is outside all space and time coördinates means also that its laws are the same in all systems.

Now let us compare this conception with that of Giordano Bruno.

V. Comparison with Bruno's Universe

Since, as we have indicated, our conception is a modernized (electromagnetic) version of Bruno's cosmology, it is necessary that we say something about the major features of Bruno's theory, especially his theory of the Infinite.

In order to gain some historical perspective, let us glance briefly at the views of the infinite entertained by thinkers before Bruno. The close harmony between the Aristotelian and Scholastic views makes Aristotle's view a useful background for our own exposition of Bruno's conception, since the latter made such wide departures from the Scholastic doctrines of the Medieval period.

Students, of course, are well aware that even before Aristotle other Greeks had struggled with the idea of the infinite. In general it may be said that the concept of the infinite was a source of perplexity to the Greek thinkers. Two writers in the field have developed this thought. Tobias Dantzig tells us in his book, *Number, The Language of Science*, that the principal stumbling block in Greek mathematics was the fear of irrational numbers and infinity (p. 199). And as Irwin Schrödinger puts it in his volume, *Science and the Human Temperament* (p. 101), "in the Greek physics the dynamic is missing," and this he attributes to the fact that, "in the case of Greek science the idea of the infinite is scarcely understood." Thus both authors agree that the idea of a limitless (infinite) process is foreign to Greek thought.

The first of the Western mathematicians to deal with these intricacies was Pythagoras. But the Pythagorean system was deeply challenged by the discovery of irrational numbers and the idea of infinity, — discoveries that shook to the foundations the entire Pythagorean scheme. Aristotle next informs us that the study of the infinite is essential to the natural philosopher in the understanding of time, number, and magnitude. To reconcile this notion with his rejection of the actual infinite, Aristotle turned from the negative side to a statement of his positive concept, that of potential infinity: ". . . that is infinite of which it is always possible, in regard to quantity, to take a part outside that which has already been taken . . ." (*Physica*, III, 6, 207a).

Aristotle, we observe, rejects an actual infinite. He has various reasons for rejecting this concept, among which is the argument that if infinity were a substance (actuality) it could be divided into parts. But just as a part of air is still air, so a part of infinity must be infinite. But because Aristotle cannot tolerate such an 'infinite regress,' he asserts that a part of infinity cannot be infinite. The same thing cannot be many infinities; therefore infinity cannot be an actuality (entity).

The next important figure in this development, — for our purposes, — is Lucretius. The views of Lucretius are interesting in their own right, but also because of their historical significance, for they represent a position midway between Aristotle and the viewpoint later set forth by Bruno. Lucretius feels that there can be no furthest point to anything. Since there is nothing outside the sum of things, there is no limitation to the universe, which is therefore infinite. He goes on to state that if we assume the laws of nature to hold throughout this infinite space, we can suppose that there are other worlds like ours, "with tribes of men and races of wild beasts." Thus there is an infinite number of worlds in an infinite universe, — an idea restated by Bruno.

Let us now glance at the typical view of the Scholastic thinkers, — that of Saint Thomas. In certain respects Thomas Aquinas goes beyond Aristotle, and this is due to the emendations required by Christianity. St. Thomas begins by defining the actual infinite as that "outside of which there is nothing." Since he holds necessarily to the transcendence of God with regard to the created world, and to the exclusion of the concept of extension from the Infinite, — because it is the act of existing which alone is infinite and perfect, — it is a simple matter for St. Thomas to extend the definition of infinity to cover the existence of God. That is to say, by identifying His perfection with existence, it is possible for St. Thomas to assert that God is necessarily infinite and immortal. Thus God is the Infinite Being, and the only entity to which the term 'infinite' may be applied. In general, medieval Scholasticism could not get a non-theistic interpretation of Infinity. It is true, however, that Nicholas of Cusa, — whom Bruno followed at some points, — did try to develop the idea of a *positive* infinity, belonging to God alone, and a *relative* infinity, which is the universe's. That is, the universe is finite in comparison to God, but infinite in relation to all created things. Thus we leave the historical background, a jumble of conflicting views, and turn to a more promising conception, that of Bruno.

In his work, *De la Causa*, Bruno begins his considerations of the infinite with two definitions. There are, he states, two kinds of infinity, extensive and intensive. The universe is extensively infinite, having no outer margin or limits, but each part of it is finite. God, on the other hand, is intensively infinite, since He has no outer boundaries, but is also composed of an infinity of parts.

Bruno introduces his consideration of extensive infinity with the question, "If the world is finite, and outside the world there is nothing, where then is the world?" Aristotle, by defining place as ". . . the innermost boundary of what contains," had been able to answer, "In itself." Bruno felt that this was a degradation of the Divine, making it Space by another name. Bruno's further criticism of Aristotle's conception of the universe is that there must then be a vacuum beyond the universe, bounded only on one side, and this is more difficult to conceive than an infinite universe. According to Bruno, there is no reason to suppose that there are no worlds beyond this; all space, instead of only one small part of it, contains matter. Thus there are infinite worlds like our own. The idea of actual infinity as held by Bruno is therefore far different from Aristotle's viewpoint.

Linking these thoughts of Bruno with our own cosmology, we note several parallels. In the first place, as Milne has noted, Bruno's claim that "the eye being placed in any part of the Universe, the appearance would still be one unto us here," is a definite forerunner of the principle, fundamental in our own cosmology, that the universe in its macroscopic features looks the same no matter from what position in infinite space it is viewed. In the second place, Bruno's notion that infinity is of two sorts, the intensive infinite and the extensive infinite, could be regarded as the prototype for our Cosmic Field, with its continuity being that of the intensive infinite, and the extensive infinite corresponding to the discrete or matter aspect. I would like to believe that Bruno, were his spirit here, might whisper: "That is exactly what I meant!"

VI. Field and Matter

In the present form of Pantheism the following propositions are asserted:

1. The Cosmic Field is infinite, that is, it is outside all space and time coördinate systems.
2. The amount of matter in the universe is infinite; that is, it is without limit.

Here are two 'infinities', — the space-time-matter universe is boundless in its spatial and temporal dimensions; while the Cosmic Field is ubiquitous and all-inclusive. But how shall we explain the interconvertibility of matter and energy, particles and field?

Careful consideration suggests the conclusion that the interconvertibility is not a result of the fact that because we make matter out of the field, an equivalent amount of energy must be converted into matter to maintain the 'balance.' There *is* a balance, but not because nature has a ledger with entries in the red and black which must balance. If both matter and the Cosmic Field are infinite in amount and extent, and if this infinity can neither be increased by addition nor decreased by subtraction, then the balance cannot be the result of nature's effort to keep the two infinities 'equally large.' That is, regardless of how much field energy is used up to make matter (for example, a galaxy), there still remains an infinite amount of energy for making other universes. Why, then, is there this interconvertibility of *matter* $\rightleftarrows$ *energy?*

For one thing, what we are saying is that the principle in nature, — whatever it is, — in virtue of which it is possible to convert energy into matter is the same principle which allows for conversion of matter into energy. That is, there is no absolute gap between the two. *But what is this principle that is responsible for the duality of particles and radiation, matter and the field?* Let us get at the answer by indirection.

In our cosmology there is a combination of two ideas: the notion of a steady-state or over-all equilibrium condition, plus the idea of a cyclic-creative process of stellar evolution within an all-encompassing Cosmic Field. The circle of the passage of energy is from its undifferentiated source in the manifest world, through the Cosmic Lens as the impersonal formative power, into the manifest physical world, and then on up the evolutionary ladder, from sub-atomic particles to mankind. At the 'end of the line' there is a feed-back of energy into the undifferentiated Cosmic Field, which completes the process and begins the cycle anew. But whether or not we can make Bruno's modernized infinite universe satisfy the equations of Einstein's field theory is a question. If not, Einstein's equations will have to go, or the cyclic-creative universe will have to go. Perhaps both will be transcended in some more inclusive view. But before looking for such a conception, let us exploit the possibilities of the present conception.

When we get to the source of the difficulty, it appears that we come upon Maxwell's equations for the propagation of waves in free space. Here matter appears as the region in which Maxwell's equations of continuity do not hold, — matter is a hole in the ether of space, so to speak. Matter continued to appear as a foreign particle in the field, until wave mechanics came upon the scene and promised a synthesis of optics and mechanics. But this promise has not been completely fulfilled. The wave-particle difficulty still baffles human ingenuity. However, various field-theories of matter have been conceived, and quite possibly the right theory, unifying the two domains, will soon be forthcoming. Certainly one great step toward an understanding of the relation of matter and energy came with Einstein's conception.

Mass is an inertial property of energy, as Einstein pointed out in his far-reaching definition. If we take the energy content of matter, $E = m \cdot c^2$, and apply this to a quantum whose energy is $E = h\nu$, the quantum behaves as if it had mass of $h\nu/c^2$. This has been verified by the gravitational star shift predicted by Einstein. Mass is therefore related to weight in a peculiar way: we can speak of mass without necessarily referring to weight, although the above-mentioned 'star-shift' shows that the particle of light also has a gravitational property. All physical energy has mass. The great riddle is to unify the field point of view (matter as energy-nodes) and the particle point of view. The equation $E \leftrightarrows mC^2$ shows the possibility in both directions; but we still lack an adequate theory. For us, this is the only case or sense in which there is a 'riddle of the universe.' But in the search for a satisfactory field theory of matter the physicist is not completely helpless, and the following sections summarize some of the relevant material which will ultimately make it possible to produce a comprehensive theory of the creation of matter. First let us say a word about the rôle of cosmic rays in nature's cycle.

VII. Cosmic Energy and the Creation of Matter

Some years back Dr. Robert A. Millikan proposed that cosmic rays are the birth cries of atoms being born out in the depths of space. It cannot be said that this idea is wrong, though how such a process is sustained is still quite mysterious.

Cosmic rays are high energy penetrating particles coming from somewhere out in space, bombarding the earth and disintegrating the atoms in the earth's upper atmosphere. These cosmic rays represent the upper limit of energy, so far as present knowledge goes.

The physicist does not understand why (how) matter can be transformed into radiation (as at Hiroshima), nor why (how) energy can be transformed into matter, as Millikan and others have supposed. But in due time these processes will certainly be well understood. In the atom bomb, which gets its energy from nuclear fission, no one particle has more than a million electron volts of energy, while cosmic ray particles represent energies of a billion or more electron volts. In the laboratory physicists are accelerating particles to the point of creating such cosmic rays artificially. This cosmic ray energy is greater than the binding energy of the nucleons, which suggests that in time man may direct this energy in such fashion as to control the arrangement energy in the nucleons. At that time man will be able to synthesize matter (atoms).

If, for the moment, we assume the existence of 'ultimate' particles, the first step in the building of a universe will consist in the integration of the hydrogen atom. The import of such a possibility is prodigious, for it means that man will be well on the road to duplicating the alchemy of nature. Indeed, man has already created trans-uranium elements, such as plutonium. Why, then, should he not create hydrogen atoms, the original substance out of which universes (galaxies) evolve?

VIII. The Mother Substance of Universes

The matter of which the cosmos is composed is amazingly uniform in nature and distribution: it consists of somewhat less than 50 per cent of hydrogen, about the same amount of helium, and the remainder (about 1 per cent) is made up of the heavier elements. Thus hydrogen has been described as the 'mother gas of creation,' which, once it is in existence, is gradually converted into the 'ashes' of helium. This accounts for the terrific energies of the stars, and gives us the solution to a problem that long has puzzled the astronomers. The story is interesting and well justifies a slight digression, following which we return to the central theme.

There are two theories of how the energy of the sun, which warms the solar system, is generated. According to one theory, the so-called carbon cycle, the energy of the sun and stars is generated in the process whereby helium is created out of hydrogen. This is a relatively rapid process. The second theory involves a process which is slower in rate, — a billion-year cycle, — but much more important as a source of energy. This is the 'proton-proton reaction.' According to this conception, two protons may pass near enough so that they stick together. Since each proton is a nucleus of a hydrogen atom, together they will thus form one atom of double-weight hydrogen or deuterium. The nearness of approach at which this 'sticking together' occurs is very exact.

Once the deuterium atom is formed, the process continues through a series of transmutations of elements involving lithium and beryllium, until an atom of helium is formed. In this process energy is released, — mass is converted into energy. This is the atomic fusion whereby a hydrogen bomb could generate the terrific energy which, in its destructive applications, far surpass the energy released by the atomic fission of the older atom bomb.

These two processes are not mutually exclusive. By these two processes of (1) the carbon cycle, and (2) the proton-proton reaction the sun generates its energy, actually consuming its own mass at the rate of millions of tons of mass a day to produce the starlight which helps illuminate the universe and warm the earth.

IX. The Arrangement Energy of Atoms

Each atomic particle, — the electrons and the nucleus as a 'particle', — spins like a top on its axis. The spin of the particle is quantized in the sense that it is an integral (or half-integral) multiple of Planck's constant divided by *2pi*.

Pauli's exclusion principle tells us that two electrons can never possess the same orbit and orbital angular momentum, with their spins in the same direction. Quite probably the 'magic numbers' (the atomic numbers of those elements with nuclei that are stable, in the sense that they do not easily react with other elements of the periodic table) are related to the phenomenon of the spin of particles in the atoms. These magic numbers (i.e., atomic numbers 2, 10, 18, 36, and 40) don't coincide with the Pythagorean magic number sequence (except that the decad is common to both), but the central thought is pretty much the same.

It is now believed that the mesons discovered by Yukawa are the offspring of the protons and neutrons within the nuclei, and that as the mesons disappear as matter, the mass is reborn in the form of energy which supplies the adhesive forces required to hold the atomic nuclei together, despite the powerful repulsive forces. The following formula represents the situation:

Atom = positive electrical charges plus negative electrical charges plus . . . . . .

The dots indicate the presence of a powerful binding energy, a nuclear glue, uniting the particles within the nucleus. It is estimated that the forces holding the nucleons together inside the atomic nuclei are a million times as powerful as the electrical forces holding the planetary electrons in their atomic orbits.

The total mass of the nucleus is always smaller than the combined masses of the protons and the neutrons of which it is composed, so that the 'binding energy' can be calculated from this 'mass defect,' through the use of Einstein's formula, $E = mC^2$.

This is a significant fact. Advocates of gestalt principles usually argue that a non-summative whole contains *more than* the sum of the properties of the parts; but in the foregoing case the non-additivity results from the fact that the whole (the nucleus) contains a net mass *less than* that of the parts. It looks as if part of the mass has been used to create the binding energy. But in any case we are dealing with a non-linear (wholistic) phenomenon.

Turning from the interior of atoms to the outer universe of stellar matter, we recall that hydrogen constitutes the major part of the gaseous material of the nebulae that are scattered over trillions of miles of space. At least several 'outer universes' are within the reach of the artificial eye of the Mount Palomar telescope, and probably others will swim within our purview when better telescopes are constructed. The important thing is that out of the turbulent motions of gaseous materials galaxies are born,[1] and our job is to find the evidence for a 'Cosmic Guiding Field' in such apparently unguided processes. The background material out of which these universes are built is provided by the atomic hydrogen, and these atoms are *products* conforming to the Vanderjagt formula:

$$P = \int_{t_1}^{t_2} (a\,dx + b\,dy + c\,dz)$$

where t_1 and t_2 are the time-limits, x is the matter (electrons and nucleons), y is the labor (work), and z is the imagination (or organizing field). *Without the organizing field there can be no atoms of hydrogen.* If we treat the 'arrangement energy' as a manifestation of the organizational factor which puts parts together in their right times and places to make products, Cosmic Imagination is seen to be at work in the creation of the mother substance of universes.

Accordingly, at the very foundation of the physical universe the *guiding field* is already at work. We surmise, therefore, that it is likely that the statistical nature of turbulent motions will ultimately be resolved into a higher order of organization.

X. Atoms, Galaxies, and Our Solar System

One problem we have not touched upon is this: Did the atoms come before the stars, or did the stars come into being before the atoms? In a sense, this is a silly question: if stars are made of atoms, how could they come into existence before the atoms out of which they are made? Nevertheless, the relation between the two is still not altogether clear, especially if there is any truth to the conjecture that the atoms of hydrogen (or at least neutrons) may be created in the region of the collapsed stars (or supernovae) which generate the conditions favorable to the creation of matter.

My own attitude would be that on this question the theory set forth by Cecelia Payne-Gaposchkin in her fascinating book, *Stars in the Making* (1952), provides a reliable guide. She supposes that stars and galaxies must have originated out of clouds of atoms or gas. Because of the distance between the stars, two galaxies (once they have evolved sufficiently) may pass through each other without disturbing the position and motion of their stars, and as they interpenetrate each other they could have the effect of cleaning out each other's interstellar dust and gas material. As Dr. Payne-Gaposchkin tells the story (p. 124):

> "Without stretching the imagination too much we may picture a spiral galaxy as an irregular galaxy rotating within an ellipsoidal galaxy, and swirled into pinwheel form by its rotation around the nucleus of the former. We begin to see the spiral structure as something churned out of the layer of dust and gas by the rotation of the system, something that is progressively twisted out of existence by its own differential rotation. So long as the dust and gas are present, spiral arms will form, and dissipate, and new spiral arms will re-form. The process will go on while there is dust and gas present; when all the raw material is used up, there will be no more spiral arms. We shall be left with a system that . . . will be an elliptical galaxy."

This is not the end of the story (nor the beginning either, for that matter), but it is an essential part of the story which puts the spiral galaxies in their proper place, — between the irregular and the elliptical galaxies, — but it does not fit the birth of atoms into the sequence in that sense that it does not explain the origin of the interstellar gas out of which universes are born. However, this cosmology is of interest to us because it does not call for the hyperdense state of the universe, 4 or 5 billion years ago, that Lemaitre's model requires. Here we have a theory which, like Hoyle's, could accept the thesis that nuclei of high atomic weight could have been formed in stars and galaxies as we find them today, without the excessively high density which the Lemaitre-Gamow explosion calls for.

If such atoms (nuclei plus planetary electrons) could be born continuously and uniformly in space (or even at privileged regions everywhere in infinite space), under conditions which always exist, we would be free from the absurdity of the *cosmic* $t = O$ concept of creation.

At the present time the problem of the origin of our solar system is not connected in any obvious way with the theory of the finitude or infinitude of the cosmos. For example, the verification of the truth (or falsity) of our infinite-eternal cosmology may not settle the dispute between the rival theories about the origin of our own solar system. None the less, the latter problem is interesting to us humans, especially since this is the problem of how our own earth, — man's local habitation, — came into being.

Much of the theorizing, by way of agreement or disagreement, harks back to Immanuel Kant's cosmological speculations. Kant's theory assumed that our solar system was once a vast cloud of hot gases from which the sun and its present population of planets evolved. Most theories since Kant's time are emendations of this theory. This is illustrated, for example, by the theory advocated by the astronomer Gerald K. Kuiper of the University of Chicago. According to him, three billion years ago the sun condensed from a vast rotating cloud of interstellar dust. But Kuiper rejects Kant's idea that this 'dust' is composed of hot gases and supposes that it represents the accumulation and fusion of 'cold' particles. As this cloud spun faster and faster around the sun, it shrank in size and flattened out into a dense ring of particles, after which the ring broke up into a number of eddies which in turn continued to shrink, thus ultimately producing the planets of the solar system.

In some ways this idea that the planets were formed from eddies in a gaseous ring resembles the theory of Karl von Weizsäcker, with the difference that Kuiper stresses more the role of gravitational attraction in producing the angular momentum. Both views, however, start from the original form of the dust cloud hypothesis as proposed by Professor F. L. Whipple of Harvard Observatory (described by him in a semi-popular article in the *Scientific American*, May, 1948). This account begins with a great dust cloud, contracting with minor turbulent motions but not rotating as a whole. Condensation and contraction, strung out in a series, spiral toward the center and grow by accretion into proto-planets. Ultimately, after other episodes in its life-history, the process ends in a system having the required regularities. According to Lyman Spitzer, now at Princeton University, the pressure of light may serve to collect the dust particles in space into the clouds postulated above.

This theory of a cosmic dust cloud as the original material of our solar system is also favored by Harold C. Urey in his book, *The Planets, Their Origin and Development*. Starting from the hypothesis of Lyman Spitzer and Fred Whipple, Professor Urey tries to explain the formation of the sun through a process of condensation of an interstellar globule having a temperature far below zero. But even if this looks good as a beginning, the difficulties soon pile up, — no matter what theory is favored. Some of these difficulties are mentioned by P. S. Palmer in his article, "Cosmic Cloud Hypothesis of the Origin of the Solar System" (*Science*, Vol. 117, 1953, 236–237), wherein he quotes the statement that "the public is being played upon and utterly misled by the dreamery of the rival mathematical astronomers and physicists." This may be an exaggeration; nevertheless, it is true that there is no generally accepted theory of the origin of our solar system.

One of the crucial problems in this field is the problem of angular momentum. No one has yet invented a satisfactory hypothesis to account for the angular momentum of the solar system in a series of evolutionary stages (including a paradoxically necessary slowing down of the sun's rotation), so that a separation of elements according to atomic weights could take place. In view of these difficulties, it is evident that a final solution may not be forth-coming for many decades. But the statement now made by some investigators, that "the general tendency is to ignore the whole problem of angular momentum," is too pessimistic and presumably only represents a passing phase in the development of an extremely difficult subject. Certainly we cannot ignore the problem in our own theorizing, and we therefore now return to this important topic.

XI. Spin in the Universe

We have referred to the importance of spin in atomic and in cosmic processes. Does the fact of spin require a finite universe? Or is it compatible with an infinite universe? To answer that question we must look to the source of spin in galactic phenomena.

According to the theory of Hannes Alfvén, Professor of the Royal Institute of Technology in Sweden, the spin of stars and sun is acquired by material bodies under the action of electric and magnetic fields. Spin, therefore, can be transferred from fields to matter, and this raises the question of the source of spin or angular momentum in the fields of space. In a recent article on this,[2] Professor Alfvén directs attention to the role of magneto-dynamic waves, a new type of effect, capable of producing (1) mechanical motion, (2) magnetic fields, and (3) electric fields. The study of such waves leads to a novel way of looking at the behavior of stellar matter. Since magnetic fields change the properties of dense stellar gases, the customary laws of hydrodynamics as they apply to ordinary liquids and gases are superseded. Among the consequences of this revised way of looking at the forces in the universe, we find a possible explanation of the behavior of sun-spots (great eddies in the solar atmosphere, similar to cyclones on the earth). Another result of the study of magneto-dynamic waves is that this also throws light on the fantastic energy of cosmic rays, which are thus accelerated in their motion just as particles are accelerated in the big laboratory cosmotron. The magneto-dynamic waves roam ceaselessly through cosmic space, but especially near the stars the cosmic rays (particles) are propelled into space with terrific energies, later to crash into the earth's atmosphere.

Another possible consequence of such waves (though Professor Alfvén does not suggest this, so far as my knowledge goes) is that they may throw some light on the space distribution of the galaxies and the turbulent motions of the matter in such universes. Thus everywhere in the cosmos we find laws of spin, which govern not only the motions of galaxies but the behavior of particles inside the nuclei and the valence electrons in the atoms, the latter being responsible for chemical affinities and integrations. Perhaps in the case of the stars, — which frequently are accompanied by families of planets, — there will be, in addition to the mechanical-electric-magnetic waves, which produce angular momentum, other supplementary rotation phenomena such as are described as *coriolis forces*. Such forces are not only important here on earth (thinking, for example, of the magnetic coriolis theory of bird navigation), but they are also significant in the cosmic scheme of things. Thus, when we transcend our own planetary coördinate system and adopt an extra-terrestrial view of things, we see our little earth revolving around the sun, and we see the solar system moving through interplanetary space as it wheels around the center of the galaxy which is the Milky Way. This lens-like galaxy, like all other galaxies, must generate a small but significant coriolis drift, and this, added to the magneto-dynamic waves, determines the macroscopic behavior of galactic systems. All things considered, the order in the universe may yet register the over-lordship of cosmic principles of harmony such as was dreamed of by Pythagoras of old in his inaudible music of the spheres.

Returning to the question that initiated the problem of this section, our answer is that up to now there is no reason for believing that the idea of spin or angular momentum applies to the universe as a whole, — the cosmos, — and we are probably correct if we conclude that spin is peculiar to local systems (galaxies, metagalaxies, etc.) and is not a property of a cosmos infinite in extent. There appears to be no necessary reason, however, why a universe of infinite circumference should not revolve, so that the 'Cosmic Lens' could have an angular velocity, — but as yet there is no experimental evidence on this one way or the other.

XII. Stellar Evolution and Galactic Magnetic Fields

The picture we form of the origin of a universe is therefore somewhat as follows: In the depths of interstellar space hydrogen atoms are constantly in process of creation. This universally diffused hydrogen constitutes the background material, — the *Cosmoplasma*, as Harlow Shapley terms it, — for building a universe. The next stage consists in the aggregation of such basic material into gases which are condensed into the stuff of which stars and spiral nebulae are constituted. One theory of how this occurs is provided by Dr. Karl von Weizsäcker's explanation. As he observes, nearly all the spiral nebulae are of the same type: a white center with two spiral arms wrapped around the center. Our own Milky Way galaxy, for example, is such a spiral, and there are millions of such spirals revealed by the large telescopes. A mathematical study of the turbulence effects (eddies and vortices) in these nebulae demonstrates that the inner parts will rotate faster than the outer parts (as is the case in our own galaxy). The total Weizsäcker picture, therefore, portrays a universe that exploded, the present nebulae, rushing away from each other, being what is left after the mysterious beginning of creation.

This theory, like that of Professors Gamow and Hoyle, gives no explanation of the origin of the material it starts with. Moreover, like Gamow's universe, but unlike Hoyle's, this conception starts with a finite system, whereas in our view we always have an infinity of universes, any one of which, however, does have its individual life-history. Moreover, while Gamow's theory and Weizsäcker's conception recognize the rôle of turbulence forces, neither cosmologist assigns any significance to magnetic fields in cosmic processes, as Alfvén's discovery of magneto-dynamic waves requires and as Dr. Enrico Fermi's recent investigations confirm. The supplementary value of the theory that fluid magnetic fields are generated in the great cosmic dust clouds dispersed along the plane of the galaxy is that these fields may then act as celestial generators of cosmic rays, some of which, in the course of time, are accelerated to escape-velocity to become free rays (particles) in space.

An additional virtue of this line of thought is that it may help solve another problem at the same time. As Dr. Lyman Spitzer, Jr., of Princeton University Observatory, points out,[3] gravitational attraction alone is not sufficient to create stars out of these cosmic dust clouds. In that case, as the authors insist, the external pressure of light would help to push these particles together, the larger aggregations after a few million years becoming dense enough to form stars.

This, of course, is an extraordinarily profound subject, and many details remain to be worked out. The overall difficulty that the present theory faces is the mechanism for the reciprocal convertibility of energy and matter, and also we have before us the problem of explaining the origin of the hydrogen atoms out of which universes are built. Out of star-dust we are born; by star-light we live; and into star-dust we will dissolve, — that is the story of creation. In a way, this story provides a curious confirmation of the thoughts of my friend, Dr. C. Hilton Rice (now deceased), as these thoughts are preserved in my volume, *The World Sensorium:*

"With our sensory perceptors we look out at the universe and bless the light that illuminates the physical world. The truth is that we see little, for moving objects quickly diminish in size and fade into the distance or disappear over the horizon. The nearby planets are indistinct objects shining by reflected light. Beyond the planets we cannot see the stars for the light they give off. We cannot see with too much light and we cannot see with too little. To sensory perception the cosmos consists of masses of matter moving through a sea of their own diffusion, like melting icebergs in a sea of water. Hence the cosmos is 'fogged' with light that both gives and obscures vision."

That there is some deep kinship between cosmic light and human sight; that there is some electromagnetic bond of fealty that unites man and nature; that in some sense the Cosmic Image-forming Lens visualizes the universe into existence; and that man in investigating nature uses light as the link that spans the abyss that separates logic and physics, — these are ideas that have haunted me for years, and the working out of a satisfactory theory about them has become an ineradicable philosophical obsession.

XIII. The Wave Mechanics of Particles

In the preceding pages we have tried to show that behind our sensorially perceived universe, which the scientists investigate with their microscopes and telescopes, there exists a superior or circumambient field-plenum which is the reservoir of organizing influences which guide the emergence of matter, life, and mind. In other words, behind the visible phenomena of nature which comprise the *manifest world* lies the ultimate realm of the *unmanifest world*, the undifferentiated plenum of the Cosmic Field.

The picture of the universe we have here tried to piece together from the fragments of human experience is based on a deep feeling of the utter futility of dealing with the problem of creation by pushing it back in time, or, still worse, of shoving it aside as meaningless. I feel certain, also, that this universe is one in which there is a double process at work: a continual replacement of the energy which appears to be lost or degraded by an inverse process whereby that energy reënters the stream of time and creativity. Thus the 'Cosmic Lens' is conceived to function in such a manner as to bring the forces of nature into constructive focus for emergent evolution in local systems.

The Field Plenum itself is eternal, infinite, uncreated, and indestructible. It is outside all finite coördinate systems, and 'space' and 'time' as we humans deal with them are finite measures of energy transactions occurring within the limitless cosmos. The term 'cosmos' is used to designate the weld of the visible manifest and the invisible unmanifest worlds. Obviously, we have here a kind of dualism: in the outer universe a dualism of field and particles, and within man himself a dualism of mind and matter. This, however, is a *relative* dualism, not an *absolute* dualism.

In order to understand the relation between the end-terms, we have repeatedly turned to the various theories that have been devised to overcome the dualities. We have looked for the solution in the general direction of a unified field theory of matter. Looking back over the path we have traversed, it appears that among the several efforts in this direction one of the most promising is the attempt undertaken by Sir J. J. Thomson and his son, G. P. Thomson. In returning to this line of thought, we are back-tracking a bit, — returning to an earlier form of wave-mechanics, — but not infrequently in the history of science it has proved rewarding to do this. One recent illustration of this has already been noted: the case of Dirac's return to the idea of an ether of space. Indeed, Dirac's revival of the ether-concept helps us in a measure in the return to wave-mechanical ideas. This is the case with the notion of *group waves*, or wave packets, which still remains a possibility for explaining corpuscles or particles as foci of field-energy.

To see how this synthesis may be carried through, let us return to Maxwell for a moment. It was Clerk Maxwell who first showed that light is not only an optical phenomenon, but an electromagnetic phenomenon as well, — that it consists of electromagnetic waves. Now in all forms of wave phenomena two kinds of processes are involved: there is (1) the transmission of energy, and (2) the propagation of wave-forms. In many cases (for light and sound transmission especially) the duality of function, — transmission of energy and propagation of wave-forms, — is not easily noted because the speeds of the two processes are the same.

To explain these dual aspects, the ether of space was invoked, and it was generally concluded that all forms of light (or electromagnetic radiation) travel in a vacuum at the same speed. This velocity, as Einstein's relativity theory emphasized, is a fundamental constant of nature. But in investigating the nature of wave-phenomena it was observed, as we have just seen, that there are two kinds of waves, called *group* waves and *constituent* waves. The distinction between these two kinds of waves and their velocities of transmission has been illustrated by Sir Joseph Thomson in his little book, *Beyond the Electron* (1928), and from this (pages 17–18) I select the following:

> "The velocity at which the disturbance or the energy moves is called the group velocity; the velocity of the waves, the wave velocity. Let me illustrate the difference by a simple example. Take the case when there are two sets of waves, and let us represent one set by a procession of men, walking in a straight line at a constant speed and with a constant distance between each man and his nearest neighbor: the speed with which they walk represents the wave velocity, the distance between them the wave length. Let the other set of waves be represented by a procession of girls moving at a different speed from the men and separated from each other by a different distance; suppose the two processions are walking side by side. If the men represent the crests of one set of waves, the girls the crests of the other set, then when a man and a girl are together the crests of the two sets coincide and the disturbance and energy are maximum at these places. Let us concentrate our attention on these places and find the velocity with which they travel. If an observer stands still at one place and waits long enough he will see a man and a girl side by side; but since the two processions are out of step the next man that passes will not pass at the same time as the next girl, and it may be a long time before he sees another couple. Could he get a richer harvest by walking forward, and if so, what is the pace at which he ought to walk?"

To answer the question, Sir Joseph enters into a mathematical analysis of the situation (here omitted), and then concludes: "We see from this analogy that though the velocity of the energy may lag far behind that of the waves, the path of the energy will be that of the waves; the waves guide the energy along the path it has to take."

It will be noted that in this situation the greater the velocity of the waves the smaller is that of the energy. The remarkable thing is that the product of the two speeds in electromagnetic phenomena is always the same, — the square of the velocity of light. In other words, *the velocity of light is a mean between the velocity of the group waves and the velocity of the guiding or constituent waves.*

The great achievement of de Broglie (in 1924) was to indicate how the wave theory and the corpuscular theory of light and of matter could both be true. This was accomplished by concentrating attention on the group wave and developing a wave theory of matter. As indicated in the above quotation from Sir Joseph Thomson, these group waves are a resultant of superposed constituent waves. Applying this kind of thinking to the electron, de Broglie showed that an undulatory theory of electrons can be developed, provided we regard the electrons as manifestations of group waves accompanied by a train of waves which the particles are compelled to follow. Here the *guiding waves* show the electrons where to go, as it were. The guiding waves that accompany the electrons do *not* travel with the speed of light; they travel much faster, and the slower the electrons (group waves) move the faster the constituent waves will move. That is, if U is the velocity of the group waves (wave packets), and v the velocity of the constituent waves, then $Uv = C^2$, where C is the velocity of light.

Since the medium required by this wave theory of matter is one in which waves travel at variable speeds, the old-fashioned ether had to be modified. Accordingly, a sub-ether was posited having the required properties. Thus the particle provides its own sub-ether in the form of waves, and these guiding waves show the particle where to go. I shall return to this. Here it is sufficient to note that this doctrine that energy-waves may travel at any speed does not contradict the teaching of relativity theory concerning the constancy of the velocity of light *in vacuo*. *But the important point is that there is no field-free space*, except as an abstraction.

The wave velocity, — as opposed to the group velocity, which is that of the electron, — is the velocity of the constituent waves which are running through the electrons. As G. P. Thomson put it in his book, *The Atom* (1930, p. 186), "the waves, in fact, must be regarded as perpetually running through the electron from behind so that the electron is always receiving a fresh supply." Since it is impossible to measure the wave velocity directly, it was (is) therefore referred to as a 'ghost wave' which directs the motion of the electron waves. Later, as a 'wave of probability,' the guiding wave was interpreted as man's power to predict the electron's appearance in a given place at a given time. That is, the certainty or 'chance' was proportional to the intensity of the wave there.

For us one interesting feature of this hoped-for synthesis of optics and mechanics is the manner in which it would solve several problems at one fell swoop: on the one hand, it gives us an indication of how the wave and corpuscular aspects of matter and radiation are to be harmonized; and, secondly, it would solve the problem of the unknown mechanism whereby guiding fields may control the course of emergent evolution. A third virtue is that, for us, it would solve the problems of the interrelation of mind and matter, since on our theory consciousness is related to the cortical fields, while the matter aspect of the brain represents the visible particle phase of the physical world.

In order to expand this last suggestion, it is necessary to bring in ideas advanced by Sir Oliver Lodge. In an article on the "Interaction of Life and Matter," in the *Hibbert Journal* (April, 1931), Sir Oliver Lodge proposed to add to the physicist's conception of electric and magnetic fields of force the notion of a 'biological field,' which would provide the medium whereby life and mind (themselves non-material) would operate on and direct material particles. This dualism of the 'field' and 'corpuscles' arises out of the distinction between *form* waves (termed *constituent* waves above) and *group* waves. Sir Oliver stated that if either of these is more ultimate it is the form waves, for group waves (or particles) are due to the superposition of a set of form waves and in this respect are analogous to 'beats' in music. The peculiarity of these form waves (Schrödinger's *psi* waves) is that they exert a controlling influence on matter without imparting energy. Thus we have at least a possible mechanism for understanding how life and mind may employ a bio-field to act on matter, thus functioning as directive agencies without upsetting the laws of mechanics.

The reader will observe that in our interpretation the wave-particle opposition is looked upon as basis for the mind-matter dualism of the 'subjective' and the 'objective' worlds, the subjective being paired off with the relatively continuous field (or sub-ether) aspect directing the behavior of the group- or matter-waves. In this interchange between ether and matter the interaction is always in terms of finite quanta, as Planck's quantum theory indicates. But behind the manifest physical (matter) universe a continuous and infinite field provides the circumambient plenum for the discreteness which appears in the particle-aspect of the visible manifest world as seen by the eyes of man.

It appears, therefore, that one of the great services of wave mechanics is that it has called attention to the limitations of the older space and time representations of physical reality. In discussing the opposition of the wave picture and the particle theory of nature, Sir James Jeans points out in his book, *The New Background of Science* (p. 251), that "the particle picture implies the possibility, and the wave picture the impossibility, of representation in space and time." Sir James then states that "the wave picture begins to appear as the true picture of reality, and the particle picture merely as a clumsy approximation to the truth, an approximation obtained by trying to force into a framework of space and time a structure which does not admit of representation in space and time." Thus, as we are told, our thoughts have become space-time bound, so that the abandonment of a space-time representation of nature is the first step on the way to a better understanding of reality. Space-time, Sir James states (p. 259), is not the framework of the world of nature, but the world of our sense perceptions. The events which affect our senses are only the outer surface of nature, — like ripples of the surface of a stream, — but the origins of these surface disturbances throw roots deep down into the stream.

And that brings us back to the medium required for wave mechanics, the sub-ether. This medium has the properties of a *super-dispersive medium*, and it is necessary to say something about that.

In the ether free from matter, — in a vacuum, — light or radiation travels with a constant velocity. But when electrical charges are introduced, the situation is altered. In an electrified space the properties are those of a super-dispersive medium: here the waves travel faster than light. That is to say, inside transparent matter the effective velocity is decreased, but inside an electrified region (*our infinite ocean of electrical density*) the wave velocity is propagated at speeds according to wave-length. Thus the constituent waves of a super-dispersive medium (or sub-ether) are guiding fields of influence which can travel at speeds approaching an infinite velocity, — with the speed of thought, as Sir Oliver puts it.

The net result of these studies, therefore, seems to be this: While the description of the physical world is dualistic, — in terms of waves and particles, — the evidence clearly indicates that the wave-aspect is more fundamental than the particle-aspect. To quote one more scientist on this point,[4] classical physics appears as a limiting case where h, Planck's constant, tends toward zero. In other words, one can derive the particle-aspect by imposing quantization upon the wave description.

It is still true, however, that two fields are required, — previously designated as the *sub-ether* and the *electromagnetic field*, — since the quantized wave-field (the 'sub-ether' of the Thomsons) yields the building stones (electrons, protons, neutrons, etc.), while the quantized electromagnetic field will yield photons and *pi* mesons, which constitute the cement that binds the particles together. The paramount problem, therefore, is to investigate the interaction between these two fields. That is the next order of business for the physicists. But surely it no longer seems necessary to resort to such extremes as *action at a distance* in order to find the principles of synthesis that will harmonize physical phenomena.

In this investigation the perplexing problem of infinity will again come up. When quantization is invoked, the problem is to derive finite physical units (corpuscles and their interactions) from a mathematics of continuity and infinity. But as F. J. Dyson[5] points out, in the mathematical manipulations in this field, — as H. A. Kramers first noted in the new quantum electrodynamics which is discussed in the next section, — the infinite expressions cancel out and the results are finite. As Dyson states (*loc. cit*): "We need not be afraid of infinite quantities. We treat them as if they are ordinary numbers, and then at the end of the calculation, when everything is expressed in terms of the observed mass m and the charge e, all the infinities drop out and the results are finite." Thus it appears possible to secure a unified conception in which there is no separation of the mechanical and electrical properties of 'particles.' The most recent confirmation of this conclusion is provided by the new quantum electrodynamics, as the following section aims to show.

XIV. Classical Field Theory and Quantum Electrodynamics

Formerly, when one spoke of *field theory*, the meaning was clear. This meant, originally, the electric and magnetic fields as Michael Faraday and James Clerk Maxwell conceived them. The fields represented a state of tension or stress in the ether of space, describable by a set of numbers denoting the strength and direction of the fields at any given point. This notion of the field, which may be designated as the *classical field*, was sufficiently general to include the gravitational field.

In the days when the idea of an 'ether of space' was still in good repute, the classical field theory visualized the field-influences in terms of mechanical stresses in a substance, an ideal (frictionless) fluid. Thus the electric and magnetic fields were pictured as two liquids having well-defined velocities or directions of flow, filling the whole of space and interpenetrating each other.

When in 1905 Einstein introduced the new ideas of relativity theory, he gave us the electromagnetic field as a complete substitute for the older ether of space. In 1916 he extended relativity theory to include gravitational fields, and then undertook the task of including both types of fields, electromagnetic and gravitational, within one unified field theory.

Now a new type of field has made its appearance to complicate the scene: not only do we have the Faraday-Maxwell-Einstein unified field, but we find also that the quantum field must enter the picture. Einstein's field theory has been most successful in dealing with large-scale or macroscopic phenomena, but relativity theory has not worked as well on the small-scale level of elementary particles. Here the behavior of the individual particles is subject to Heisenberg's uncertainty principle, based on the discovery that particles do not possess exact positions for precise instants of time. Quantum fluctuations give statistical results averaged over periods of time. These quantum fluctuations are not observable on the level of large-scale behavior, but are important when (for example) one studies the effects of an electromagnetic field on a single atom.

One important component of the present quantum field theory is the idea of a 'reaction force,' referring to the electron's *self-field*, which reacts back upon the behavior of the electron. This introduces a novel and significant idea: the notion that empty space, — or a *vacuum*, — possesses dynamic properties and even has a creative potency, so to speak. In the interaction of matter, field, and empty space, a vacuum interaction becomes very complex and cannot be described by any simple mathematics.

The experimental evidence for the field reaction dates back to the year 1947. The physicists, Willis Lamb and Robert Retherford, associated with the group at Columbia University led by Dr. I. I. Rabi, devised a way to measure the effects of electromagnetic fields on single hydrogen atoms. Using the new techniques of radio-frequency familiar to radar experts as micro-wave cavity resonators,[6] they showed that the field reaction on an electron existed and did indeed produce a quantitatively measurable displacement of the spectral lines of the hydrogen atoms. This Lamb-Retherford experiment, indicating that quantum fluctuations are a part of the total effect of the fields, is the best evidence available for believing that the quantum field theory is correct. Thus the new quantum electrodynamics, first proposed on theoretical grounds by H. A. Krámers (who, until his death, was Lorentz's successor at Leiden), indicates that the field reaction on an electron cannot be separated from the ordinary mechanical (inertial) properties. Further investigations along these lines by A. A. Bethe (Cornell), Julian Schwinger (Harvard), and Dyson (Cornell) have solidified the theory considerably.

The consequences of this new way of looking at the situation are rather surprising. When the two sets of concepts, the ideas of quantum mechanics and relativity theory, are put together, there emerges, almost automatically, a third idea, — the idea that the world is built of elementary particles. As Professor Dyson puts it in his article:

> "The picture of the world that we have finally reached is the following: Some 10 or 20 qualitatively different quantum fields exist. Each fills the whole of space and has its own particular properties. There is nothing else except these fields; the whole of the material universe is built of them. Between various pairs of the fields are various kinds of interaction. Each field manifests itself as a type of elementary particle. The particles of a given type are always completely identical and indistinguishable. The number of particles of a given type is not fixed, for particles are constantly being annihilated or transmuted into one another. The properties of the interactions determine the rules for creation and transmutation of particles."

Another consequence of this line of thinking is that it lends support to the idea of *gestalt* and *emergence*, notions which play a fundamental role in our own philosophy. This point concerning the wholistic nature of physical processes has been stated by Dr. Alexander Stern,[7] as follows:

> "It is of interest to note that the elementary particles, which are more than a billion times smaller than living cells, have this in common with them. They are both complex, interacting systems that must be considered as wholes. No observation is possible on these elusive fundamental units, living and nonliving, that would reveal the nature of the interaction between their component systems."

A further consequence of quantum electrodynamics is that it helps to refute the thesis of the positivists who want to build the world out of observables and exclude non-observables from science. This point is well made by Dr. Stern in these words:

> "... the explanation of the Lamb shift and the anomolous magnetic moment of the electron as the *measurable consequences of the unobservable field and charge fluctuation of empty space interacting with the electron ... is that the real in physics encompasses more than the directly observable and measurable.*"

And what do others have to say about these new developments? Without entering upon a thoroughgoing survey, it is sufficient for my purpose to glance only at Einstein's attitude toward quantum-probability-uncertainty physics. In the fourth edition of his book, *The Meaning of Relativity* (1953), Einstein says in his new Appendix that his theory runs directly counter to the main current of modern physical thought, in the sense that he still believes in a 'field theory' rather than the 'particle theory' favored by most physicists. Thus he continues his argument with the quantum physicists who are "convinced, as a result of the success of the probability-based quantum mechanics, that one must abandon the goal of complete description of real situations in physical theory." Einstein is determined to find such a description, and states that he sees "in the present situation no possible way other than a pure field theory, which then, however, has before it the gigantic task of deriving the atomic character of energy."

My own theory about this dilemma is that Einstein's unified field theory and the quantum field theory are not merely trying to say the same thing in two different languages (a kind of solution that might be proposed by peace-makers), but that these two types of hypotheses are operating on two different levels of being. Both theories seem to me to contain elements of truth, but the truth that is in each of them is included in our own two fields, the *ether* and the *sub-ether*, i.e., the space-medium for interactions of the *manifest world* and the field-plenum of the *unmanifest world. This leads to two kinds or levels of communication*, as we shall see in the next chapter.

For our purposes, the important thing to remember is that our Cosmic Field, or Ocean of Electrical Energy, is closer to the sub-ether of the Thomsons and Lodge than to the electromagnetic field of Faraday and Maxwell and the unified field of Einstein, all of which belong close to the manifest world of reality. Our Cosmic Field goes even deeper into the foundational continuum than the quantum field just discussed, which may be regarded as a mid-way bridge between the manifest and the unmanifest worlds. The constituent waves which fill the Cosmic Field are the guiding fields of influence which supply the archetypal forms behind the emergence of 'matter' on all levels of evolution. But in any case, all three conceptions (Einstein's unified field, quantum electrodynamics, and our own Cosmic Field) have at least one thing in common, — *the rejection of the fantastic fiction of an empty and uncreative space as the passive receptacle into which matter is put*, a theory which has made impossible a satisfactory philosophy of nature. However, given the notion of the Cosmic Field, it becomes possible to work out a decent theory, even to the point of solving the problem of the 'uniformity of nature.'

XV. The Cosmological Principle and Uniformity

As already noted, John Stuart Mill argued in his treatise, *A System of Logic*, that the principles of the 'uniformity of nature' and the 'law of universal causation' are the foundation of inductive reasoning. Among the several attempts at providing a justification for this principle, one of the least controversial is that advanced by J. N. Keynes in his *Treatise on Probability*, where he argues that positions in space and time are irrelevant to generalizations which have no reference in themselves to any particular spatio-temporal relations.

Some writers have attempted to dispense with this principle of uniformity as being unnecessary or even meaningless. But it seems to me that it is still useful, at least as a descriptive statement. For example, as previously noted, there is reason to believe that all hydrogen atoms are alike, and this is a type of 'uniformity.' Again, the proposition in Einstein's relativity theory termed the *principle of covariance*, namely, that the general laws of physics are expressible in a form which is independent of the frame of reference (choice of space-time coördinates) is certainly another form of the uniformity of nature concept. The most recent form of this supposed uniformity, proposed by Milne, is called the *perfect cosmological principle*, and asserts that the view of the universe obtained from one point of view (a spiral nebula, for example) is the same as the view from any other. This postulate of the temporal stability of the structure of the universe has become an integral part of the steady-state universe. It should therefore reappear in our own cyclic-creative universe, as indeed it does, except that, for us, uniformity reflects the eternality of archetypal forms in the unmanifest world of the Cosmic Field. These archetypal patterns are exemplified in the manifest world of physics, — for example, the spiral structures of energy-knots in space-time. This is what I mean by the statement that the infinite Cosmic Field is 'outside' all space and time coördinates, — that is, its laws (archetypal forms) are the same in all finite systems.

This principle that the universe would look the same no matter where we happened to be was stated in an earlier century by Bruno when he insisted that "the eye being placed in any part of the universe, the appearance would be still all one as unto us here." For Bruno, as for Bondi and Hoyle, this implies that there must be an infinity of worlds. But the 'new cosmology' permits these worlds to rush off into the infinite depths of space, while new matter is created to replenish the matter that disappears from sight, — and this was no part of the cosmology of Bruno. Bruno, presumably, would not object to 'creation,' *provided no special act of God were required for this.* Unfortunately, the Bondi-Hoyle cosmology simply has no theory about this. Here our own theory has the advantage.

This all hangs together in our view. As part of our hesitation in accepting the 'expanding universe' interpretation of the 'red shift' of the spectral lines, we must necessarily question the theory of 'creation' and 'expansion' as developed by Hoyle, even when we agree with him that the universe is infinite spatially.[8] If, as Hoyle believes, the distant nebulae recede into the depths of space at a relative velocity equal to (or even faster than) the speed of light (without contradicting relativity theory), it follows that the other distant parts of the universe cannot interact with ours, since no reciprocal *causal influence* can be transmitted faster than the velocity of light. *In such a view there can be no cosmic causality*, and so one must hold that matter is not created out of the field of energy (as I hold), but out of nothing! The creation of matter may be responsible for the pressure toward expansion (as Hoyle believes), but the expansion taking place in the non-observable parts of the universe can have no connection with the creation of matter in our observable part of the infinite universe. This seems philosophically very unsatisfactory. The only sensible cosmology seems to be the modernized form of Bruno's cosmology: all parts of the universe look the same from any point of view, and the overall equilibrium is maintained by an information system wherein each part 'knows' what is going on in every other part of that cosmos. This, if true, confirms the mind-matter monism of Bruno, so that our cosmology is panpsychic as well as pantheistic.

On our cyclic-creative theory 'cosmic time' does not have a unique or unidirectional arrow, even though living organisms and the ladder of emergent evolution do exhibit an irreversible arrow. There is no inconsistency here. Time in the sense of an irreversible series of instants, having a beginning and an end in some finite manifest history, simply does not apply to the infinite cosmos as a whole. It may be that the origin of the experience of duration lies in the motion of the human organism relative to the field-plenum. As I once proposed, — even before Eddington and Jeans, — in the brain there is a one-way increase of entropy to which our consciousness responds; thus the rate of time lapse could be a function of body temperature (as Hudson Hoagland has demonstrated), and this, in turn, could be a kind of physiological 'modulation' superposed on the underlying flow relative to a medium which resembles the *Aether* of the Stoics, suitably refashioned into the Cosmic Field.

Our idea about these matters was well stated by Bruno in his book, *The Infinite Universe and its Worlds*. Here Bruno presents the following debate:

> *Elpino:* How is it possible that the universe be infinite?
> *Filoteo:* How is it possible that the universe be finite?
> *Elpino:* Do you mean that one can prove this infinity?
> *Filoteo:* Do you mean that one can prove this finitude?
> *Elpino:* What an extravagance of fantasy!
> *Filoteo:* On the contrary, how narrow your view!

While Bruno does not tell us this, one suspects that Elpino represents the Aristotelian viewpoint, while Filoteo might very well be a pseudonym for Bruno himself. Certainly he (Filoteo) is representing Bruno's point of view.

XVI. Summary: The Infinite and Eternal Cosmos

Looking back over the path we have traveled, it may appear that we have wandered far afield in our search for unifying principles. And yet such is not the case. There is a deep kinship between stellar dynamics and atomic behavior; between Fermat's principle of optics and Hamilton's principle of dynamics; between the radiation paths of optics and the trajectories of particles; between wave fronts of radiation and the surfaces of constant action of mechanics. All this is known to students familiar with the wave-particle nature of light. The problem, — for us, — on the formal side is simply to formulate a mathematical theory of the hyper-dimensional vector spaces with Hamiltonian operators that is consonant with our concept of emergent dimensionality.

In a general way we have committed ourselves to the thesis that the most hopeful promise of a solution resides in the line of thought opened up by de Broglie. Some informed readers may object, pointing out that de Broglie later abandoned his 1927 synthesis. But in reply, I would observe that de Broglie has recently returned to his earlier formulation. The reasons why the original theory seemed faulty, and the explanation of its revival in a modified form, are given in Chapter 10 of de Broglie's recent book, *The Revolution in Physics* (New York, 1953). Here the 4-field is restored as the agent guiding the particles.

All this has been a part of our survey of atomic theory. Now let us reverse our microscope and turn it into a telescope (so to speak), and summarize the results achieved through our contemplation of the wider cosmos, — the hierarchy of galaxies.

As part of the total enterprise of the integration of knowledge we have surveyed the thought-patterns in the field of cosmology. We have examined the most recent cosmogonic speculations as they are set forth in the hypotheses of Lemaitre,[9] Gamow,[10] Hoyle,[11] and others. After proper consideration, we have inclined toward the conclusion that *the 'expanding universe' interpretation, at least when this 'big bang' theory is associated with the revamped form of the special creation theory of Genesis, cannot be considered as philosophically sound*, and is therefore not to be regarded as a permanent feature of enduring scientific thought. All things considered, it still seems that the most satisfactory cosmology is that provided by the modernized form of the Pantheism of Giordano Bruno, — the cyclic-creative universe, infinite in space and without origin in time, with no 'beginning' or 'end' of either.

Difficult though the conception of the infinite may be (thinking here of Brouwer's criticisms of the completed infinite), our foregoing revised form of Bruno's cosmology receives a measure of support from E. Finlay-Freundlich's monograph on *Cosmology*.[12] Here Professor Finlay-Freundlich refers (p. 2) to "Lambert's idea of a hierarchic structure of the universe." This turns out to be the theory that matter is so distributed in space that stars combine to form galaxies, galaxies combine to form super-galaxies; and so on. Thus from each rank on the hierarchic ladder we can step to the rank of the next higher order, and so forth to infinity. This type of cosmology has not yet found its place in modern theory; but the idea of an infinite amount of matter in an infinite space could, under suitable restriction, satisfy the requirement of finite values of the gravitational forces in each volume element of an infinite space. Such a universe would be 'static' in the sense that no large-scale changes in the distribution of matter and no unduly high velocities would occur. A hierarchical universe also satisfies the 'cosmological principle' in the sense that, apart from local irregularities, the cosmos presents the same aspect from any place at any time.

An interesting feature of Finlay-Freundlich's presentation is the argument (p. 23) that the universe with a hierarchical structure is an 'expanding' universe, that is, the transition to a space of infinite volume has to be done by exhausting an infinite sequence of concentric shells, all centered around the observer's place. This follows from the Doppler interpretation of the 'red shift,' it is asserted. I see no reason why the present cyclic-creative universe formulation cannot accept the hierarchical cosmology, provided experimental evidence is favorable to it. According to Hubble, there is no observational evidence of more than one system of the second order, but this may be due to an observational limitation. It could be that a modernized Bruno cosmology required the hierarchical structure. At this point I can do no better than quote Bruno's words:

> "It has seemed to me unworthy of the divine goodness and power to create a finite world, when able to produce beside it another and others infinite; so that I have declared that there are endless particular worlds similar to this of the earth; with Pythagoras I regard it as a star, and similar to it are the moon, the planets and other stars, which are infinite in number, and all these bodies are worlds."

Only a slight modification is required to bring Bruno's statement into line with the architectonic of the hierarchical universe.

The picture, therefore, we secure as a final reward for all this far-ranging speculation is as follows: the cosmos as the endless hierarchy of sub-systems is open to plus and minus infinity, at least in its spatial aspects. With respect to time, our theory states that the idea of time does not apply to the 'cosmos as a whole'; that is, the cosmos has no origin or end in time, though it is always true that this or that particular system (solar system, galaxy, etc.) does have a temporal origin in this or that region of space. This may be represented as follows:

COSMOS : INFINITE — ETERNAL

$$+\infty$$

$$\text{Super-galaxy}_1 = \int \begin{array}{l} {}_{t_2}\text{Galaxy}_1 \int_{t_1}^{t_2} (\text{matter, labor, imagination}) \\ {}_{t_2}\text{Galaxy}_2 \int_{t_1}^{t_2} (\text{matter, labor, imagination}) \\ {}_{t_1}\text{etc.} \end{array}$$

$$\text{Super-galaxy}_{11} = \int \begin{array}{l} {}_{t_2}\text{Galaxy}_1 \int_{t_1}^{t_2} (\text{matter, labor, imagination}) \\ {}_{t_2}\text{Galaxy}_2 \int_{t}^{t_2} (\text{matter, labor, imagination}) \\ {}_{t_1}\text{etc.} \end{array}$$

$$-\infty \quad \text{etc.}$$

From this it is clear that when we speak of the birth or death of a universe, we refer to the precipitation of particles (atoms such as hydrogen) into some particular finite universe (nebula). But this still leaves us with a bottomless mystery: why is there a cosmos at all? This is the one question to which there is no answer. Like Margaret Fuller, we must accept the universe! Whether this is easy or difficult depends upon one's philosophy or religion. But like it or not, the universe is here to stay. Aside from the 'goodness' or the 'badness' of human life here on earth, if one but lifts up his eyes to the stars at night, surely he will find some sympathy for the thoughts and feelings of Pascal as set forth in the following eloquent passage:

> "Let man then contemplate the whole of nature in her full and grand mystery, and then turn his vision from the low objects which surround him. Let him gaze on that brilliant light, set like an eternal lamp to illumine the universe; let the earth appear to him a point in comparison, with the vast circle described by the sun, and let him wonder at the fact that this vast circle is itself but a very fine point in comparison with that described by the stars in their revolution round

the firmament. But if our view be arrested there let our imagination pass beyond it; it will sooner exhaust the power of conception than nature in supplying material for conception. The whole visible world is only an imperceptible atom in the ample bosom of nature. No idea approaches it. We may enlarge our conceptions beyond all imaginable space; we can only produce atoms in comparison with the reality of things. It is an infinite sphere, the center of which is everywhere, the circumference nowhere."

This is a moving passage. With slight modifications, the last sentence of Pascal's description would provide a fair picture of one function of God in a pantheistic universe: the Cosmic Imagination quite possibly could be thought of as an Infinite Lens "the center of which is everywhere, the circumference nowhere."

At this point, — if the question has not already come up, — the reader is likely to ask whether, in the pantheism here outlined, we are not being served up the theory of Sir James H. Jeans that the Supreme Architect of the Universe is a mathematician. The reply is that if this, in the mind of the reader, is interpreted to mean Berkeleyan idealism, — that the whole physical world is but a set of ideas in the mind of God, — then this certainly is not a correct description of the foregoing variety of pantheism. It is true that Bishop Berkeley, far ahead of the plodding physicists of his day, bored his way through inert Newtonian matter to something like the sub-material continuum of Einstein's unified field theory. It is also true that when the physicists today interpret 'particles' in terms of field-theory, informing us that 'matter is non-matter in motion,' this confirms Berkeley's thesis in a sense. But the Cosmic Field as we conceive it is inseparably welded to the universe of 'matter' which is the body of Divinity, — the 'word made flesh,' if you wish. It is clear, therefore, that our Cosmic humanism is not Berkeleyan idealism by any stretch of the imagination, — cosmic or human, — since the manifest universe is as real as the unmanifest universe.

This conception, imperfect as it must be, has a kind of symmetry about it that is philosophically satisfying. According to present ideas, the energy of matter comes from an unknown source and proceeds into space toward an equally unknown destiny. But if the *source* and the *sink* of energy can be tied together in the manner indicated, we have an explanation of where the atoms get their energy and why the universe has not run down long ago. Thus, in the cyclic-creative cosmology (to reiterate), the circle of the passage of energy is from the undifferentiated source in the field-plenum, through the Cosmic Lens into the manifest physical world, and then on up the evolutionary ladder from subatomic particles to mankind. At the end of the line there is a feed-back into the ocean of the Cosmic Field, which completes the process and begins the cycle anew. All this is on our level of reality. What happens on the higher levels, the levels of meta-galaxies, I have no way of knowing.[13] One world at a time is enough.

FOOTNOTES CHAPTER X

[1]On this point see the article, "Turbulence in Space," by George Gamow, *Scientific American*, Vol. 186, 1952, 22-26.

[2]Cf. "Electricity In Space," by Hannes Alfvén, *Scientific American*, Vol. 186, 1952, 26-29.

[3]Cf. "Interstellar Polarization, Galactic Magnetic Fields, and Ferromagnetism," by Lyman Spitzer, Jr., and John W. Tukey, *Science*, Vol. 109, 1949, 461-462.

[4]Cf. "Fundamental Particles," by H. S. Massey, *Science Progress*, Vol. 40, 1952. 193ff.

[5]Cf. "Quantum Electrodynamics," by F. J. Dyson, *Physics Today*, Vol. 9, 1952, 6-10.

[6]For a description of this experiment, see "Radio Waves and Matter," by Harry M. Davis, *Scientific American*, September, 1948 (Vol. 179).

[7]See the valuable article, "Space, Field, and Ether in Contemporary Physics," by Alexander W. Stern, *Science*, Vol. 116, 1952, 493-496.

[8]It is important to keep in mind that those who believe in the expanding universe (and that includes Lemaître, Gamow, Einstein, Eddington, Shapley, *et al.*) rest their case in considerable measure on the famous red shift, or Doppler effect, which refers to the shift of the spectral lines (coming from the extra-galactic nebulae) toward the red end of the spectrum. This is the Hubble interpretation (recession formula). My own theory inclines to the view that the alleged Doppler effect *may* be due to the presence of inter-galactic matter (possibly invisible atomic hydrogen, as Dr. T. Weiner proposed to me), roughly proportional in amount to the distance away from us, which would cause the shift of the spectral lines. However, it is possible to believe in the expanding universe and still hold that the universe is infinite (unlimited) in size.

[9]Cf. *The Primeval Atom*, by Georges Lemaître, New York, 1950

[10]Cf. *The Creation of the Universe*, by George Gamow, New York, 1952.

[11]Cf. *The Nature of the Universe*, by Fred Hoyle, New York, 1951.

[12]Appearing in the series of the *International Encyclopedia of Unified Science*, University of Chicago Press, 1951.

[13]Formerly there seemed to be a fatal objection to an infinite universe, in connection with "Olber's paradox," to the effect that in a universe filled to infinity with stars the sky should be ablaze with an infinite amount of light. But C. V. L. Charlier showed that there is a way out of the difficulty, provided one has a proper idea of the distribution of galaxies per unit volume of space. On this matter see the article, "The Supergalaxy," by Gerard de Vaucouleurs, *Scientific American*, July, 1954, Vol. 191.

11

THE SOCIAL BASIS OF CONCEPTUAL INTEGRATION

"The result of conventional science teaching has not been a critically minded type of scientist, but just the opposite. The longing for the integration of knowledge is very deeply rooted in the human mind. If it is not cultivated by the science teacher, it will look for other outlets. The thirsty student takes his spiritual drink where it is offered to him."
— Philipp Frank, *Modern Science and its Philosophy*

I. Integration and Human Institutions

The theme of the present study is synthesis. We are concerned with the unification of knowledge, with conceptual integration as a basis for social synthesis. The unity we are seeking in this investigation is subjective and objective, psychological and social, — the goal of harmonious inner life and unified social operations.

Obviously the process of integration as it takes place in the individual is conditioned by two sets of circumstances: (a) the psychological constitution of the human person, and (b) the social matrix within which the individual grows to maturity. We have elsewhere[1] touched upon the ways in which personality traits limit man's capacities for having and interpreting experiences. In the present chapter we are concerned primarily with the cultural framework within which conceptual integration must occur.

Throughout the history of the Western World, it has been the function of the institutions of higher learning to formulate and carry out the all-important work of the integration of knowledge. But now, in our contemporary world of conflicts and cross currents, it is clear that these institutions are falling far short of their goals. It is abundantly evident that the results of their efforts are far from satisfactory, especially in the fields of the social sciences, the humanities, and kindred fields. Here confusion about methods, data, and purpose is very conspicuous. And yet it is equally certain that until we have a socially recognized body of individuals who can compare their insights and arrive at coherent formulations of their 'combined operations,' we shall continue to have a multiplicity of interpretations of these partial visions of intellectual synthesis and cultural integration.

This failure to attain the goal of the integration of knowledge is due to a number of factors. Among such, we find the existing limitations of human nature, the sheer complexities of the problems, and perhaps also the fact that the world is still evolving in someways: for example, there is the possibility that the fundamental constants of physics, the mass of the electron, the diameter of the universe, the velocity of light, and so on, are changing. If this is so, the synthesis of knowledge into systematic unity is doubly difficult, because nature won't stand still long enough to allow us to investigate her sufficiently.

The question posed by Robert Lynd's book, *Knowledge for What?*, is still unanswered. It will remain unanswered as long as our theories are inconsistent and our knowledge incomplete. All our efforts at unified knowledge will fall short of the goal, and society will remain confused, while our systems of belief are fragmentary and fail to aggregate to a formal whole.

If, however, the problems seem difficult, we can at least take comfort in the reflection that we understand better the conditions for the successful prosecution of the task. It seems evident that there are two conditions that must be satisfied if we are to achieve the progressive unification of knowledge: that is, in the first place, we need a *common method of procedure*, and secondly, we need *social institutions*, staffed by trained personnel, capable of using these methods in integrating the materials secured through the use of these techniques.

Let us first consider this problem of methodology.

II. Methods of Integration

There is a widely held belief that at least for the integration of the results of scientific advance there is one and only one method of procedure to be employed in building up bodies of knowledge and synthesizing the results in these specialized fields into a comprehensive theory of nature and of man's place and possibilities in the wider universe.

The recommended method is, of course, what is known as the *scientific method.* But when one looks at the striking fact of confusion in our world, the conclusion is suggested that the intellectual and social disorganization we face is due to one or the other (or a combination of both) of the following possibilities: (a) scientific method *is* adequate wherever it is used, but it has not been used long enough in the social field to achieve an integration of knowledge, or (b) scientific method is *not* adequate for all areas of human life, and confusion results from the fact that scientific method is not sufficient and we have not yet discovered any satisfactory substitute for it.

Before we can attain clear views on these matters, we shall have to decide whether scientific method as the social scientists understand it (and in so far as there is a unity of opinions) coincides with scientific method as the physical scientists interpret it. One problem here, of course, is whether, for example, psychology and sociology must necessarily employ the techniques and data of introspection (i.e., rely upon inner experience), and, if so, whether the intrusion of these subjective elements adds something in the social sciences which is over and above the methods and data of the physical sciences.

My own view of this problem is that physics and psychology both start with what is consciously experienced: physics does not *eliminate* the human observer but only standardizes the rôle of the observer. If this is so, scientific method is pretty much the same regardless of the field in which it is employed. It would also be adequate to the job in all fields where it is utilized. To show that this is so, let us turn our attention to the possibility (our second alternative) that scientific method may not be adequate for all areas where human beings respond in various ways. If it turns out that scientific method is not adequate to settle all questions by a proper interpretation of all phenomena, it may well be that our social confusion arises out of this lack of a commonly acceptable method for determining what views human beings should hold on various controversial questions.

I have in mind here particularly the fields of religion, politics, and economics, fields wherein human beings make judgments, express views, advocate opinions, — fields wherein decisions, put into practice, frequently result in political conflicts, religious wars, racial tensions, and the like. Should beliefs in these fields of religion, art, politics, and the rest, be submitted to the tests of logic and right reasoning? Can such beliefs be validated by science, or are they extra-logical in nature? Are we here dealing with emotional attitudes, esthetic interests, and other extra-scientific reactions which lie, at least in part, outside the boundaries of reason and logic?

III. "Scientific Method" as the Guide to Life

To relieve this discussion of some of its abstractness, let us consider the views of one investigator, Karl Pearson, — scientist, statistician, geneticist, and eugenist. His classic, *The Grammar of Science* (especially Chapter II, dealing with the "Canons of Legitimate Inference"), points out that:

> "while logically trained minds which are able to draw inferences frequently neglect to do so, the illogically trained, on the other hand, unfortunately devote a large part of their ill-trained energies to the production of every kind of cobweb of rash inferences; and this with such rapidity that the logical broom fails to keep pace with their activity."

Speaking as a 'scientist,' Pearson then gives us some examples of such fallacious inferences, and observes that they are:

> "... screened beneath an unlimited flow of words, and not thus exhibited in their naked obscurity. When we recognize how widely inferences of this character affect our conduct in life, and yet grasp how unstable must be the basis of such conduct, how liable to be shaken to the foundations by the first stout logical breeze, then we understand how honest doubt is far healthier for the community, is more social, than unthinking inference, light-hearted over-ready belief."

Professor Pearson states the *canons of legitimate inference*, and among them are these two:

I. Where it is impossible to apply man's reason, that is to criticize and investigate at all, there it is not only unprofitable but anti-social to believe. To believe in a sphere where we cannot reason is anti-social, for it is a matter of common experience that such beliefs prejudice action in spheres where we can reason.

II. We may infer what we cannot verify by direct sense-impression only when the inference is from things known to unknown things of the like nature in similar surroundings.

One problem which the canons of Pearson bring into focus is the problem of the place of esthetic, religious, and philosophical judgments in human life. I believe it is clear that the implication of Pearson's view toward religion is one of disapproval. Without defending organized religion, I believe we may say that his general view greatly over-simplifies life situations. Pearson fails to recognize that there is an area wherein beliefs are only partly rational (e.g., politics, economics, the arts), and yet where it is sometimes necessary to act as if we knew the answers when in fact the only decision we can make comes from the 'heart' or 'conscience', — a thalamic response, as general semantics says. Bertrand Russell recognizes this in one way when he affirms that the field of values lies outside the scope of science. But Russell does not have the right answer, for he attributes a rationality to science which presupposes an elementalistic psychology of human nature. Small wonder that Russell insists upon a separation of 'facts' and 'values.'

Both Pearson and Russell assume a division of functions which is old-fashioned 'faculty' psychology. Moreover, this view ignores the doctrine of those philosophers who believe in what may be termed *non-propositional truth.* According to this view, a great drama or poem, a profound religious experience, a moving symphony, — these may express something about human life which is quite as significant as the propositions of physics or astronomy, and if the meaning of this experience is communicable in some manner, then these experiences as examples of human creativity may reveal something about man, and therefore something about the universe in which man lives, which places limitations upon the all-sufficiency of scientific method *when conceived narrowly and then employed as the sole method of arriving at an understanding of man and nature.*

Pearson's theory that we should not hold beliefs in those areas where knowledge does not exist because this prejudices action in fields where knowledge is available, sets up the following division: (a) *fields where knowledge exists, — the sciences*; and (b) *fields where knowledge does not exist, — religion, poetry, metaphysics.* Our own view is that it is not correct to say that there are two distinct fields; we ought not set up such a sharp dichotomy, for the distinction is a matter of degree. We also criticize Pearson for assigning a function to science on the assumption that man should be 'logical' and guide his actions exclusively by the canons of scientific method, when in fact the organism-as-a-whole functions in life-situations in a manner which is not in accordance with Pearson's elementalistic theory of human nature.

The view I here present is that man has potentially many dimensions to his nature, and to the extent that he permits some of these dimensions ('capacities') to remain dormant he is only partially human. This results in what we term *fragmented living*, as compared with *total living*. Let us expand this idea.

IV. The Causes of Fragmentation

This situation in which men content themselves with being only partially human is a result of a number of causes. One of the most obvious conditioning factors is social in nature. We live in a world where specialization of function (division of labor) is already well established, so that our activities from infancy on are channeled into narrow compartments where each of us is more or less an 'expert' trained along given lines. Thus, broadly speaking, there are scientists whose business it is to carry on research, using their reasoning powers as they think out their problems; artists and poets whose business it is to cultivate man's aesthetic life and provide emotional satisfactions for mankind; clergymen, lawyers, teachers, and the like, whose business it is to supervise the ethical aspects of our society, and so on.

If there is anything that a scientific humanism aspires to, it is for a synthesis of the attitudes represented by the fields of science, religion, and the arts. Planetism is the enemy of elementalism. Planetary humanism is opposed to the harmful cultural atomism and psychic fragmentation which elementalism encourages. The vicious consequences of atomism are indicated by John Dewey in his statement: "There is no more significant question before the world than this question of the possibility and method of reconciling the attitudes of practical science and contemplative aesthetic experience."

In addition to the factor of specialization of social functions, which parallels the complexity of social structures in evolving societies, one other factor shares responsibility for the emergence of elementalism, namely: *a false theory of human nature*· The widening breaches that separate social classes — brainy scientists, emotive artists, sentimental clergymen, and the like, — merely reflect the psychic schisms in human nature: emotion vs. intellect, reason vs. the passions, imagination vs. memory, contemplation vs. overt behavior, etc., etc. All this is a heritage of a 'faculty psychology' which is now obsolete.

Planetary humanism insists that this manner of fragmenting human nature, and the correlative ways of building a society, are passé and must go. In previous studies it was suggested that the false dichotomy of a sterile intellectualism and an irrational emotionalism which runs through much of modern life, separating religion and politics from the life of reason and excluding science from the fields of art, religion, and public administration, is the unfortunate but inevitable consequence of elementalistic analysis and the social atomism which stem from it.

Up to the present, however, this discussion has been carried on in rather general terms. No procedure for harmonizing science with the aesthetic life in music, poetry, and the other fine arts has been proposed. Accordingly, we need to suggest in more detail how the aesthetic and the scientific dimensions of human existence may be brought into conjugate relations.

V. Elementalism in Language and in Culture

We begin by referring to the well-known work of Ogden and Richards, *The Meaning of Meaning*, where the several functions of language *as they see them* are presented. The elementalistic theory of psychic atoms, which provides the theoretical underpinning of much of our cultural fragmentation, is illustrated in the Ogden-Richards analysis of the functions of language in terms of the types of purposes that language serves, namely, the emotive function and the cognitive function. The supposition that there is a dualism of an emotive use of language and an intellectualistic use of language is certainly Aristotelian in spirit and reflects a faculty psychology from which, as one might suppose, such enlightened individuals as Ogden and Richards should be free. That this addiction to dualism is not an isolated phenomenon, but is shared by other theorists, is indicated by the fact that the Logical Positivists also have succumbed to this traditional elementalistic type of analysis. Here is the dichotomy that is set up:

THE WAYS IN WHICH LANGUAGE IS EMPLOYED:

I. COGNITIVE USE OF LANGUAGE (*Reason*)	1. *Formal mode of speech.* (purely symbolic, e.g., mathematics) 2. *Material mode of speech.* (factual statements, e.g., physics)
II. EMOTIVE USE OF LANGUAGE (*Values*)	1. *Poetry and Religion.* 2. *Metaphysics and politics.*

This analysis of the two types of judgment, — judgments of the cognitive function and judgments of value, — is the consequence of a theory of human nature in which emotions can be isolated from the intellectual life. This mutual exclusiveness reflects the two-valued logic of the *either-or* antithesis: if a response (judgment) illustrates one of the alternatives, it excludes the other. As the Logical Positivists would put it, "there is no logic in ethics, and there is no ethics in logic." In our own analysis of the situation, we hold that these two types of response are not necessarily exclusive of each other; indeed, we go further and assert that there never is a response which is purely intellectual or purely emotional, — all responses in man are organismic, a fusion in which one, it may be the emotional, may prevail over the other, the rational; but a sound psychology will recognize that ideas are always emotionally conditioned and emotions in man are ideationally guided in some degree.

If we adopt the following symbolism, the several classes of response and types of judgment that are logically possible are four in number, as follows:

F = *judgments of fact* (intellectual)
V = *judgments of value* (emotional)

(1)	(2)	(3)	(4)
FV	FV′	F′V	F′V′

The interpretation of the four classes is this: (1) judgments that are both fact and value responses; (2) judgments of fact, but not of value; (3) judgments of value, but not of fact; (4) judgments neither of fact nor of value. While (4) is a logically possible class, it is really a *null class*, in the sense that it has no members (i.e., there are no human responses that lack both intellectual and emotional content); and (2) and (3) differ only in degree in which emotion and reason are present. Cases of the complete absence of emotion (pure judgments of fact) and the complete absence of ideation (pure judgments of value) represent limiting cases in which one or the other is reduced in amount to the vanishing point, i.e., they approach zero as a limit, without actually reaching it.

The oppositions which tradition sets up between these two types of activity and the interests they represent may be visualized in the following manner:

CONSEQUENCES OF ELEMENTALISM IN PSYCHOLOGY

Judgments of Fact	Judgments of Value
Intellect	Emotion
Reason	Feeling
Science	Aesthetics (Poetry, Art, etc.)
Ethical Neutrality	Morals (Ethics, Religion)
Logic as Scientific Methodology	Love, Hate, etc.
World As Is (Statements of Fact)	World As It Ought To Be (Emotional Valuations)

Let us examine in more detail the contrasts between science and the religious-aesthetic attitudes, as they appear in this dualism:

SCIENTIFIC ATTITUDES	RELIGIO-AESTHETIC ATTITUDES
1. *Function:* to understand.	1. Provide emotional outlets.
2. *Approach:* 'Artificial', — Scientific method is an austere discipline; it is contractive in effect.	2. 'Natural', — child-like and unrestrained. Expansive.
3. *Goal:* objectivity and impartiality.	3. Arouses emotions of beauty sublimity, awe, fear, etc.
4. *Point of view:* dehumanizes nature. Secondary qualities (colors, sounds, etc.) are regarded as subjective.	4. Anthropocentric: unifies the subjective and objective by humanizing nature through *empathy*.
5. *Type of analysis:* is *atomistic*, dealing with microscopic mechanisms as the most real things in the cosmos.	5. Is integrative, through the *phenomenological* and appreciative attitudes, responding to macroscopic wholes or unities.
6. *Tendency:* reads nature's 'meaning' backward, in terms of ultimate elements, and therefore 'mechanistic.'	6. Reads nature's meaning forward, and interprets nature in terms of the highest, and therefore 'idealistic.'
7. *Technique:* analysis of wholes into parts.	7. Appreciates wholes as totalities.
8. *General orientation:* 'Thinking' by way of piece-by-piece study, with limited objectives. Planal orientation.	8. Responding in terms of synthesis, with more inclusive apprehensions. Global orientation.

With this background, let us summarize our results up to this point. As previously noted, we live in a world where individually and socially we are coerced by atomism and fragmentation; we have the specializations of religion, art, science, and others, and these appear as the social analogues of volition, emotion, reason, and the like. Here is the psychological-cultural pattern:

I. What we call 'science' concentrates on the 'truth' aspects.
II. What we call 'religion' concentrates on the 'goodness' aspects.
III. What we call 'art' concentrates upon the 'beauty' aspects.
IV. Philosophy is the expression of the total self as it integrates these interests and activities in the individual and harmonizes their purposes and expressions in society.

Philosophy strives for unity. It is devoted to the complete synthesis of all the phases of man's nature. Unlike science (as now conceived), it cannot ignore art, emotion, and the esthetic; unlike religion, it cannot claim to have divine knowledge or revealed truth. That is to say, philosophy is multi-dimensional: it is the expression of the whole man, of total living, integrating the manifold interests of human nature. This global view which philosophy seeks to attain may be said to represent a *volume-element*, as opposed to the elementalistic or fragmented disciplines each of which represents a *line-element*. It is for this reason that we have suggested the term 'planetism' as a designation for the integral or global outlook.

If we apply these principles to some specific case where an individual is forced to deal with a situation as a whole, — for example, in the field of statesmanship, — we would point out that a great social leader must be able to function as a creative artist, one who is not merely concerned with the 'truth' of the atomic propositions of social science, but who aims at what we have called congruity, — a sort of general fitting in with the general pattern of a total situation. It is obvious that this admits of degrees; it is not two-valued but multi-valued. As it is stated in the author's passage in the volume on *Planetary Democracy* (page 170), this is the way the theory works:

"The test and measure of congruity must be more complex than plain yes or no compatibility or logical consistency; it must embrace all ethical and esthetic principles. Further, it must take into account the entire situation, — be thoroughly organismic. Here is how it would operate: Suppose a playwright or a novelist is working out the actions of one of his characters: he must make certain

> that such actions are congruous, not only with the character already depicted, but with the character in the particular surroundings in which he then is, taking into account the influences and reactions of the other characters in the drama. Congruity must be with the whole picture or pattern. The action which the character performs must be psychologically, ethically, and esthetically congruous. Here the rules of classic logic are inappropriate, and the new formulation must be more complex and flexible than traditional logic permits.
>
> The new application of this formulation will be in the production of art combined with science. The successful practitioner will require the possession of a large humanity, a Shakespeare, combined with a Newton wielding his instrument. Congruity thus appears as a kind of non-propositional 'truth' revealing the extra-logical 'meaning' of life, of human aspiration and the progress of civilization."

This, I believe, is the sense in which planetism would recognize and sanction 'pragmatism' in politics.

One way of trying to comprehend the biological alchemy whereby judgments of fact are harmonized with value-judgments is provided by the doctrine advocated by Mary Everest Boole, that "we *feel* as our ancestors *thought;* as we *think* so will our descendants *feel.*" This formulation, translated into biological terms, would mean that processes that started out on the cortical level are pushed down into the thalamic level, or even lower into the sub-cortical levels. If we think today as our descendants will feel, this means that judgments of fact, which are now the products of intellectual activities, will end up as apprehensions of value, — feeling-attitudes. But in all cases, judgments of value and judgments of fact will be specialized phases of an organism-as-a-whole process. This head-heart synthesis, or cortico-thalamic integration, should express the human search for wholeness.

In passing, it may be noted that on this point of the interaction of reason and emotion the present view seems to exhibit an advantage when compared with Professor F. S. C. Northrop's dualism of the *theoretic* and *esthetic* components of consciousness. One weakness in Professor Northrop's philosophy is that he leaves us with an irreducible dichotomy which is hardly any improvement over the traditional dualism of mind and matter. In the present view ideas get transmuted into feelings by the same biological alchemy which underlies the fixation of Jung's 'archetypal memories' as a kind of racial inheritance. What this alchemy is we have tried to surmise in our previous surveys of this problem in *The Promise of Scientific Humanism* (Chapter XIV) and *Planetary Democracy* (page 196).

That the 'hunger for wholeness,' as it may be called, is an important item in the motivation of scientific research is one of the fundamentals of a scientific humanism, and to show why this is so, and then to develop the implications of this discovery, it will be necessary to examine the social bases of scientific concepts. This we shall reconsider in a moment. In the mean time, however, let us first retrace our steps a bit and examine a related problem: the place of "intuition" in science.

VI. Science and Intuition

It should be evident that we agree wholeheartedly with Pearson's thesis that the goal of science is the complete understanding of the universe. But the universe in its totality includes living systems and conscious human beings, and science must also explain the facts of life and mind if it is to be complete.

To explain organisms or living systems, Bergson has argued with much persuasiveness that we need something more than intellectual analysis, i.e., breaking protoplasmic systems up into their constituent parts. We agree with Bergson that empathy ('einfühlung') is required, — we need a kind of sympathy or 'feeling with' what we are studying. This may well be akin to the esthetic feeling by means of which one appreciates and enjoys ('understands') the music of a symphony as played by the orchestra. But this 'understanding' need not be anti-intellectual: one can appreciate or apprehend the meaning of a whole (a gestalt) without abandoning reason and intelligence. The striving of a living organism to satisfy a desire (urge) can be understood by another living system if he uses insight. Yet this does not commit us to Bergsonian vitalism. The intellect is not merely analytical; it also has the function of synthesis: putting the parts together to envisage it as a totality. Such synthesis is indeed the function of philosophy, as we have repeatedly emphasized. That is why, in the previous section, we protested against the elementalism which splits human activities into atomistic functions and faculties.

This apprehension of things as wholes is not a miraculous event; insight is not independent of previous experience, when one includes phylogenetic experience ('instincts') as well as ontogenetic experience ('intuition'). Moreover, the insight we are here discussing has its place even in the formulation of physical theory, no less than in the theorizing in biological science. Henri Poincaré, Einstein, and many others have utilized and justified intuition and recognized that in trying to create a unified picture of reality the scientist is like the artist who is trying to create a meaningful whole as his interpretation of experience.

It is true that these insights have their origin in the individual consciousness, and that they are socially validated by others later on. This fact calls attention to the possibility for distinguishing between the problem of the *origin of hypotheses* and the question of how to *test the validity* of hypotheses that may have been discovered in one way or another.

One might suppose that it would be possible to allow that ideas may come from any source or condition whatsoever, — delirious fever, alcoholic intoxication, drug addiction, religious experiences of a spirit world, or whatever non-rational source you wish, — provided only that the test of the *validity* of the idea is by way of rational justification: the hypothetico-deductive procedure of scientific method. But careful scrutiny of the implications of this idea reveals that it may commit one to a very dubious procedure: if you allow a person to believe that his ideas come from the gods or the spirit world, he is not likely to accept the social criterion of publicly verifiable knowledge as the test of the validity of what he puts forth. It may even be the command of the spirits that one defy the social test! In a word, only those persons who get their ideas from right sources (reasoning by analogy, insight, or mere summary induction) are likely to have the right intuitions and be willing to test them by the right methods. Traditionally dogmatism and the appeal to extra-rational sources of information seem to go together.

Intuition as a 'revealed truth' independent of human experience is too private, too variable, to provide the solid foundation for science and philosophy. The test of the truth of hypotheses must be by way of the hypothetico-deductive system which science has finally evolved.

In this connection, it is pertinent to say a word about the traditional, — and now obsolete, — distinction between the 'sciences' and the 'humanities.' This dualism is based on the idea that man's nature and behavior lie outside the natural sciences. The earlier German distinction between the natural sciences ('naturwissenschaften') and cultural or spiritual sciences ('geistenwissenschaften') no doubt reflects this supposed dualism. It is true that man's 'spiritual' nature does lie outside the concepts of traditional mechanistic behaviorism. But gestalt theory, organismic theory, and emergent evolution interpretations are entirely adequate to comprehend human nature. Accordingly, the warfare between the sciences and the humanities no longer has reason for being. *Man's nature is open to investigation by science, and the results, even when achieved through the use of introspective methods, can be put into the form of communicable, verifiable knowledge.* My life is private to me, and your life is private to you, but you and I can compare our experiences and arrive at mutually acceptable conclusions.

The possibility of success based on such a democratic method, — social agreement by competently trained investigators, — implies something about the nature of the human mind which still remains to be determined. With respect to the human organism, it implies that all minds on a comparable cultural level conform to a common structure; if a publicly sharable body of scientific knowledge is possible, this means that all scientists can attain the same insights and compare the implications of these insights. With respect to the wider universe of which the scientists are a part, it implies the existence of some common and universal base, or *harmonic base*, as it has been called, with some kind of sympathy or resonance between the human thinker and the substructure of the universe that man may grasp. But that is a profound issue which deserves separate consideration.

We have stressed the importance of getting rid of the confusion about the methods of science. We see no great gap between the physical and the social sciences, and the passage back and forth should not be blocked by high walls and 'spite fences.' We believe that the social sciences do not introduce any essentially new factors into their domain: all science starts with what is given to (or in) consciousness. For a physicist, this immediate experience may be a color spectrum with Fraunhofer lines, and his problem is to find what chemical elements produce such lines and analyze the structure of the atoms responsible for them. For a sociologist, his immediate data, given in direct experience, may be the segregation of peoples in geographical areas along lines of color bands similar to Fraunhofer lines. The physical spectrum and the social spectrum are both examples of what comes to us as immediate experience, and we then interpret experience in terms of atoms vibrating and human beings responding.

So far as method is concerned, the procedure in its broadest features is not different, for both groups of sciences, — physical and social, — try to think as objectively as they can about the materials they collect, classify, and organize.

What is important about the 'objectivity' of the scientist is not whether he does (or does not) exclude empathy, einfühlung, 'anthropomorphism,' or other elements of 'subjectivity,' but that he should not be guilty of wishful thinking and find 'facts' that are not there, or fail to see facts that are there. It does not matter if a physicist, perhaps in the spirit of Whitehead, is persuaded that atoms are organisms and therefore holds that atoms have souls, so long as in his thinking about the structure of atoms with souls he is able to follow the facts and get equations that enable him to describe the structure of these ensouled atoms and predict their behavior.

VII. The Social Basis of Scientific Concepts

In the preceding pages the problems of the 'integration of knowledge' and 'cultural integration' are discussed as if they were correlative subjects. Some critics will protest against this intimate association, arguing that the function of a university is the organization of knowledge, a purely intellectual affair that has no relation to programs of 'social reform.'

The view here presented is somewhat different. It is based on the conviction that the problem of the 'integration of knowledge' (i.e., the intellectual unification of the principles accumulated by the various natural sciences) can be solved only as we succeed in achieving a harmonization of the cultural interests in art, religion, politics, and the rest. This view maintains that there is a close parallelism between the confusion existing with respect to the fundamental concepts of science, physical and mathematical, and the confusion about the purposes and values characteristic of modern life, socially and morally.

Many social scientists have tried to work from the physical to the social sciences; but there are few scientists who have worked in the opposite direction, who have recognized the influence of cultural factors on the development of physical theories. In our own view we seek to go in both directions, from physics to sociology and from sociology to physics. In terms of our Temple of Knowledge, this means that there is an interaction between all levels, not only vertically between the highest and the lowest levels, but also on the second level through a cross-wise interaction between the special sciences which provide the pillars of the temple. Among the consequences which flow from this interdependence, we find the implications which we have already investigated under the term, 'geometry and ethics.'

This thesis will not be accepted without an argument. Since there are those who at first blush will reject it, how shall we strengthen the case? That the social sciences are decidedly 'framework conscious,' in the sense that they realize that they function within a social context, will not be contested. But how about the 'exact' sciences? Does our view imply that even in these fields integration is impossible without a corresponding cultural integration?

Those who would have us believe that the 'exact' sciences are not related to the culture-patterns of human society for their discovery of truths in their fields will find no support for this view in the ideas of Irwin Schrödinger (Nobel prize winner) who is in a position to speak for physics. Schrödinger quotes Zola as saying that a work of art is nature seen through the medium of a temperament, and then asks whether the same is not true of science.

Obviously such sciences as history, politics, economics, and others, are colored by the individual temperament of the researcher as well as by the collective temperament which constitutes the society of the time. But we have usually regarded the exact sciences as being free from the effects of this human temperament. We have thought of them as objective studies, more dependent upon laboratory equipment than on human nature and values. But in his volume, *Science and the Human Temperament*, Schrödinger does not share this view. He recalls the many thousands of experiments that might have been made but were never attempted. He points out that, the *selection* of experiments rests largely on human factors: first, the personal inclination of the researcher, his likes and dislikes of subjects, and so forth, and secondly, the social temperament, which controls laboratory policies and facilities, endowments, the time available for research in the particular society in which the scientist finds himself, and so on. These things depend upon the social enlightenment of the society.

To see that the state of science is a direct reflection of the social temperament, consider the relative discrepancies of the state of scientific research in China, India, Russia, the democracies, and the rest. The direction of research rests on human factors. Research in war time and in times of peace move in different directions, due to the urgencies of the occasions. So ultimately the direction, volume, and quality of scientific research are related to inner compulsions, aspirations, and the collective imaginations of human groups.

VIII. Archetypal Fields Supporting Integration

In order to provide further support for the thesis that science is not an independent, self-sufficient atom of activity unrelated to the cultural *milieu* in which it lives, we appeal also to the viewpoint set forth by Professor Tobias Dantzig in his book, *Aspects of Science.* This author thoughtfully observes that there exists a category of ideas which are indispensable to scientific thought, and yet they derive their validity from neither logic nor experience. As he says, they seem to antedate all experience; they reveal the existence of a sort of collective mind which seems to sublimate and mold the experience of the race along preconceived patterns. To this category of ideas (which Dantzig calls *articles of faith*) belong some of the most fundamental conceptions of science: the causal connection of events; the rational character of the cosmos; inductive inference; the infinite; simultaneity; space and duration; matter and motion. All these notions, when analyzed, turn out to be tinged with such collective predilections.

While Dantzig gives no explanation of these 'predilections,' his language suggests a familiarity with the ideas of Carl G. Jung, the Swiss psychiatrist. In any case, since we are already committed to a Pythagorean-Platonic metaphysics of archetypal forms, suitably modified into the modern notion of *guiding field*, Jung's theory of archetypes will be accepted as the psychologically correct theory of 'collective predisposition.' In the preceding chapters we have already laid the basis for this metaphysics, with the implications of Pantheism in formulating our epistemological theory.

It is in the spirit and tradition of Pythagoras and Plato that we put forth the conception of archetypal patterns as formative fields. In the type of cosmology here espoused, these guiding fields are found to operate on all levels: on the bottom-most rung of the ladder of emergent evolution in the transformation of undifferentiated cosmic energy into particles; on the biological level through the *individuation fields* which control embryogenesis; on the psychological level in the *cortical fields* associated with mental fields; and on the highest human level through the integrative fields responsible for social synthesis. *For us the Cosmic Imagination is that organizing field of influence in nature which puts parts together in their right times and places to make products.*[2] In the cosmos God is that immanent guiding field which makes the universe what it is. In man, creative imagination is the god-like quality which strives to give coherent form to that which was without form. The creation of a planetary civilization requires the collective imagination of mankind, and when men have created the electromagnetic society of the future, the quality of deity will have found its newest habitation. In this manner the philosophy of panpsychism makes possible the epistemological doctrine of isomorphism and the cosmological theory of emergent evolution.

IX. Pythagoreanism, Semantics, and Cybernetics

What, then, is the answer to the question: Does the applicability of the symbolism of mathematics to the formal structure of nature validate the Pythagorean-Platonic thesis that mind finds mathematics in nature because it was there to begin with? Our considered reply to this is that the structure and functioning of man's mind and his nervous system exemplify the laws, — the uniform modes of operation, — of a common patterning which is that of mathematical logic. The common base is the primordial experience of a temporal flow in a linear order — an insight-experience more fundamental than that of the classical Aristotelian 'laws of thought' or the Euclidian 'axioms' of geometry. It is this universal and primordial experience which provides the promise of an ultimately universal symbolism for planetary communication.

Of course, when one comes to consider a symbolism for universal communication, one must consider also the naturalness of the iconography or ideography. A 'natural' symbolism would, so far as possible, be based on innate psycho-biological dispositions to respond. Interestingly enough, the rejuvenation of the Pythagorean-Platonic explanation of the universe in terms of the 'regular solids' of Plato may turn out to be psychologically sound. I am thinking here of C. G. Jung's conception of *archetypes*, which in its philosophical implications certainly leads into a Platonic realism. If one could begin with mathematical archetypes, — squares, triangles, circles, spirals, and so forth, — as psychological *potentialities of ideas* which make possible a conceptual science of mathematics, one might then proceed upward into physics, biology, psychology, and sociology, by way of a natural symbolism for isomorphic structures on all levels. Jung's theories, however, are not generally accepted, especially in the United States where empirical trends are the fashion at the moment, so that this project remains only a preview of what might be undertaken.

One important illustration of the power of an invariant symbolism free from elementalistic frameworks is found in the equations of *spherical harmonics*, which provide the formal isomorphic structures expressed in such apparently diverse fields as the flow of heat, light, electricity, magnetism, stream lines, and conformal mapping. Here we find that spherical harmonics comes into its own, and, beyond the Fourier series, Legendre, Bessel, and hypergeometric functions find their applications.[3] When we finally learn to unite this level of investigation with the 'spiral action of time' in the non-linear functions of the nervous system and the mind which is its wholistic field manifestation, we will be well on the way to describing the very highest spatio-temporal organizations which the universe has thus far succeeded in creating out of the womb of generation.

The presence of non-linear circuits as well as linear circuits in the organism is recognized by Dr. McCulloch.[4] As he points out, in the linear circuits (feed-backs), when you *add* causes you *add* effects; but in the non-linear circuits, adding causes does not add effects. In the non-linear cases (such as relaxation oscillators) the mathematical description can sometimes be brought into the category of linear relationships by juggling the mathematics so as to find a new variable, say the logarithm of the variable, in terms of which the oscillation can be treated as sinusoidal (linear). As McCulloch points out, the 'logarithmic nature of mapping' makes it possible to find a layer of the cortex to give the required magnification or diminution of the cortical field to correspond to the figure of the visual (retinal) field.

But we must be careful not to misinterpret this. The fact that it is possible (sometimes by 'juggling the mathematics') to analyze the complex forms of brain waves into a number of different sine wave frequencies may lead to what Professor H. J. Jasper[5] has termed the 'Fourier fallacy', — the idea that all frequencies actually occur as periodic phenomena of cell groups within the brain. Apparently McCulloch is not entirely free from this fallacy, for it is only unwittingly that he recognizes the operational reality of gestalt principles. In our own language, such non-linear action-patterns are like *gestalten* with field-properties analogous to a public time, transposable across the parts.

X. Recapitulation: The Dimensional Nature of Thought-Systems

The history of Western culture is the story of recurring crises, of problems that arise, are faced, and overcome, — only to reappear in a transmuted form. Today we face our greatest crisis: the need for creating a unified philosophy to synthesize the findings of our separate sciences and integrate our discordant theories of nature and of human nature. In our own attempt to respond to this challenge, we have concluded that the new synthesis will arise out of the cephalization of a world organism which will thus provide the sensorium for an electromagnetic society.

This, as we view it, is the proper goal for a program of the unification of knowledge. Since the future grows out of the past, even when it transcends it, a study of the history of thought provides us with the memory basis for the planetary action-fields which will emerge to be transposable across the social whole. It is for this reason, — that is, to remember what has been achieved and use this as a basis for building the next level of synthesis, — that man must, from time to time, summarize and evaluate his advances, just as we, in passing from chapter to chapter, have sought to integrate what we may have attained. In order to gather together the materials for our summary, we must review the series of crises which culminated in our present 'moment of becoming' with its challenge and promise for the future.

As we have seen, our Western culture stems from the branches of ancient Greek civilization, and beyond that, back to the trunk of the earlier civilizations of the Egyptians, Babylonians, Israelites, Sumerians, and possibly even to Iranian and Hindu sources.

The beginnings of Western science (knowledge) come largely with Greek rationalism. But even here, at the outset, the rational-scientific and the mystical-religious impulses are still fused, and this is especially clear in the case of the ancient Pythagorean brotherhood, a religious-scientific sect which provided us with the first great synthesis, — the original example of what can be achieved when head and heart are linked together in harmony. Let us, therefore, note how the Pythagoreans faced up to the problem of synthesis, and then failed to measure up to the challenge of the first great crisis.

It is no exaggeration to say that much of Western philosophy, science, and even religion, is a flowering of Pythagorean mysticism. For example, all Occidental thought has had to orient itself toward the tradition of intuitive or self-evident truths ('axioms'), which reveal themselves in the eternal structure of geometrical forms and number patterns as these undergird the visible world and appear in the human mind as the absolute structure of mathematical order. This fact has been well stated by Bertrand Russell in his *History of Western Philosophy* (Chapter III), where he tells us that he can think of no man who has been as influential as Pythagoras in the sphere of thought, for what appears as Platonism (on the basis of which Aristotle and Euclid erected their own thought-structures), when analyzed, is found to be Pythagoreanism. The whole conception of an eternal world, revealed in the intellect but not to the senses, is derived from him. But for Pythagoras, Russell continues, Christians would not have thought of Christ as the Word; and when the Declaration of Independence states, "We hold these truths to be self-evident. . . ." it is modeling itself on Euclid. If, as Russell argues, the eighteenth century doctrine of "natural rights" is a search for Euclidian axioms in politics, then indeed the Pythagorean brotherhood was the true progenitor of the Western world's rational culture.

Following Pythagoras, we come upon Plato. Any adequate survey of the course of mathematics, philosophy, and religion, must certainly take into account the prodigious influence of Plato and Platonism. As is known, mathematics played a decisive role in Plato's philosophy and in his theory of education, as is evidenced by the inscription over the portal of Plato's Academy: "Let no one ignorant of geometry enter my door." In some quarters it is the custom to cast aspersions on Plato's theories in mathematics and regard them as mere curiosities. For example, in his book, *Mathematics for the Million*, Lancelot Hogben, after referring to the "queer freemasonry of the Pythagorean brotherhood," describes (p. 23) the *Timaeus* of Plato as a "fascinating anthology of the queer perversities to which the magic of symbolism could be pushed."

In fairness to Pythagoras and Plato — as we have pointed out — this derogatory attitude reflects in considerable measure the predilections of the contemporary empiricist. To one who is closer to Platonic realism, and therefore out of sympathy with the modern positivist, there is much in Plato that is still philosophically significant. This point can easily be made by reference to the *Platonic solids* which have played such a role in mathematics, science, and philosophy. Let us recapitulate this story.

The inherent value of this half-forgotten chapter in the history of mathematical philosophy can be emphasized by bringing into focus the statement of H. S. M. Coxeter, who, in his systematic work on the *Regular Polytopes*, quotes Sir D'Arcy W. Thompson, well-known author of *Growth and Form*, as remarking that Euclid never dreamed of writing an Elementary Geometry: what Euclid did was write an excellent account of the Five Regular or Platonic Solids. These solids have fascinated scholars since the time of Pythagoras; but since Plato discussed them in the *Timaeus*, they are usually referred to as the *Platonic solids*. The tetrahedron (a pyramid constructed upon a triangle), is the simplest of the five solids, the others being the octahedron, the cube, the icosahedron, and the dodecahedron.

Plato, it will be remembered, assigned a cosmological meaning to these geometrical figures. In his architectonic there was a correspondence between the four easily constructed solids and the four natural elements: fire, air, water, and earth. The fifth solid (the dodecahedron) was the shape that enveloped the whole universe.

Quite properly, this phase of Plato's cosmology, — the association of the four 'elements' with four of the regular solids, — has taken its place in the museum of obsolete scientific theories. Many will add that the remainder of this tantalizing doctrine also seems like 'queer perversity,' to use Hogben's words. But before completely dismissing Pythagorean-Platonic mysticism, it is well to observe that we have discovered, as Coxeter points out, that three of these solids, the tetrahedron, cube, and octahedron, are found in nature in the crystals of various substances, while the two more complicated regular solids cannot form crystals, but need the 'spark of life' (as Coxeter puts it) for their occurrence, being observed in the skeletons of small animals in the sea.

When one contemplates these facts, more fully set forth by the writer in the book on *Nature, Man, and God*, one wonders whether Plato's fundamental theory is so far-fetched. One wonders, too, about the appropriateness of those easy witticisms of the critics who ridicule Sir James Jeans's proposition that the Supreme Architect of the Universe is a mathematician. It is true that we can no longer believe in the Euclidian-Newtonian theory of space as the *Sensorium of God*, to use Newton's own words; but surely the discarding of the traditional framework of classical physics, the absolute space and time of Newtonian science, did not entirely wreck the Pythagorean-Platonic philosophy: certainly Sir James knew as much about 'relativity' physics as our modern positivists.

The world today still has to face this issue of the relation of mathematics to nature, and it may well be that philosophy will sometime find the Pythagorean thesis has been substantiated. This difficulty with the Pythagorean-Platonic synthesis (a difficulty compounded much later by the rise of the non-Euclidian relativity physics), and other problems, arose to plague the Greek thinkers. It was not alone the difficulties created by the failure of the Greeks to hit upon the concepts of *zero*, or other ingenious notions which Hindu and Arabian mathematics were to discover later, but rather the challenge to the Pythagorean thought-system presented by the discovery of irrational numbers and the idea of infinity which shook the foundations of Pythagorean mathematics. Thus started a controversy that still rages: is the concept of the mathematical *infinite* a safe concept, which will not lead the human mind into contradictions?

Our own solution to this problem has emerged as our investigation has proceeded. But before summarizing this statement of our view, we must recall briefly the intervening events, between Pythagoras and Brouwer, thus bringing up to date the unfolding story of mathematical progress.

As we portrayed it, the struggle of man is the search for freedom, the struggle against ancient limitations. In the field of mathematics, this is a struggle for breadth of outlook and conceptual generality. After the magnificent beginnings of the Greeks, came the slumbers of the middle ages, and it required the catalyst of Hindu-Arabian mathematics to stir the medieval world out of its somnambulance. Shortly after we come upon the superb developments associated with Descartes, Leibniz, Newton, and the other creators of modern civilization.

The invention of the calculus by Newton and Leibniz was a tremendous step forward. But here, precisely at this point, new problems were uncovered as old viewpoints were transcended. The calculus of Newton and Leibniz, while giving for the most part correct and important results, lacked a sound logical basis. The philosopher Berkeley argued that the calculus was so illogical that no mathematician could object to the doctrines of theology. Reference to one problem will suffice to indicate the nature of the issue. Division by zero is not permitted because the result is not a number, but in the usual form a number is introduced, which is not zero, and various manipulations are then made, in the end this number being called zero. This subtle kind of juggling may escape the unwary, but to the critical mind it came as a challenge to further research in the field.

Nothing much was done about the matter for over a century, but from 1800 on such men as Lagrange, Cauchy, and Weierstrass strove to put the calculus on a logical basis. This was done by reducing the problem to one of numbers without reference to geometrical notions. An accepted description of Differential Calculus is that it enables one to find the tangent to a curve at a given point, while the Integral Calculus gives the area under the curve. Because of these formulations and other factors, earlier mathematicians attempted to justify the calculus by geometrical arguments, and got nowhere. The solution, as presented by Weierstrass, dealt with the question of finding a number which would differ from a second number by an amount less than a third number.

The analytic geometry of Descartes had already shown that there is a connection between algebra and geometry, and it was due to the emphasis on the 'algebraic' side that further steps toward a solution became possible. It is not difficult to see a correspondence between ordinary numbers and the points on a straight line; then, near the beginning of the nineteenth century, several investigators discovered a connection between complex numbers (involving $\sqrt{-1}$) and the points on a plane, and thus by placing the foundations of the calculus on the properties of numbers, mathematicians were encouraged to base all mathematics on arithmetic. This was accomplished by Frege and Peano, who set up the necessary postulates and definitions and from these derived the contents of mathematics. This deductive apparatus is not the Aristotelian logic, but a more inclusive logic whose history we have already surveyed. As we have seen, George Boole invented an algebra of logic about 1850. The x's in this logic were interpreted as classes, and some of the rules seem odd when compared with the older logic (for example, $x^2 = x$), but the great merit is that it thus becomes possible to explicate more complicated inferences by the operations of the symbolic machinery.

The effect of all these developments has been to stimulate intellectual activity into energy-bursts of mental expansion. Some of the major experiments, such as the development of non-Euclidian geometrics, non-Aristotelian logics, and non-commutative algebras, were regarded as impossible in earlier ages. Thus these new departures are like mutations in biology: they go beyond the ancient forms to create innovations that transcend the old forms.

In a sense, therefore, thought-systems in mathematics and logic may be likened to the chromosomes of the soul: out of these genetic bases of past achievements comes the morphogenesis of new patterns, — the social institutions of mankind as the nerves and flesh and blood incarnation of a world organism. Like the serpents of the caduceus, the spiral thought-forms and the ever-evolving social institutions are intertwined as theory and practice weave together the embryogenesis of an electromagnetic society. Thus like the spiral arrangements of protein chains in the chromosomes of proliferating cells, the spiral forms of the planetary embryo follow a pattern of emergent evolution. This, then, gives us the theme of our summary.

XII. Mathematics as the Chromosomes of the Soul

When one looks carefully into the history of these successive thought-experiments of scientific thinking, one becomes increasingly conscious of the constant interaction between the 'theoretical' and the 'practical' aspects of the human adventure. In our preceding chapters this has repeatedly been noted, and some reiteration of the theme seems appropriate.

Just to have a place to start, let us go back to the notion of 'force': everyone knows that a force is a *directed* quantity, — therefore, as the physicist puts it, forces are *vectors* which must be added geometrically, as in the case of the simple 'parallelogram of forces' where the *resultant* represents the addition of vectors. 'Energy,' on the other hand, turned out to be a *scalar* quantity (that is, *not directed*), and therefore must be added arithmetically. Here the practical value for physics of the mathematical formulation was immediately evident. From the fact that a directed quantity like gravitational force, which in Newtonian mechanics is a vector-quantity that varies inversely as the *square* of the distance, can be treated as a scalar quantity that varies as the *first power* of the distance, Joseph Lagrange was able to handle problems where several gravitational masses interact (as in the solar system) by describing the influence of a body at any given point in space in terms of the 'gravitational potential,' a term earlier employed by Laplace.

This in itself was very gratifying, for it provided elegant solutions to many problems of physics; but other values soon accrued. Upon the foundations thus laid, the derivative concepts of 'scalar fields' and 'vector fields' as the media for the continuous distribution of some function throughout space (e.g., 'stress') could be based, and from there it was possible to go on to 'tensor fields' which represent stresses in the four-dimensional space-time of relativity theory. First developed by Ricci and Levi-Civita, tensor calculus turned out to be useful in Riemannian geometry, the non-Euclidian geometry that Einstein employed so effectively in the physical theory of relativity.

Between the earlier mathematico-physical explorations of Newton, Laplace, and Lagrange, and contemporary electrodynamic mathematics, comes one of the very greatest of the thought-explorations or mutations: the mental experiment carried through by Sir William Hamilton, the Irishman who invented *Quaternions*, the representation of imaginary numbers in the field of a complex domain. Here again, as usual, the practical or somatic applications were soon forthcoming. When, as noted above, the idea of *potential* had been extended to 'fields' other than Newton's gravitational field, it was next applied to the electromagnetic field. Since it was clear that the lines of force in such fields are not straight lines, a new mathematical device was called for, and Hamilton provided this when he transformed 'ordinary' algebra into quaternions with their right vectors, called *right versors*, designating the operation of *rotation*. The practical fruits referred to above came into being when Clerk Maxwell and Charles Steinmetz put Hamilton's quaternions to work in electromagnetic theory. Still later, developments on the theoretical side were extended by Grassmann in his beautiful generalization dealing with manifolds of points ordered in any number of dimensions.

In retrospect, we see now that this is all a part of the process whereby a science of 'generalized space' was, and is, being created, — a process which reaches its finest level of generality when the mathematicians extended the concept of 'space' to include 'phase space' as a notion which makes possible 'energy-levels,' 'wave-functions,' 'resonance,' and other highly abstract ideas which supplement and even supersede the older mechanical viewpoints in scientific thinking. The analogous idea of *function space* as a class of vector functions, extending the notion of space into a *class of functions*, reemphasizes the progressive emancipation, but at the same time again calls attention to the correlative need for strengthening the logical foundations of science.

For this reason, our concern in the present volume is with the formal foundations of system-structures. In such investigations fundamental questions in the philosophy of mathematics and logical theory, — the formal foundations of all science, — come up for review. According to our own hard-won conclusions, it is not possible to show that logic is more fundamental than mathematics, nor that mathematics is more fundamental than logic. We have proposed that any formal system appears as a logic when it is interpreted as applying to classes, propositions, and inferences, as such; but when we deal with a manifold of elements that are ordered according to transitive, asymmetrical relations (serial order), we enter the domain of what traditionally has been considered as a branch of mathematics. The manner in which we pass from arithmetic as a linear ordering of discriminated elements to geometric manifolds (planes, solids, polymorphs) as ranges of functions of several such intersecting or congruent orders, rising eventually to the highest manifolds of n-dimensional space, has already been outlined. The manner in which the empirical integrations of manifolds emerge from the basic and primordial experience of temporal flow has also been discussed, especially in relation to Brouwer's intuitionism, which has yielded a solution to the problem of Pythagoras in terms of the *dynamic infinite* of a process philosophy.

Thus we orient ourselves in the midst of an intellectual hurricane. As Kurt Lewin has shown,[6] the traditional Aristotelian mode of thought is based on the idea of an ontologically immutable essence, made up of the sum total of characteristics which a class of objects has in common. This traditional logic gives us a static world with an unbridgeable chasm separating the universal types and those individual deviations which depart from the class types (or essences) and thus are reduced to the status of 'accidents' beyond the scope of the real and typical.

Such a logic and metaphysics only creates obfuscations. The modern logic is attempting to overcome this opposition and establish a nexus between the universal and the particular. As Ernst Cassirer has pointed out in his volume, *Substance and Function* (1923, p. 224), it is by way of the relation of these two moments wherein the universal and particular stand within a system of complementary conditions that the real is apprehended. Thus the individual is not an isolated accident, a deviation from the type or essence, but it is an element in an ordered manifold. Accordingly, the particular has something of the character of universality, and universality is always exemplified in particulars.

As opposed to the 'essence' theory of Aristotelian logic, the non-Aristotelian logic presents a field-theoretical approach wherein 'relations' are not accidental, but inherent aspects of a universe of intersecting dimensions of behavior-stuffs of increasing orders of complexity. Thus in the new logic, substance is relativized, and our conceptual architectonic is adjusted to the dynamic nature of the universe.

In a philosophy of becoming wherein a non-Aristotelian mode of thinking is applied to the temporal order as the basic intuition of life it is possible to work toward a philosophy of nature akin to the limitless universe of Giordano Bruno. This is an open universe in the sense that evolution is more than illusory because the time-series of organic wholes are non-linear functions of levels of reality which arise in emergent dimensionalities upon a foundational manifold, — the space-time-energy continuum of cosmic interactions. In this pyramid of emergence we have found both freedom and order. But what will come after the emergence of the next level, — the cephalization of the electromagnetic society of the future? This I do not profess to know.

But this we do know: it is now one world, — or none. Social imagination must make this vision a reality, and this can be done through a unified symbolism, a planetary semantics, and a world philosophy. In all this speculation there is one important point that must not be overlooked: when we attempt to envisage the form of the electromagnetic society of the future, we must keep in mind that there can be only a relative autonomy for the two halves of any armature, — in a dynamo or in the earth-armature. That is, there can be no 'world sensorium' if the East-West opposition loses its relative polarity. The two hemispheres must be two halves of one whole, and if the two cerebral lobes of the earth-organism work against each other they will destroy the halves because they will destroy the whole. Obviously, therefore, the time has come to take the next step from political segmentation to social cephalization. This means world federation, of course. The electromagnetic society is even now at the point of emergence. Will it break through to reality? A definitive answer to this question will be attempted in the last chapter of this work.

XIII. Summary: Man on the March

It is obvious that things are on the move here on this planet. In this changing world nothing seems permanent and abiding. The old maxim, 'the more things change the more they remain the same,' is no longer even a half-truth. Ancient institutions and time honored beliefs are fluid and evanescent. The demon of acceleration is at the throttle, so to speak, and is speeding up the rate of social change.

As one attempts to peer into the future and discover the over-all direction of this change, it becomes increasingly clear that strong forces of unification are at work. The planet is becoming 'one world' in a physical sense. This, however, is not an unmixed blessing, for new social problems arise from this physical unification. The end-result of this process would seem to be one of the three possibilities: (1) *world destruction* through the military uses of atomic (nuclear) energy, because the peoples of the earth who have been brought closer together by mechanical integrations can't learn to live together in peace; (2) *world fascism,* because nations have been forced to live together under a system of giant enterprises such as international cartels; (3) *world federation* of the nations of the world into a universal industrial and political democracy, resting largely on the basis of voluntary agreements.

As he triumphs over space and time, man is unifying the planet into a technological one-ness, and this very unity surely will culminate in some kind of cultural unification. But what sort of integration will this prove to be? If we rule out universal annihilation in another world war, it would appear that on either of the last two alternatives we will get unified society. On either possibility the future of man may be described as 'global.' But in case (2) we shall have *planetary slavery;* whereas in (3) we shall achieve a *planetary democracy.* It is a commonplace that the radio, airplane, television, and the like are telescoping time and distance. Further conquests of these air-age and ether-age advances will result in a wide enslavement of mankind under the domination of those who control the engines of science, —

or else these mechanisms will be utilized by free peoples everywhere to build their own world community. In that case we shall have attained the third possibility. This is the consummation devoutly to be wished, of course. But to attain this consummation something like a psychic unification will also be necessary, and that is the concern of the next two chapters.

FOOTNOTES CHAPTER XI

[1]See my volume, *WORLD PHILOSOPHY: A Search for Synthesis,* Chapter III. Investigations in this field have been advanced considerably by Charles W. Morris in his book, *Paths of Life.*

[2]The first detailed statement of this Pantheism was given in my article, "The Evolution of Cosmologies," *Philosophy of Science,* April, 1952. Chapter X of the present volume presents a more complete statement.

[3]For a further exposition of these matters see the volume, *Spherical Harmonics,* by T. M. MacRobert, 1947.

[4]See W. S. McCulloch's article, "A Recapitulation of the Theory, With a Forecast of Several Extensions," in *Teleological Mechanisms,* Annals of the New York Academy of Science, 1948, Vol. 50.

[5]Cf. "Charting the Sea of Brain Waves," by Herbert J. Jasper, *Science,* 1949, Vol. 108, 343-347.

[6]Cf. "The Conflict Between Aristotelian and Galileian Modes of Thought in Contemporary Psychology," by Kurt Lewin, in *A Dynamic Theory of Personality,* 1935, p. 5.

12

OPERATION WISDOM: THE WORLD BRAIN IN ACTION

"We need not content ourselves with the bare statement that modern physics is no longer mechanistic; it is possible even to see, though vaguely, how it can make a positive contribution to the biologist's field of interest. Here again, it is the Exclusion Principle that leads the attack on the problem of organization. Briefly stated, this problem concerns itself with why component parts of organisms develop functions when compounded; why they show different laws of behavior in their togetherness than when each is alone."

— Henry Margenau

I. The Unity of Scientific Knowledge

In the preceding chapters we have been concerned with the problem of the organization of knowledge in its several areas: physical, biological, and social. We have viewed the problem of modern culture as the problem of extracting from these fields the common principles upon which we may build a philosophy of science. How may these principles of synthesis contribute to the development of a universal world-view?

Here on earth, and viewed from present concepts of the story of evolution, we picture the curve of planetary development as a series of cycles which can be bent into the spiral of a time-binding synthesis. Though not a prediction of things to come, this can be realized as an imaginative preview only if we accept the challenge to make sense of that which otherwise is nonsense. History can be made meaningful by reinterpreting the past, that is, the past can be freed from the pathos of time, if we salvage the pageant of history from the dark domain of chaos and futility. By a kind of projective geometry of the imagination we have drawn a curve of social change, but the following of that curve is not a 'law' of nature. It is up to man himself whether he will snatch the panorama of planetary evolution from the frustration of the meaningless.

We have also called attention to the fact that philosophy, to fulfill its historical rôle, will have to discover and bring into being a new synthesis. Such an integration of modern knowledge will accept scientific procedures and data as providing its tools of research and corpus of principles. Thus will it be possible to find unity in variety, simplicity in multiplicity, permanence in the flux of events. Thus will it be possible to provide a world philosophy based on a valid and verifiable cosmology. But before opening up the final facet in the story of unified knowledge, let us pause for a moment and glance backward in time and survey briefly several historical examples of this quest for the simplicity in nature.

II. Visions of Simplicity

We have already paid homage to the Pythagorean-Platonic synthesis as the first great movement in this symphonic progression of human thought, so let us next take note of Archimedes as one of the great simplifiers in Western thought. This ancient physicist of Alexandria had an ecstatic vision of the beautiful simplicity of nature when he observed that if he could only find a place for a fulcrum, he could move the world. Copernicus found that fulcrum when he hit upon the idea of taking the sun as the center of the system of wheeling planets. What a magnificently simple idea this was, and yet how fraught with implications! This transition from the ancient geocentric to the modern heliocentric cosmology, shifted the center of gravity of the universe and the pivot of man's thought. Well might Galileo, rising to his feet after bowing to the will of the Church to tower above those who would stop the forward movement of both matter and mind, mutter to himself: *and yet it moves!*

And the world has continued to move, until Einstein, like a modern Joshua, stopped not only the earth, but the entire system of motions. Here a movement of thought seemed to halt the movement of matter. Three centuries before, Descartes, flushed with the vision of a mathematical-physical universe, uttered the famous words: "Give me space and movement and I will construct the universe." Einstein, intoxicated with another vision of the power of mathematics, exclaimed with equal fervor: "Give me the four-dimensional space-time continuum, and I will construct the universe. But it shall not move! For I now show you how three-dimensional dynamics is absorbed into four-dimensional statics."

With no less a flair for the great simplicities, the modern behaviorist has also appeared on the scene, to proclaim with equal ardor: "Give me organic movements — nay, give me only physical movements — and I will construct what you call *mind!*" Thus was Descartes spurned by the physics and the psychology that he helped so much to create. For his *cogito ergo sum* ("I think, therefore I am") the modern behaviorist would substitute the axiom, *respiro ergo sum* ("I breathe, therefore I am"). Thus speak the great lovers of simplicity.

In the present formulation a sustained effort is made at recovering the all-inclusive vision of an earlier age of science. Relativity theory and behaviorism undoubtedly have their contributions to make to the modern synthesis, for have we not described our own effort as a *universal behaviorism*, a *monism of action?* But it is doubtful whether either relativity theory or behaviorism, taken singly or together, can give us an explanation of the *complex simplicity* of the world in which we live.

The central idea of our philosophy of simplicity is based on the conviction that nature, like a clever actress, covers her simple designs with secondary embellishments. But when it is asked, "If nature is so simple in her schemes, why haven't we learned her secret long ago?" the answer may be given by paraphrasing the poet: the intellect is a dome of many-colored glass which stains the white radiance of simplicity with the local hues of partial aspects. In more prosaic terms this means that our brains are prismatic — each facet of our reasoning machinery reflects a fragmentary part of the whole, which can only with great difficulty be resynthesized into a single master-vision.

Our thinking apparatus is a kind of cortical analyzer (to borrow a term from Pavlov), which breaks up the harmony of the cosmos into many separate chords. Since the process of integration is less habitual than differentiation, it is naturally difficult to reconstitute the whole from the dismembered parts. Notice how nature accomplishes with ease that which the intellect reconstructs with difficulty: I throw a book across the room, and then I ask the physicist to plot the curve of the trajectory. No synthesis from the microscopic details will enable him to integrate the total macroscopic situation. I speak a few words, and ask the expert in acoustics to recreate mathematically the sequence of words which cost me so little effort. In terms of harmonic analysis (fundamentals and overtones), this would be a difficult achievement. While this may only prove that what some people say is more interesting from a mathematical viewpoint than it is in terms of word-meanings, nevertheless, it also demonstrates the principle that organisms can solve rather remarkable mathematical problems by what in his book on *Mechanics* Ernst Mach has termed 'instinctive knowledge.' More recently, this kind of knowledge has been discussed by Walter B. Cannon under the designation of the 'wisdom of the body' — a kind of wisdom which in its own domain seems superior to the 'wisdom of the mind' which man is attempting to apply in the sphere of social action.

We are told that all the complicated machinery that man has devised consists for the most part in the combination of a few elementary mechanical principles and operations: the lever, the screw, the wheel, and a few others. The living body employs mechanical principles with ease and efficiency, though man, — the thinker, — employs complicated mathematics and fills ponderous tomes of learning in his straining efforts at explaining that which his own body accomplishes with almost effortless efficiency. Indeed, the situation reminds one of the argument on the part of the mathematician who was convinced that a cat could not jump through an open window because, as the cat passed over the sill, the head of the cat was in the future and the tail of the cat was in the past!

Whatever Zeno with his paradoxes of motion may have believed, cats do jump; the world does move; man is in motion; history is in the making; and humanity is on its evolutionary way. Accordingly, if we are to proliferate a world psycho-somatic organism with its own functional simplicity, we must wonder: what will this social simplex be like when it does emerge?

We have observed that our universe is a universe of action — energy integrated through time. But what is the unit of mental life? Is there a quantum unit for psychical response? How can we integrate energy through time on the social level? And what is the next advance on the human level going to be? These questions can only be answered through reasoning by analogy, — a study in isomorphism, — as we strive to envisage what happens on level after level of nature as she rises on the ladder of emergent evolution. Our vision of new possibilities must grow out of the study of what nature is and what man is, and how nature and man may go about the task of producing a higher level of organization. By taking advantage of the laws that operate, man may help to determine the new actualities that he hopes to realize.

In our form of scientific humanism the assignment is to work out the consequences of the idea that the next level of human evolution will see the emergence of a social organism with a planetary civilization as its action-pattern. This possibility of world unification through what is termed an economic-political-ideological synthesis can be attained only if we exert a supreme effort at harmonizing our scientific, religious, esthetic, economic, and educational programs. The social embryology of world unity calls for (1) a subjective-psychological transmutation of human nature, and (2) an objective-social transformation of man's institutions, both representing a kind of spiritual alchemy. That is to say, the proliferation of the coming world organism calls for psycho-social mutations. How can this be accomplished?

III. The World Psychosomatic Organism

In order to make crystal clear to the reader the main objectives of scientific humanism, let us resort to an analogy. This takes us back into the past. According to the story of biological evolution, unnumbered ages ago simpler organisms, the only kind that existed then, were mere colonies of agglomerated cells. Lacking a central nervous system, they had little capacity to learn by experience; they could not adjust themselves to new features in their environments. These lowly organisms could not anticipate future emergencies. But when the processes of biological evolution produced the higher organizing mechanism called the central nervous system, the animals that possessed this invention were better able to survive under more complex conditions.

Today the human race has reached the place that these lowly organisms had attained when, in order to forge ahead, it became necessary to evolve the central nervous system. On the human level our problem is now that of achieving something in the way of social action comparable to the integrative action of the cerebro-spinal axis. Cephalization — bringing things to a head — makes unity of purpose, mobilization of energies for planned action, a possibility. In the same way, socially integrated behavior will make possible unity of social purpose and intelligently planned action.

Our human world is at present like a low grade organism: it is an acephalous affair, segmented like a tapeworm, with no brain and no efficient organization as a whole. If society is to get ahead, it must become a high-level organism and acquire a brain and organs for coördinating its vast multiplicity of now random activities. The time has come to take the step from social segmentation to political cephalization. This is one of the basic propositions of scientific humanism. It points to the need for the growth and cephalization of a world psychosomatic creature, a social organism-to-be. But a high-grade organism has not only a nervous system — it has also a mind. And if we are to have a world organism with a world brain, we must also have a world mind. This world mind would be the world philosophy of a planetary civilization, — a scientific humanism functioning through the lives and thoughts of mankind.

If we fail to provide the machinery for such a world brain, all humanity will be headed for destruction. It is either mass creativity or mass psychosis. Our politicians do not realize this yet — they have a blind spot that prevents them from seeing the importance of the subjective factors. They fail to see that we need not only new social mechanisms, but also new values, new attitudes, new motivations. In a word, *we need not only the political synthesis of a World Federation in which the Eastern and Western hemispheres function like the right and left lobes of man's brain, with the seat of the United Nations serving as the point to decussate the World Brain's social nerves, but we need also a planetary way of living, a planetary way of feeling, and a planetary ethics to supply the action-patterns for our giant electromagnetic society.*

This means that we must first create a loyalty that will transcend nationalism, patriotism, and narrow ideologies. Loyalty to man must become the central, global motif, replacing limited loyalties with a universal loyalty to a world community. To place limitations upon the broadest concepts and plans is to invite disaster, for anything less than fundamental changes in our views and attitudes will encourage the drift toward conflict and chaos and will in the end prove fatal.

Humanity today is being strangled by the institutions men have created in the past and are now trying to transcend. The world we live in is moving so rapidly in its recurring crises that we can no longer leave it to unguided social forces to produce social cohesion. These forces must be regulated by man's collectively polarized intelligence. This means that fundamental changes in our ways of thinking are a prelude to the economic and political changes we shall have to embrace. Those who belong to the ranks of scientific humanism are human beings with the physical and mental equipment we know so well, but they seem to have caught the gleam: from their point of view they see something important, namely, that the peoples of this earth must learn that accidents of birth — color, nationality, religion, and the rest — are not so important as learning to live together. Loyalty to man's planetary destiny is the only ideal in this world big enough to dominate the total personality and elicit our collective enthusiasm.

This is what is needed. But as it is now, we deal with problems in piecemeal fashion. We do what is expedient at the moment. What so many of our "experts" in social matters fail to realize is that *mere political truces will not make a world organism, because a high level organism is impossible without a central nervous system and a world mind to function through it.* The world mind for the social organism will come into being when we have learned to match the inventor and technologist — men who on the physical level have created a physical unification of our planet — with the social inventor of cultural communications: such researchers must discover ways of creating a mental unity of mankind.

This can be done only by achieving the highest possible synthesis — a world civilization in which are united the philosophy and religions of the East and the sciences and technologies of the West. *To attain this goal we shall have to persuade the Russians to take over their share of convolutions of the world brain and work in harmony with the rest of the social cortex.* Thus we see, now more clearly than ever, the need for a great, unified, conscious change in human relationships. This is an enormous enterprise. But as the energy of evolution reverberates in human consciousness, as we grow through tensions, trials, and gropings, so also grows the will to the new society. This growing aspiration is a portent of the approaching time when the hopes and strivings of all mankind will reach fruition. That is still the promise of scientific humanism!

But we have been holding forth this 'promise' for several decades. How shall we make good? The time has come to deal with this problem realistically.

IV. The Great Transitions

In examining this problem of biosocial integration, let us consider the field of biological evolution to see whether we may find, lower down in the scale, some forerunners of the type of transition we have in mind when we contemplate the possible modes of development for a coming world organism.

Let us begin with the homely observation that an army travels on its belly. Crude as this truth is, it brings to light the fact that some of the activities of society are like the progress of an earth-worm: first of all you pull up the rear end, and then you thrust forward the front end (some worms work on the opposite principle, a biologist informs me). But in any case, such an organism is capable of locomotion, the directed action which leads toward progress in space — provided it has enough food to supply the necessary energy. An animal is fitted to engage in a high level of coördinated response *if it gets a head*, i.e., if the creature has a cerebro-spinal axis. The moral of the story, on a higher level, is that humanity needs to be cephalized by acquiring a sensorium, if it is to make comparable progress — no longer in space but in space-time.

The problem of creating this super-organism with a world brain is analogous to the problem of how nature was to pass from the single-celled animals of long ago — for example, the ameba — to the multicellular organisms higher in the scale. The theories about this have been recorded for us by Dr. Libbie H. Hyman,[1] as follows.

Dr. Hyman starts with the proposition that since metazoans (many-celled living creatures) develop from a single cell, the egg, this means that phylogenetically they originated from protozoans (single-celled creatures). The probability is that the many-celled organisms resulted from the consolidation of a *protozoan colony*. The older supposition that the ameboid protozoan are the most primitive animals and must be looked upon as ancestral to the metazoans is now displaced by the belief in a flagellate ancestry, according to Dr. Hyman. Among the reasons for this change of opinion is the resemblance of the animal sperm to the flagellate protozoan. The probability now appears to be that the metazoa arose from the colored holophytic flagellates (like sponges, cœlenterates) by way of colony formation, followed by loss of chlorophyll and the assumption of holozoic habits. While Dr. Hyman does not explain this technical language, presumably she is referring to the transition from plant to animal — "phytic" to "zoic." Moreover, she unfortunately does not tell us much of how this transition may have occurred, and to supply the missing pieces

I quote the following paragraph from another source:

> "Something of the nature of the problem may be seen in the case of chlorophyll and its congeners, which are crucial to all physical life. Chlorophyll A is a molecule containing as many as 136 atoms: $C_{55}H_{70}O_6N_4Mg$. In this molecule the last atom, Mg (magnesium) is enormously significant. For though this chlorophyll constitutes the green element in plants, through which sunlight is poured to convert sap into sugar, thus making all plant and animal life possible, the substitution of *one* copper atom for the *one* magnesium atom converts the chlorophyll into another life element altogether, an element essential to lower animals — the substance haemocyanin — while if the one magnesium atom is supplanted by one atom of iron, we have the red blood haemoglobin of the higher animals, including man."[2]

Thus does nature accomplish one of the most remarkable of her achievements, the biological alchemy whereby higher forms of life are produced.

The next problem we encounter in following the progressing story of this transition is the question of when and how the primitive metazoan, once it came into existence, adopted the principle of equatorial cleavage, which is the starting point for cell differentiation, so essential a feature of the metazoan individual as contrasted with a protozoan colony. The theories to explain this are too numerous and too complicated for discussion here, but Dr. Hyman favors the theory of Metchnikoff, who surmised that the blastula-like flagellate ancestor became the two-layered creature by the wandering of cells from the surface to the interior, particularly cells loaded with food. The process produced the organism known as planula, where surface cells catch food in a flagellate manner and pass it in part to the interior for digestion. Thus the locomotory and food-catching functions are combined in flagellates.

Having brought us thus far, Dr. Hyman then leaves the morphological phase of the question to consider the physiological aspects. She points out that the difference between a spherical colony of protozoa and a spherical multicellular individual (like Volvox) is obviously a functional one. In the first case, the cells act in independence of each other and the colony rolls about aimlessly. In the second case, the cells act in coördination, the colony is polarized and swims always with one pole forward, and each cell is no longer capable of all possible functions. Such coördination can result only from a relation of control of one part of the colony, namely, the anterior pole, over the rest of the colony: the relation is one of domination and subordination, as Professor Charles M. Child terms it.

How does such a relation come about? In the last analysis, it would seem that it can happen only through the influence of surrounding factors. Organization on the plane of multicellular organisms involves as its steps the following: functional polarization resulting from environmental exposure, coördination of the cells conditioned by a dominance-subordination relation, and finally morphological differentiation (division of labor) with reference to the axis of polarity. When this level of biological organization has been attained, the constituent cells of a multicellular individual lose their capacity for independent life; each of the cells gives up some of its liberties; and they must all coöperate with other cells to perform the functions of the individual as a whole. This means that some cells must accept the position of subordination as they submit to being governed by the dominant parts.

As one surveys this story of the transition from one level of biological organization to a higher level, a transition that occurred for the first time ages ago, can one doubt that many of the principles involved here can be transposed to the coming level of the social organism? Can one doubt that the wisdom of the body foreshadows a corresponding wisdom of the social organism of the future?

All this, of course, is a part of the record of what has already happened. As we look to the future, what are the prospects and the strategy of human evolution? This is one of the important problems for the makers of blueprints for a coming planetary civilization.

V. Creative Semantics: A Map of a Territory-To-Be

The drawing of blueprints for the planetary social organism is no easy thing. This is a matter of forming an imaginary map of a territory-to-be, and then constructing a program for its accomplishment. This is a project for what we have termed creative semantics, as illustrated in DIAGRAM XVIII (p. 397)

Some years ago, in my volume, *Humanistic Logic*, it was pointed out that an analogy can be set up between scientific reasoning as a sending out of mental tentacles into the external universe to anticipate further sensory experience and the ameboid (or flagellant) movements of unicellular organisms. It may turn out that this is no mere analogy,

DIAGRAM XVIII
CREATIVE SEMANTICS

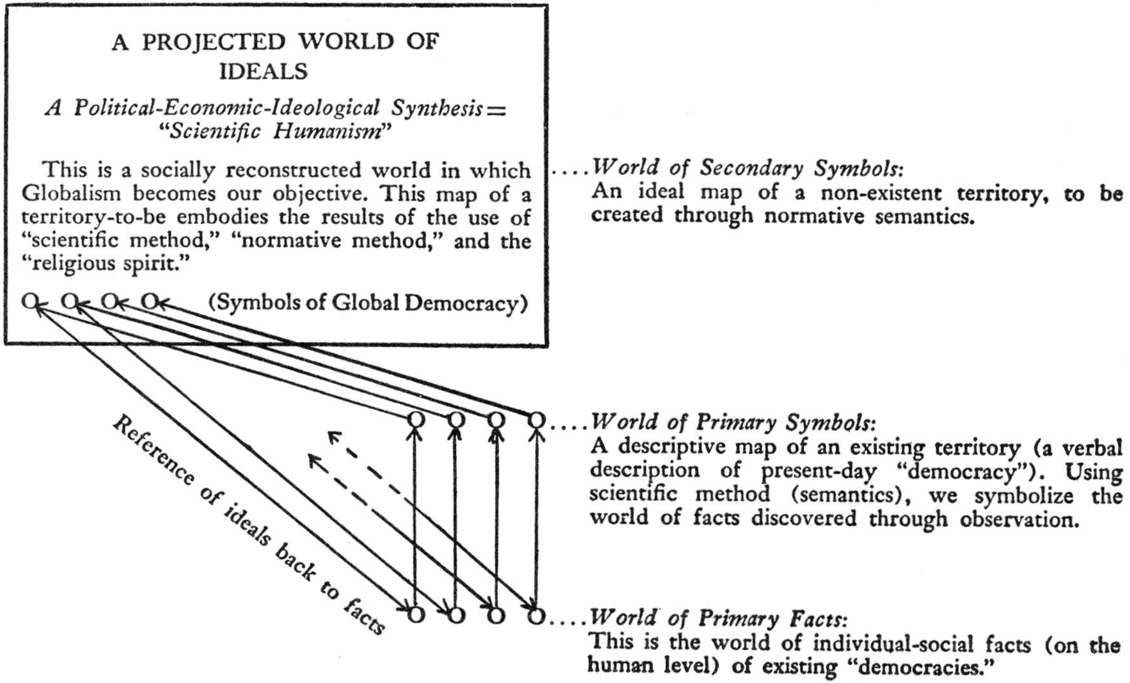

A PROJECTED WORLD OF IDEALS

A Political-Economic-Ideological Synthesis = "*Scientific Humanism*"

This is a socially reconstructed world in which Globalism becomes our objective. This map of a territory-to-be embodies the results of the use of "scientific method," "normative method," and the "religious spirit."

(Symbols of Global Democracy)

....*World of Secondary Symbols:*
An ideal map of a non-existent territory, to be created through normative semantics.

Reference of ideals back to facts

....*World of Primary Symbols:*
A descriptive map of an existing territory (a verbal description of present-day "democracy"). Using scientific method (semantics), we symbolize the world of facts discovered through observation.

....*World of Primary Facts:*
This is the world of individual-social facts (on the human level) of existing "democracies."

but indeed the fundamental mode of locomotion of intellectual as well as spatial progress. Just as in biological evolution the eye develops as anticipative touch, and sight finally becomes the major medium for distance reception, so in imaginative constructiveness the fulfillment of visions of a reality-to-be is a matter of realizing a desire to see, so that the whole plan of nature from ameba to man represents the same "reaching out" of protoplasm. Creative thinking is a kind of feeling of one's way through the universe, a form of social cytotropism or neurobiotaxis. The manner in which a creative semantics may pass from a map of the world of facts to a map of a territory-to-be is indicated in our DIAGRAM XVIII.

The ameba explored its universe by projecting its pseudopodia into the space about it. Here the enlargement of the environment is a result of a tentative groping into the unknown. But the scientist is also an explorer, a voyager along strange shores and over untracked continents. He projects his mental pseudopodia, those intellectual tentacles, into space and time to reach out even to the stars in their anticipations of experience. And if it be true, as some believe, that in mental activity a similar type of ameboid movement occurs in the nerve cells of the brain of the thinking man as he ideally explores new worlds of conceptualization, then reasoning becomes in fact the experimental-exploratory activity, only on a much more subtle and intricate scale, which we observe in organisms that feel their way by trial and error through the universe of micro-organisms.

Many individuals today are working creatively toward a new eye-brain-mind layout, social in its operations. Bishop Berkeley, who, ahead of the plodding physicists, bored his way through Newtonian matter to something like an energy-continuum, was much given to speculations about a new kind of vision. A new vision, far beyond what Berkeley had in mind, alone can save society, — if salvation there be, — with an all-seeing eye and brain for the world brain that will enable the guardians of the future to mold the topological structure of human institutions into the form of unity.

The approximate meaning of this turns out to be as follows: The making of blueprints for the territory-to-be is a kind of reaching out into a new dimension of reality, an imaginative locomotion on the social level of individuals who are striving to create a time-binding synthesis, a field-plenum dynamics of history. Just as within the nervous system there is an embryological elaboration of a cell-structure under the compulsion of a stimulus pattern, due to a migration toward the source of the irradiating energy, so on the social level there can be an analogous migration of the neuroblasts (individual men) who are converging into the emergence of a social cortex or world sensorium. This onward-upward surge is comparable to the ameboid movements, or flagellate activity, of individual cells; and the cytotropism of the neuroblasts in the embryonic nervous system constitutes the three-dimensional analogues of the extra-neurobiotaxis of the social neuroblasts (human individuals) in the hyperdimensional manifold of the World Brain.

VI. Neurobiotaxis and Biological Integration

Our program is to find a social analogue for the doctrine of neurobiotaxis, as this doctrine has been developed by C. V. Ariens Kappers and others. According to Kappers' theory, the developing neuroblasts (embryo nerve cells) are polarized: there is a difference of electrical potential controlling the developing nerve cell so that it grows toward the region from which the largest number of excitations come.

Kappers' doctrine was intended to explain such phenomena as the shifting of position of nerve cells, a common phenomenon in growing organisms. For example, the regeneration of a cut nerve fiber, as it grows toward the muscle which it originally innervated, has its embryological parallel in the growing axon of the neuroblasts. These migrations are analogous to the form of behavior known as taxis or tropism. Kappers claims that the evidence shows that the topography of cell-groups in the spinal cord, mid-brain, and fore-brain is determined by the regions where the largest number of excitations reach the cell. Thus the doctrine of neurobiotaxis maintains that the direction of the developing embryo nerve cells is governed by the bioelectric processes which result from stimulation. That is to say, if several stimulative charges occur in the nervous system, the outgrowth of the chief dendrites, and eventually the growth of the cells, takes place in that direction from which have come the largest number of stimulations. This means that the developing neurons are polarized, and that the axons grow out in the direction of the excitation current. The method of growth is comparable to the process of electroplating, and Kappers' term 'galvanotropism' is therefore quite appropriate.

If we carry this doctrine of neurobiotaxis to the next higher level of emergent evolution, which, if we are correct, is on the way to being formed, how shall we picture the social neurotropism which is to produce the cortex for the world sensorium? Clearly we must find some social analogue, a psychotropism, as it will be termed, for the principle that cells bathed in the irradiation field of a stimulus pattern grow toward the source of stimulation. In seeking the answer to this enigma, I shall have recourse to the work of Dr. N. Rashevsky of the University of Chicago, whose investigations in the field of mathematical biology have already been referred to. Dr. Rashevsky[3] claims to have established certain conclusions, the most important of which, for our purposes, are as follows:

1. Attraction and repulsion of cells are two forces always present in cells which are irritable and metabolize.

2. Two irritable cells, which influence each other so as to excite mutually, will attract each other.

3. In highly irritable cells attraction always prevails, and this may be the basis for the formation of diffuse nervous systems in lower animals and ganglia in higher animals.

4. The forces of attraction between highly irritable cells result in such phenomena as are described by Kappers as neurobiotaxis and neurotropism by Cajal.

5. In an aggregate of cells derived by consecutive division from one cell, we find that in the early stages of such an aggregate it will assume, under the influence of the above forces, shapes familiar to the embryologist, such as the blastula, gastrula, neurula. Arranging all forms in a series according to an increasing amount of irritable cells, we find a remarkable analogy with the actual animal forms. The lowest, almost shapeless, correspond to mollusks, with very low developed diffuse nervous systems; others to arthropods, with more concentrated ganglia; the highest to vertebrates with pairs of limbs and one chief ganglion mass — the head.

These conclusions, which become more significant as we pass from the earlier ones to the later ones, we believe can be transposed to the higher human social level. But is such a transposition valid?

On our theory the social organism — the electromagnetic society — is a giant cell-colony. That some sort of laws are transposable from individual cells to cell-colony or multi-cellular developments is evident from the simple fact that the body of a multi-cellular organism, with its own laws of macroscopic behavior, is itself a population of cells. Since this may not be obvious to others, let us consider some of the difficulties, before going further.

VII. Difficulties Facing the Organismic Theory

The first difficulty confronting our organismic theory of society is the objection that society cannot be an organism because it lacks some of the essential parts of an organism. This objection has been taken care of by Charles M. Child. In his classical work, *The Physiological Foundations of Behavior* (1924, p. 270), he states:

> "Objections such as those that human society is not a big animal, that it has, for example, no stomach, no muscles, etc., etc., are just as true of many organisms as for society. It has been said that the social mind has no sensorium. But do not the individuals in relation to each other and to the environment constitute the sensorium of the social mind just as truly as cells and cell groups in relation to each other and to the external world constitute the sensorium of the individual mind?"

This is certainly an answer to one major criticism. From our point of view, however, the criticism has some validity: to the extent that it points to a genuine need — the need to create a world brain to serve as the synthesizer of social behavior-patterns.

The second difficulty that is likely to occur to the reader is that even though we humans may enter functionally into the cell-colony which constitutes the world brain, we as individuals cannot be conscious of the emergent social mind of which we as individuals constitute the component elements. In reply we may point out that even if this be true, this does not invalidate the organismic theory. We believe, therefore, that *our failure to be aware of our functioning as creative agents in the fabrication of the world brain for which humanity provides the living body is not a fatal objection.* For one thing, we have the parallel case of individual neurons as structurally distinct anatomical units, while yet these units function as parts within the brain-as-a-whole, being participants in a gestalt pattern of behavior.

If we look back to what happens in earlier biological levels of evolution, we find examples of where organisms may experience the internal manifestations of behavior *before they have attained a level of development such that the organisms are consciously aware of the significance of these internal manifestations.*[4] An example of experience without conscious awareness of the behavioral meaning of such experience is cited by Jennings[5] in the mating behavior of pairs of paramecia. In discussing this situation, Jennings states: "The infusorian has no awareness of the complex social system into which its behavior fits, for the good reason that there is no way in which it could acquire the data requisite for being aware of it — even if it has the capability of conscious awareness." It is interesting to note that Jennings supposes that the seeking of mates is the origin of both social behavior and self-consciousness as the awareness of the meaning of behavior.

The foregoing observations not only tend to weaken the objection to the organismic view, but also refute the statement of those persons who assert that 'society' is a high level abstraction, because the lower level units alone are real. Such critics will affirm, for example, that you can't reform 'society'; you can only reform the individuals in society — if that. But precisely because man is at once subject and object, — an individual with personal awareness and an imaginative super-observer of the cell-colony-being he is helping to create, — man has the unique capacity to change society by changing himself. Whether we do in fact ever produce a social organism with the functional characteristics of an emergent whole is up to man, scientific humanism insists. This is not fixed by divine or natural law, except as these reach up into human consciousness. Granted the material basis and the necessary social imagination for such an emergence, how shall man operate on the factors available to create the world sensorium? This is our biggest problem.

VIII. The Embryology of a World Brain

The problem now is one in social embryology. To integrate the cells of our social cell-colony strong binding forces, based on attraction of units, must be brought into play. Here reasoning by analogy (isomorphism) seems to be our most useful tool.

Let us first recall what Dr. Paul Weiss points out in his chapter on 'Differential Growth' in his book on *The Chemistry and Physiology of Growth*, where he discusses the orientation of growth between two centers in terms of 'attraction.' In general, it may be said that any physical force capable of affecting the orientation and aggregation of molecules (e.g., electrostatic fields) can accomplish this migration or attraction. And even more specifically, Dr. Rashevsky's research, as already noted, indicates that the irritability of metabolizing cells sets up forces of attraction which draw the cells into a convergent movement toward cephalization. And just as the cerebral hemispheres, — the 'specific organ of civilization,' to use C. J. Herrick's term, — were thus elaborated, with the cortex as the vehicle of highest metabolic rate and the synthesizer of reactions, so, we anticipate, the separate cells of the coming world brain will get into functional harmony and produce the giant sensorium. In that day, just as human electro-encephalograms now represent the scanning reactions of the alpha rhythm sweeping over the cortex, so the planetary pattern reactions of the electromagnetic society will play like signs over a bank of lights, — world brain waves moving over the earth's surface. If, in colloidal systems, as Dr. N. Rashevsky has shown, a resonance between two chemical reactions is possible in the sense that their mutual influences increase with the decreasing differences in their proper frequencies, why can't there be a similar tuning of resonance (psychotropism) effect on the level of social synthesis, so that our neuroblasts may mutually attract each other into the convergent proliferation of the world sensorium?

The geometry of a world sensorium will perforce conform to the principles of the emergent dimension, — the elements of the lower ensemble being organized in a new way to produce a higher organization with its isomorphic properties, these macroscopic properties being public (phenomenal) properties transposable across the social whole. In commenting on the fields associated with growing organisms, Professor Henry Margenau[6] observes that these electrostatic potentials at all points on the two-dimensional surface determine the growth of a three-dimensional, complicated, and finely organized object (such as the salamander head). The implication of this, as Margenau sees it, is that "a three dimensional structure appears to be mapped out on a two-dimensional surface," — which he regards as comparable to the biological traits imbedded in the small space of a chromosome.

From our point of view, this, carried to the next level of emergence, means that the geometry of a world brain is already mapped out on the isomorphic base of surface-relations among human beings, and that from the space-time relations of our neuroblasts social embryology will elaborate a world organism. Here the planetary symbols of Bliss's semantography will provide the media for communicating the world philosophy of a scientific humanism.

IX. Imagination as the Creative Force

What people need today is imagination. The unrest of the world, due to fear of tomorrow, will be transmuted into the tidal delight of seeing the progressively unfolding meaning of human history. If we can form the *great vision,* there can be a tremendous uprush into consciousness of the big idea behind planetary history.

The central difficulty with scientific humanism has been that it has tried to put an immensely simple message into *words*, whereas such a message should be written into the choreography of a universal picture language. In our topology of humanity this appears as a language of motion, a psychosocial motion or spiritual caravan. If it were possible to use the full play of mass media on an international level, the all-world drama of earth-history could lift up the lives of peoples everywhere by sheer evocation of god-like qualities from within.

In a word, scientific humanism seeks to create a space-time drama of epic proportions which shall embody and express the social analogue of Minkowski's space-time continuum of relativity theory. Just as physics interprets physical events in terms of field influence curving the space-time manifold, so in our organismic theory social patterns, like spatio-temporal relations, are manifestations of curvature: no human act is isolated — it, too, is a part of a field-plenum dynamics which unifies the parts, bending the world-encircling arc of history into the spiral of a time-binding synthesis. When this superlative mission, *Operation Knowledge,* as been accomplished, society will no longer be the acephalous and amorphous thing it now is, but man will have brought into being the planetary organism with its world brain as the proper organ of integration. (See DIAGRAM XIX, p. 405)

X. THE MYSTERY PLAY OF HUMAN EVOLUTION

Having indicated how we may draw together a few of the tangled threads of evolution into some sort of pattern, we turn to the question: what is the meaning of this mystery play which is life itself? Here is my own best guess.

Men speak across the abysses of space and time and try to communicate something of the burden and the mystery of this awesome drama. These exploratory gropings have been examined — and we see that they do not appear to justify any claim to final interpretation. The fugitive efforts at unification that man has thus far achieved are only prefigurations of the possible meaning of a cosmic symbolism still to be deciphered. And yet they *do* seem to point beyond themselves to some pattern of meaning yet to be revealed. What could this

DIAGRAM XIX

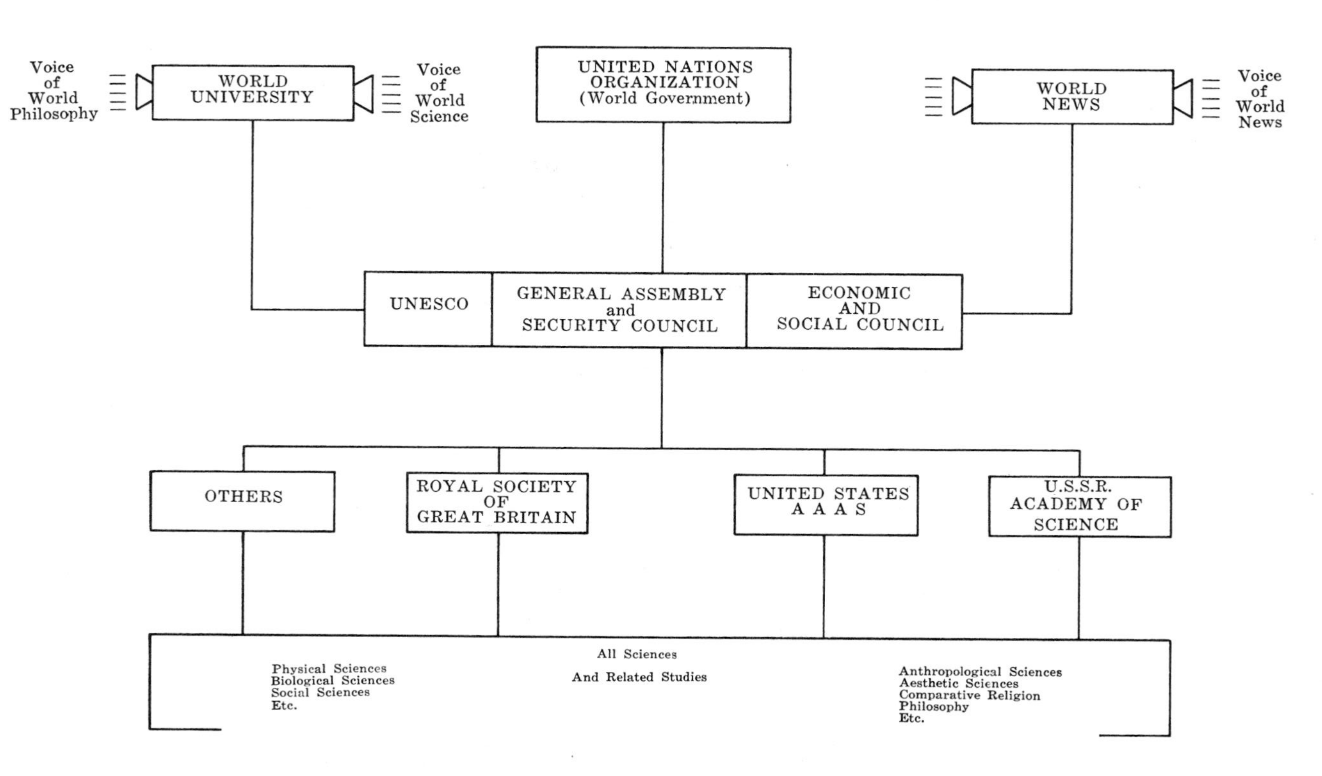

THE WORLD BRAIN IN ACTION

more ultimate meaning be? What is the message unfolding in the moving scroll of world history?

Perhaps in this coming insight, still to be clarified by the processes of time, there will appear to be a confirmation of the wonderful theory of Dr. Clark Hilton Rice, as this was sketched in fragmentary form in my book, *The World Sensorium:* here it turns out that sound and light are nothing other than the voice and vision of a great Cosmic Imagination which is communicating with itself across the two-faced screen of the human brain as it registers sensory images coming from the 'outside' and extra-sensory images from the 'inside.' Hooked up with the auditory center, the brain becomes a motion picture house in which each person is viewing the 'passing show' of the outer world. If we switch on the radio-television (ear-eye) receptors, we get sound-pictures from the external world; and if we turn the inner dial, we may receive the "news flashes" from the Cosmic Imagination as precognitions of things to come.

Here on the earth, the World Sensorium would provide the body-structure for the World Mind. This World Mind is not some coming form of World Government, — which is a political entity like Lord Tennyson's *Parliament of Man,* — but a world philosophy. The World Mind has its memory-basis in the pools of knowledge in all fields, reservoirs constantly growing in depth and breadth with the expansion of human understanding. By taking thought, all enlightened peoples may tap these pools. Each individual takes what he can contain, and what he does with these borrowed insights depends on his imagination and moral orientations.

Such a theory offers a measure of hope that we will ultimately have World Government, because we have reason to believe that the causal influences initiated by all the ethical geniuses who have dreamed and worked for such a thing are even now pushing against our evolving culture-patterns, in every country of the world, striving to imprint this idea upon man's consciousness and pour the energy of a universal desire into the emerging social organism.

This is an all-out effort. If we fail to serve as the creative outlets for the morphogenetic energy and do not proliferate the structure for the World Brain, all humanity will go down to destruction. We can be sure that we are facing the greatest reactionary movement of history, for this is the last ditch for the 'rule or ruin' people in politics, business, and the authoritarian churches, who have their counterparts in every country of the earth. If, however, enough thoughtful persons can focus on the idea of world unity, we may be able to visualize a social image and a body of ideas. If the minds of men can be concentrated into a coherent image of world unity, something in the nature of a collective thought-form, the bad "scenes" on the screen of human consciousness might be dissipated. In that event we would have the emergent social scanning of the universal symbols meaningfully transposable across the earth's surface. At this point, therefore, we return to an earlier problem temporarily put aside in preceding chapters.

XI. The *PSI* Layer and Parapsychology

We have already pointed out that communication can occur on two different levels: (a) the level of the manifest world, where space-time relations of causality obtain, and (b) the level of the unmanifest world, where a sub-ether serves as the medium for guiding influences. As part of this 'dualism,' we have also proposed that in (a) there is a time-lag in the transmission of information, since, as the theory of relativity teaches us in the case of light, the effects are delayed relative to causes by an amount equal to or less than the finite velocity of light. But in our cosmology we hold that the Supreme Imagination, functioning through the Cosmic Lens, is able to maintain a macroscopic steady-state because it 'knows' the conditions prevailing in 'local systems.' Accordingly, in (b), the unmanifest world of the cosmic field-plenum, there is no time-lag in the transmission of information. Here the medium does not involve 'mass,' 'space,' and 'time' features, for in a superdispersive field energy influences are not so limited. On the level of 'celestial cybernetics' there is no time-lag for the reason that there is no overall increase of entropy, and this relates to a cosmic causality which undergirds the manifest world of sense perception.

If now, as we have proposed, there is a cosmic mind (Supreme Imagination) which knows its own body because this body emerges from the bosom of the unmanifest world, does it not follow that the mind of the human being is related to its own bodily states by way of a similar field-matter dualism? If so, may it not also follow that these human cells of society are in turn the neuroblasts in an emerging world sensorium and that direct, extra-sensory communication between individuals will make its appearance as organismic integration progresses? In that case it begins to look as if maximum communication on the level of the world-mind can occur only as maximum communication on the level of sensory perception is achieved, *because the only way to integrate individuals into a world-brain is by way of the manifest symbols of mass-media communication* (i.e., conversation via radio, telephone, television, etc.). Thus a world-level symbolism, the planetary semantography we have called *wholingua,* is required if the world is to be saved from disaster.

The paradoxical thing is that if we get a planetary civilization based on world understanding, the unmanifest world-mind seems to be rendered superfluous. This, however, is not a genuine paradox, for it overlooks the fact that there can be no manifest world unity (world government, for example) unless there is also an unmanifest world. We conclude, therefore, that there can be no effective and universal *ESP* unless we create a unified symbolism for the level of sensory perceptions. This means — to repeat — that manifest communication and unmanifest communication must develop together, if they are to develop at all.

In the preceding chapters we have speculated concerning the nature of this planetary symbolism, and since we are now approaching the end of our journey, it will be well to review the requirements as we see them. A survey of these requirements for a planetary symbolism yields the following desiderata:

(1) *This planetary symbolism must be capable of representing the world as it is on all levels.* Mathematics provides an adequate symbolism for representing the facts of physical science, but it is presently not adapted to symbolizing the content of the religious and esthetic experiences. As we have seen, the mathematical logic type of approach to the problems of communication was outlined by Leibniz in his *Nouveau Essais* (1704), and later extended by others. But even before Leibniz's proposed reforms, the French philosopher René Descartes had suggested Chinese ideographs as providing a possible universal symbolism.

One difficulty with mathematics and symbolic logic and Chinese ideography is that their 'vocabularies' and 'rules of syntax' are so intricate as to require specialized training for their mastery. Moreover, the symbolism of mathematical logic is emasculated of emotional content, which a popularly employed symbolism must possess. To be sure, there is a 'mathematical basis of the arts,' which has been studied by Birkhoff, Schillinger, and others, but this is no symbolism for art appreciation. We must therefore find something more adequate than the symbolism of mathematical logic.

(2) *It must be psychologically meaningful to the common man.* This means something for the symbolism of our planetary iconography; but it also has implications for the education of the 'common man,' namely, that there must be a minimal standardization of experience in our mass education. In the new era, 'literacy' must be broadened to include a familiarity with *Wholingua*, — after it has been created!

Among the possibilities in this area we find the artificial or synthetic languages, such as Esperanto, Basic English, and others, which are sometimes referred to as 'auxiliary' languages. At the present time, *Interlingua* seems to be making most headway in getting itself established. But here, again, we do not have the fulfillment of our ideal.

(3) *It must possess the capacity for universality.* That means *Wholingua* must be as simple as possible. But it must also be consonant with the principles of *orthosynthesis.* If the art-science of a planetary iconography is a space-time form of experience, it must be capable of representing the static and the dynamic, the structural and the functional. At present, the 'movies' with a sound track come closest to satisfying this requirement.

This third requirement recalls the work of C. K. Bliss whose *Semantography* represents a sincere effort along these lines. A universal picture language should be useful in the service of otherwise illiterate peoples who could thus communicate on the level of common needs and purposes. But would such a language meet the needs of scientists who deal with high-level abstractions? In any case, Semantography is a written language — one which cannot be spoken — and this places a limitation upon its usefulness.

This therefore brings us back to *Wholingua* as a possible universal symbolism. This language is still to be created. Perhaps, as a beginning, it could borrow from Bliss's Semantography. If one could find common units of symbolism which are psychologically natural because they rest on the archetypes of the Jungian collective unconscious, which supposedly reside in all human beings, we might combine these with Bliss's picture writing and produce Wholingua. In favor of this possibility, we have the fact that such mathematical forms as the five Platonic solids (built upon triangles) are archetypes of the sort that Jung has in mind. But what is missing in the Platonic solids are circles. But even with the addition of this, one still misses the dynamic factor. To get the dynamic into the 'picture,' one must introduce spirals — and then use one's imagination in visualizing the dimensions higher than the two dimensions of a flat surface. This last thought makes it desirable for me to digress for a moment and return to my earlier discussion of spiral forms in nature.

In my volume, *Nature, Man, and God* (1951, p. 90), there is an analysis of the psychology of perception and conception, where I considered the views of Dr. Paul Schilder as set forth in his book, *MIND: Perception and Thought in Their Constructive Aspects*. Here, in dealing with the psychology of geometry, Dr. Schilder pointed out that in the development of the experience of children, we must not separate perception from movement. This is so because there is no perception without motility (as experience with children demonstrates), for genetically the psychological unit is not a point, nor even a straight line, but loops and curves — as in arm movements. This idea that movement is the basis of the organization of the optic field and that internally organized gestalten evolve through a progressive integration of functions gives us the basis for Mary Boole's 'spiral action of time' and Korzybski's theory of 'time binding' in terms of the screw spiral.

Later in this volume, I then pointed out (p. 104) the similarity between the views of Dr. Schilder and Dr. Joseph Schillinger in their analyses of experience. Dr. Schilder, the psychoanalyst, observed that visual motor configurations (gestalt perceptions of movement) are dependent upon principles of constant motion of a whirling (vortex) type, with an associated radiating component, and this description duplicated in a surprising degree Schillinger's summary of the projection of a melody. Here we have an interesting illustration of a transposable form (gestalt) from the fields of visual and auditory experience, *both arising out of the abstract beauty of the dynamic, logarithmic spiral.* It is also significant that on the psychological level the logarithmic curve is used to plot the goal gradient of human effort and achievement. Keeping all this in mind, does it not appear that we are correct in suggesting that a planetary choreography which combines the drama of the time-form of experience with the chiaroscuro of the space-form may well be the precursor of a new art for mankind?

In any case — whatever new art-form may arise — the advance from one rung on the ladder of emergence to the next calls for the supplementary process of mutation. If the next big step is now at hand, the new system of intercommunication that will come into being will create its own scanning devices for an all-world symbolism.

When the neuroblasts of the giant embryo have proliferated the structure of the world sensorium, the symbolism will function on two levels. In the first place, there will be the 'secular' significance of history as observed behavioristically. And in the second place, there will be the inner spiritual meaning, connected with its own level of communication.

We have already dealt with the secular meaning of history, so that, for the moment, nothing needs to be added to our discussion of this topic. With respect to the inner or spiritual meaning, we note once more that this takes us into a consideration of the second kind of communication. Let us therefore return for a moment to this type of level of communication.

We have posed this question: if humanity is the emerging social cortex of an embryonic world organism, does this not suggest the possibility that there is (or is being created) a "psychic ether" analogous to (or identical with) the super-dispersive sub-ether as the foundational continuum for the functioning of the constituent waves of the archetypal universe? If the psychic field is an *emergent* medium, could it be that this *Psi*-layer surrounds the earth like a Kennelly-Heaviside layer, reflecting the thoughts and images of mankind as the ion blanket reflects radio waves of certain frequencies back to the earth? Here we have no knowledge. It is a well-known fact that a medium which is 'transparent' to one octave of frequencies may be 'opaque' to another. What is required is that we have information about the phase and group velocities of the radiation.[7] It may be that *Psi* influences which originate on this planet are earth-bound, because there is an umbrella (*Psi*-layer) which prevents the frequencies from escaping, just as the ion blanket operates in reverse in shielding our globe from excessive ultra-violet rays from the sun. Is it possible that such a layer might provide a vehicle or medium for the manifestation of parapsychological phenomena as these have been studied so intensively by Dr. J. B. Rhine? At present such manifestations as telepathy, for instance, are flickering and fitful at best. Whether one receives such messages may depend not only on subjective factors (innate talent, for example), but also on where one is on the earth's surface with respect to the source of the message at the time of the sending. That is, the reception of the message (even though in a sense independent of distance, i.e., velocity of transmission in the medium) may depend on where one is, in the same way that good radio reception depends on one's position relative to the radio waves that are reflected back to the earth.

We are frank to admit that this hypothesis exploits an analogy, — the possible isomorphism obtaining between a human brain and the world sensorium still to be created. In the individual human brain the electrical activity of the cerebral hemispheres is revealed by the brain waves which can be tapped at the cortex as alpha rhythms. But another (though related) way of studying brain waves was reported at the annual meeting of the A.A.A.S. at Philadelphia (December, 1951). On this occasion Dr. John C. Lilly explained how a new type of television circuit had been constructed in which the electrical activity of the brain of a living animal is changed into patterns of light and shade.

As reported in the *New York Times* (December 29, 1951), the special apparatus designed to study the activity of the brain in relation to psychological processes consisted of twenty-five electrodes, placed on the brain of a cat in an area of one tenth square inch, plus twenty-five amplifiers and twenty-five glow lamps, placed before a motion picture camera. Connections are made with the electrodes and amplifiers so that the apparatus functions like a crude television set, turning electrical brain waves into visible light and shade. The local 'apparitions', some of which appear spontaneously from within the brain and others in response to external stimuli, are parts of larger forms which move within wide areas of the brain. Thus they resemble atmospheric clouds which appear in the air, grow to larger size, and then disappear into thin air. Perhaps, therefore, if our homomorphic imagery is sound, the apparitions of the world cortex are the gestalt patterns which are the electroencephalogram semantography of the planetary brain.

In speculating about the *Psi*-layer we have posed the supposition that above and around the earth there is perhaps a psychic ether which provides the field for the phenomena of parapsychology. It is not clear to what extent such phenomena as telepathy, clairvoyance, and the psychokinetic effect might find an explanation in this higher energy-field, linking individual minds into a genuine psycho-social continuum. But at least we would have here a medium with properties sufficiently different from those of the space-time relations of the engineer's middle-scale universe to serve as a matrix for paranormal manifestations.

To suppose, as we do, that the constituent waves of the Cosmic Field, or sub-ether, are transmitted with something approximating an 'infinite velocity' is in effect to say that the usual properties of space and time do not apply to the Cosmic Field. The Cosmic Continuum is outside the space and time coördinates of all finite frames of reference. Thus the Field may possess properties that underpin the relations exhibited in *ESP* — i.e., the inverse square law does not apply. In brief, the Cosmic Imagination could be the 'All-Knower,' and precognition and clairvoyance are then evidence that the 'omniscience' of the Cosmic Field may filter down into human consciousness, so that what is the 'future' in a given finite cöordinate system may be 'present' in the Cosmic Field. Accordingly if what the Cosmic Field is aware of can appear in human consciousness, such consciousness can 'know' what is distant in the space and time of the manifest world, the world of 'physical' relations.

Obviously this approach has implications for parapsychology. For one thing — as we have emphasized — it means that *evolution is not yet finished with the human organism, for still higher functions are in process of development.* Furthermore, we surmise that Humanity is a god in embryo, a developing being with those psychic powers of omniscience and omnipotence which man hitherto has assigned to his god. Such a theory of the source of man's extra-sensory powers would be in harmony with the view of E. Servadio[8] that telepathic experience may be an original and archaic way of establishing understanding between individuals which, in the course of time, has been replaced by sign communication. Servadio does not believe that telepathic transference can be produced experimentally on a rational and conscious level. But this fact — if such it be — that telepathy cannot be reproduced at the logical-rational level does not mean that it cannot be reproduced. According to our own three-level scheme of orientations, the coming superlogical level could reinstate a type of unity which would make it appear as a kind of regression to a more primitive mode of response, when in fact it is an adumbration of a coming unity. In that event, *ESP* and *Psi* phenomena generally are flickering and fitful anticipations of the integration of a giant organism in which humans function as neuroblasts of the world sensorium — cells in the social cortex which the electromagnetic society is beginning to proliferate.

If some of the foregoing ideas seem a bit unorthodox, the reader should remember that these are times when all traditional patterns —

intellectual as well as social — are in the melting pot. New molds are being cast, and some of these are surely destined to possess more enduring values. One reason we have for entertaining a bit of confidence in our conclusions is that they are never entirely novel, having been adumbrated in one way or another by this or that thinker — as the following reflections once more indicate.

XII. The "Vital Force" or the "Cosmic Imagination"

We have already seen that the idea is not new that living systems are super-mechanical, — that living matter is 'disentropic' in maintaining its organization at the cost of the environment. So far as I am able to discover, the first thinker to suppose that life may escape the tendency toward the degradation of energy was the great Helmholtz. He, at any rate, was the first scientist to gain a clear notion of 'energy' as something different from 'force.' Following Helmholtz, other scientists continued this debate as to whether organic systems obey the second law of thermodynamics. The vitalists argued that the phenomena of living systems are not deducible from this law. Hans Driesch, for example, suggested that *entelechy* may suspend the operation of this law. Henri Bergson also held that *l'elan vital* could retard the tendency toward the degradation of energy. As he put it in his great work, *Creative Evolution*, whenever energy, descending the incline indicated by Carnot's law, meets with a cause of inverse direction, *there life appears.*

This idea that living systems are supermechanical because a 'vital force' lifts the organism above the level of physical laws has never been a part of my philosophy. Life is supermechanical — yes — but so are atoms and molecules! As physical organisms endowed with imagination (organizing fields), they are supermechanical in the sense that the Newtonian-Laplacian classical physics, — the physics of particles without fields, — is not adequate for the description of their behavior. So what we assert in our philosophy is that life is supermechanical, but it still obeys the laws of energetics. If there seems to be a paradox here, I hope it will be resolved in the following paragraphs.

In my early articles dealing with this problem, I pointed out that the second law need not be interpreted to imply a tendency toward 'disorder,' but a tendency toward a new kind of order. My own views on this matter were influenced by the applications made of the second law by Gestalt psychology. Moreover, even before Eddington and Jeans, I had proposed that in the brain there is a one-way increase in entropy to which our consciousness responds, and thus the rate of time passage as experienced in consciousness (Bergson's *duree*) is a function of body temperature. The soundness of this approach was demonstrated when Hudson Hoagland[9] showed that the human time-sense is a function of the velocity constants of the chemical reactions of the brain. Later I modified my own view to the extent that the velocity of the unidirectional passage of conscious time was regarded as a physiological 'modulation' superposed on the underlying velocity relative to a Cosmic Field (sub-ether) which is the Infinite-Eternal Continuum which maintains the cosmos as a going concern.

If it is possible to simplify all this, we come out with the following: *communication is the process whereby nature produces second order or complex simplicities out of first order or simple simplicities.* That is to say, when particles on the same level dynamically interact with others of the same kind to produce an emergent whole with gestalt properties, there is communication between the parts of the new whole. Thus, as atoms interact to produce molecules, and molecules interact to produce cells, and cells interact to produce multicellular organisms, and humans interact to produce a world organism, it is as if one of the constituents of the whole said to its fellow-members: "this is what I have to offer; now what do you contribute?" In this process there is a degradation of energy, as indicated by the entropy principle, and this represents the tendency of the system to lose potential energy to its environment.

However, even though the entropy principle applies to the systems, this does not explain fully their wholeness: dynamic interactions by way of media are required (electrostatic fields of force in the case of atomic syntheses), and the concepts of statistical mechanics are relevant; nevertheless, in so far as an archetypal field of influence is involved, this has no mass-inertia-entropy properties. Whether there can be "interactions" *between* archetypal fields (e.g., physical fields and biological fields), I am not prepared to say. This could have some bearing on the possibility of the *psychokinetic effect*, — if this is genuine, etc. On that matter I prefer to reserve judgment, for the present.

In this synthesis of cosmology and epistemology we are generalizing the notions of information, communication, and cognate ideas. Atoms are considered to be organisms, and organisms are regarded as collections of atoms, but atoms are societies of selves in the same way in which a multicellular organism is itself a population of cells. Such self-integrating multiplicities are held together by interlacing lines of communication for the acquisition, retention, and transmission of information. In our scheme, therefore, the process of communication through the interaction of parts of an emergent whole does not necessarily introduce 'disorder'; it may only tend to bring about another and wider type of order or unity. Information-transmission may therefore be indicative of the trend of local statistical ensembles toward more inclusive organizations with transposable public times and a higher level of social signals.

When all is said and done, however, it must be admitted that we still have two types of communication. In the first instance, at the bottom level of nature, where the ultimate constituents emerge from the Ocean of Electrical Density which is the Cosmic Field, there is communication between the parts in the peculiar sense that there is information available in the atom as a whole; but this, we note, does not rest upon a point-to-point transmission. That is to say that the organizing field, — without *mass*, because mass is a feature of the manifest or particle-universe, – controls the behavior of the parts by something like 'action-at-a-distance,' and this 'instantaneousness' resembles the 'infinite velocity' transmission in a sub-ether. The facts in the case have been well stated by Margenau, and I quote [10] his summary:

> "Here physics has the following to say. Consider first the process of building up a complex atom from its constituents: the nucleus and the extranuclear electrons. To understand it, the Exclusion Principle is required only in its qualitative form. The first electron added to the nucleus may move in any way permitted by the laws of motion. The second, if present alone, would settle into the same state as the first; *but the presence of the first electron forces the second into a different state of motion.* To put it crudely, the second electron somehow 'knows' the first is there, even though it did not interact with it by forces. Nor is this of purely theoretical consequence, for among other things the prescience of the second electron makes the compound diamagnetic, whereas the first alone gave rise to paramagnetism. The third electron, when added, must take a different state from the other two, thereby generating new properties of the result-

ing structure. As the process continues, all the elements in the periodic table with their different chemical characteristics are formed."

But while we thus recognize a kind of communication in this case which does not involve time, on any higher levels of the manifest world the transmission of information does 'take' time. On the human level, for example, the velocity may be fast (radio) or slow (surface mail), but in any case it involves a finite velocity. However, if there be such a thing as telepathy, clairvoyance, and the other data of parapsychology, we have here to appeal to the space-free and time-free properties of the sub-ether to provide a basis for such massless, timeless, spaceless phenomena as *Psi* data exhibit.

The one great problem we have left, then, is the ever-baffling riddle of why nature is not satisfied to remain on the first level of manifestation (hydrogen atoms), but insists on climbing up the dimensional ladder of reality. At various points in the development of the present viewpoint alternative answers have been given. At one time we sought the explanation in terms of resident fields of the microscopic constituents which strive to produce a macroscopic field by integrating the parts into a more inclusive whole which is magnetically self-contained. On other occasions I sought to show that the slow accumulation of an angular momentum to create a macroscopic spin effect, an off-at-right-angles emergent dimension, was the explanation. Thus the Cosmic Lens might even have *spin*, and this influence of the field on matter might introduce a spiraling effect in nature that creates macroscopic integration. If somehow we could relate this second alternative to the presence of a 'precognitive' imagination in each physical organism and suppose that this provides an inherent striving toward a new order of relatedness, creativity would be both a spiraling effect and evidence of the activity of a Cosmic Imagination. At the risk of a slight digression, let me follow this up momentarily.

Astronomers still do not understand why galaxies develop arms, nor why these arms have a spiral form. One possible explanation may be found in the new *magneto-hydrodynamic waves* recently studied by Professor Hannes Alfvén (see his book, *Cosmical Electrodynamics*, 1950). It is now known that intragalactic space is permeated by magnetic fields, produced quite probably by electric currents circulating in space. If so, a galaxy such as ours is an immense electromagnet, with currents circulating through the turbulent gases that swirl about and along with the galaxy as it revolves around its center.

In our own cosmology, especially as outlined in my 1954 *Scientia* article, it is proposed that the *Cosmic Lens* is able to transform field energy into matter, and in that connection (i.e., the spin of the Lens) reference was made to Professor Alfvén's magneto-hydrodynamic waves. If angular momentum can be transferred from field to matter, we have some confirmation of our Pantheism based on the idea that the Cosmic Field exercises an overlordship in relation to material systems.

From these developments it is but one further step to make use of Professor Felix Ehrenhaft's view that there are not only the presently recognized forces, the force of gravity, the magnetic action of electrical currents, and the recently discovered magneto-hydrodynamic effects mentioned above — but there is a new force, the electrical action of magnetic currents. If it be true that there are magnetic currents which flow through the universe, we might have here, not only a bridge between the Cosmic Lens and the magneto-hydrodynamic forces involved in galactic rotation, but also a span between the electromagnetic phenomena of brain activity and mind which somehow maintains a causal connection with its own body, so long as it is tied to that body. With that vague suggestion, I leave the matter for the present.

Whatever the explanation of the integration of microscopic constituents into macroscopic unities to produce new rungs in the ladder of emergence, it is undoubtedly true that biological evolution is the history of systems undergoing irreversible changes. Therefore, as a principle of irreversibility, the second law of thermodynamics does have a relevant application to biological evolution. The applicability of the second law to living systems has been questioned not only (as we have seen) because of the suspicion that life may be supermechanical, but also because the thermodynamic definition of entropy was applicable only to closed systems which reach time-independent equilibrium states of minimum free energy, whereas living systems are able to maintain themselves in a steady-state by importation of materials (therefore no longer 'closed' systems) rich in free energy. Therefore, to apply thermodynamical principles to living systems, it was necessary, as pointed out by L. von Bertalanffy[11], to extend the boundaries of classical thermodynamics by the addition of new hypotheses to cover the open systems of life processes.

Accordingly the application of the second law to living systems may also allow for other principles (of field physics, for example) as having relevance. But if the present cosmology is on the right track, no modifications of the second law of thermodynamics will make it applicable to the universe as a whole. That is to say that it is not a law of the Cosmos, for the cosmos is not a spatially closed system but rather, it is open to plus and minus infinity. Quite probably the entropy principle is a feature of each and every 'local' system, — metagalaxies, galaxies, planetary systems, with their evolutionary trends, — but the one place where reversibility does obtain is in the cosmic energy-matter cycle. It is in this peculiar sense that the cosmos is 'closed' — though, as noted before, it is 'open' in relation to the emergent dimensions which are pyramided on the base level foundation. On the whole, the processes of assimilation are compensatory to the processes of dissimilation. To that extent creation balances destruction — an eternal rhythm. If, with respect to the widest feedback, there is a complete reciprocity between field and matter, we have a picture of a reality which is making itself in a reality which is unmaking itself, to use Bergson's phraseology. This view is reminiscent of the Oriental doctrine of samsara — a serpent swallowing its own tail!

From all this it appears that our universe is one of polarities and complementarities. There has to be irreversibility of processes in local (finite) systems in order that there can be reversibility of the cosmic feed-back; there must be corpuscularity in the manifest world in order that there can be the continuity of the field-plenum which is the unmanifest world; there is time, change, directionality, and purpose in the manifest world though there is no time, change, or teleology in the unmanifest world; there has to be a world-mind if there is to be a world-body — but the world-body which is matter must continually destroy itself in order to replenish and sustain the Cosmic Mind. In these polarities, there is no question of priority: each pole is necessary to the other.

XII. Summary: Archetypal Forms and Orthosynthesis

What confronts us, at the present time, is an immense problem in programming: a production number such as this old world of ours seldom witnessed. To say that man must first write the play before he can enact it is to miss the point: he is writing the play *now*, as he lives it, a 'psychodrama' such as Moreno never conceived. The simple fact is that the dénouement can be unfolded only as the curtain rises on the next act of the cyclodrama and man is forced to create a planetary meaning in order to find out what it is all about. Even the Cosmic Imagination does not know the 'end of the story' — for the Supreme Imagination is personified on the human level in evolving man. Is man equal to the self-transfiguration which this programming calls for? And if so, how can this be brought about?

The poet William Blake speculated that the 'fall of man' occurred when man's intellect was separated from feeling and imagination. The restoration of the unity of personality which Blake envisioned is what Northrop Frye described as 'fearful symmetry.' The 'symmetry' of man will have been consummated and the evils of fragmentation overcome when man returns to a higher-level atonement — the psychological 'garden of Eden' which has variously been described as the head-heart synthesis or a cortico-thalamic integration.

The synthesis as we here project it will lean heavily upon the contributions and symbolisms of the arts. In this connection, we have seen that in terms of what tradition has given us, music and mathematics are the only forms of expression which approximate a universal appeal and invariant symbolism. Moreover, since the one, music, is primarily emotional in its appeal, while the other, mathematics, is predominantly intellectual — to use elementalistic terms — we observe that they provide the best examples of the aesthetic component and the theoretic component of Professor Northrop's duality as set forth in *The Meeting of East and West.* Together, these two provide the basis for the 'meeting' as a synthesis of the intuitive experience and the objectively oriented methodology.

Such discoveries of the *universals* of a world philosophy advance the cause of unity and confirm the surmises concerning the deeper analogies of Oriental and Occidental thought. If it be true, as some scholars argue, that *Maya* of India is *electrons* in Western science, and *Akasha-Kala* is *space-time*, in a manner which harmonizes East and West, subjective and objective, ancient and modern, then indeed the goal of the unity of knowledge becomes a legitimate object of pursuit. Already in music and mathematics, therefore, we possess two languages — emotional and intellectual — which, between them, may provide the basis for further developments in the direction of an all-world symbolism for mankind. After many tentative gropings, humanity will proliferate the forms of an invariant iconography transferable across the social whole, providing us with maximum freedom from special linguistic frameworks. In this fashion man may eventually cast off the mental shackles of elementalistic frameworks and create a wholingua for a planetary civilization. This emergent synthesis of a new simplicity, erected upon the eternal foundation of archetypal forms, is what we mean by *orthosynthesis*: the science and the art of conscious and creative evolution.

When we speak of orthosynthesis as an art, we have evidently assigned an important rôle to the aesthetic component of social embryology. But what *is* the rôle of the arts in humanity's great experiment in spiritual alchemy? To discover the possibilities, we must ever and again return to the distinction between the 'arts of space' and the 'arts of time' as these supposedly indicate the structural-static and the functional-dynamic features of the aesthetic experience.

Under the first category tradition has placed painting, sculpture, architecture, and the like, while within the second were placed music, poetry, drama, and the rest, where "meaning" as dependent upon the temporal development of a theme is what is important. In the main, the arts of space have a visual appeal, while the arts of time have an auditory and kinaesthetic appeal. But the most significant thing is that certain art-forms, such as the dance, the cinema, and drama, span both fields — they are space-time arts.

To exploit this situation properly, let us return to the thought that someday mankind may reinstate on a higher level the type of psychic unity which perhaps prevailed on a more primitive level (the 'garden of Eden'), before this unity was fragmented into divergent paths of social evolution. If such a restoration of unity be attainable, it will come through a new art-form with a universal symbolism and appeal that will fuse the arts of space and time. While science would provide the formal principles of construction, the ultimate appeal would rest upon the aesthetic components. The creator of this new art-form would be the man-god whose coming Emerson foretold.

To portray something of the potentialities of a new planetary art-form, let us recall the theme of the Apostle Paul's speech on Mars Hill, where Saint Paul interprets to the Athenians the meaning of their statue to the "Unknown God." It is significant, however, that long before the beginnings of Christianity, Stonehenge stood as a circular symbol of a still earlier form of religious worship. The student, meditating on these deep impulses of awe and reverence, may wonder whether a renascence of worship might not find its present personification in a kind of globalized Stonehenge as a planetary sacrament, symbolizing God's plan for man because it embodies mankind's godlike capacity for self-recreation through social embryology.

Is it not Emerson who somewhere quotes an antiquarian as saying that Stonehenge is God's scheme for the world? This reminds one of Sheldon Cheney's statement that the coming feature of housing will be a reduction of opaque, fixed wall sections, so that — to use a kind of projective geometry — the entire world becomes our movie screen, and we sit in our glass houses by the side of the road friendly to man. The Stonehenge circle then expands and the whole world becomes a stage, with the sweepaway sliding off into the horizon that expands to planetary proportions. On that day, when the Supreme Imagination communes with man, we might stage a great visual drama, a play on an immense scale, which will stir our imaginations and we may then see ourselves as actors on a stage as big as the world itself. This would mark the beginning of a new era in the cyclodrama of mankind.

Taking light as the oldest symbol of ethical aspiration, we could use the movie cathedrals as community centers: each a Plato-cave of shadowgraphs, working through an alchemy of light and sound, to epitomize the space-time drama of our planet as the analogue of Minkowski's four-dimensional continuum. Every home equipped with television would become a part of a planetary cathedral and each spectator a participant in a wholingua communion service. This pantomime would portray the cyclodrama of humanity. Using a central clocking broadcast to act as a universal drum for movie houses and homes alike, we would build up a tremendous stirring through all the countries of the world. This gathering of the energies of humanity through an all-world drama would lift us up, cast a spell over the human race, and we would at long last visualize man's rôle on the earth's revolving stage.

What would happen if all the members of the human family were thus to imagine the same thoughts at the same time, everywhere on the world's great circles? It would be as if, at some agreed upon time, a kind of planetary hour of sunrise for all mankind, all peoples of this terrestrial globe were to turn to a universal mecca and hearken to the prayerful intonations of a sort of Polar Muezzin at the very roof of the world. This would be a universal invocation — an orthosynthesis of symbolism — in terms of a choreography of meaningful movement in the cohesive sequence of a planetary drama.

But to what purpose? What could man accomplish by this cycloramic experiment? This is for man to decide. If we could get this play of epic proportions before the mind's eye, we could condense the space-time meaning of the drama — and man might see himself in the setting of social embryology as the head-end or advance wave of evolution, precipitating the skeletal structure of a new mode or level of existence.

From all this it must certainly be obvious that our form of Humanism — a Cosmic Humanism — is no parochial, man-centered theory. Ours is a bipolar philosophy with the infinite cosmos outside as one pole and man himself as the other, with human civilization as the complex product of their interactions. The awesome function of education is to elevate the modes of existence in the spiral of human evolution. But on all levels, reconstruction of the older order must accompany the creation of the new. The cosmos is an eternal rhythm of destruction of the ancient and the creation of the new.

The question as to which will ultimately triumph — good or evil — is a meaningless question. Neither good nor evil, construction nor destruction, will ultimately triumph because both are correlative processes. A utopia in which everything is good, where all problems are solved, would be a dull world. Total security in a static universe is a tired liberal's dream — or a sign of senility — and in neither case presents a worthy fate for man. The most that we can do on the human level is create faster than we destroy. It is this fact of the freedom of man to plot his curve of self-evolution which makes us somewhat hopeful of the future.

FOOTNOTES CHAPTER XII

[1]See the article on "The Transition from Unicellular to the Multicellular Individuals," in *Biologica Symposia*, Vol. III.

[2]Quoted from the Editorial Summary by F. L. Kunz, in *Main Currents in Modern Thought*, December, 1942.

[3]Cf. "Foundations of Mathematical Biophysics," *Philosophy of Science*, Vol. 1, 1934, 176-196; and "On the Physical Nature of 'Cytotropism,'" *Journal of General Physiology*, Vol. 15, 1932, 298-306.

[4]The importance of this was first pointed out to me by Dr. William M. Martin. See his article, "Consciousness as Organismic Physiological Functioning," *Psychological Review*, Vol. 54, 1947, 99-115.

[5]Cf. "The Beginnings of Social Behavior in Unicellular Organisms," by H. S. Jennings, *Science*, Vol. 92, 1940, 539-546.

[6]Cf. "Particle and Field Concepts in Biology," by Henry Margenau, *Scientific Monthly*, Vol. 64, 1947, 225-231.

[7]The problem of the mathematical properties of media which are superdispersive or possess superconductivity is complex and difficult. Readers who are interested in this topic may consult the article, "On the Theory of Superconductivity," by H. B. G. Casimir, in the cooperative volume, *Niels Bohr and the Development of Physics*, edited by W. Pauli (1955). See also T. L. Eckersley's Letter, "A Quantum Relation in Large Scale Electric Wave Phenomena," in *Nature*, Vol. 119, 1927, p. 234.

[8]Cf. "Psychoanalysis and Telepathy," by E. Servadio, *Imago*, Vol. 21, No. 4.

[9]See the discussion, "The Chemistry of Time," by Hudson Hoagland and O. L. Reiser, *Philosophy of Science*, Vol. 1, 1934, p. 351.

[10]Cf. "The Exclusion Principle and Its Philosophical Importance," by Henry Margenau, *Philosophy of Science*, Vol. 11, 1944, 187-209. The lines at the beginning of the present chapter are quoted from this article.

[11]See his article, "The Theory of Open Systems in Physics and Biology," *Science* Vol. 111, 1950. 23-29.

13

ARCHETYPAL HUMANITY: AVATAR OF SYNTHESIS

I. The Challenge of Parapsychology

The aim of the present chapter is to outline a possible explanation of 'parapsychology,' a term which designates the extra-sensory phenomena of the human mind exhibited by extra-sensory perception, telepathy, clairvoyance, and psychokinesis. Taken together, these phenomena are designated as *Psi*-phenomena. It is becoming clearer with each passing decade that the explanation of *Psi*-phenomena requires a completely integrated philosophy, one which, when it appears, will seem quite fantastic from the viewpoint of present-day science. But the facts, if substantiated, are themselves astonishing, and a satisfactory theory to explain them can hardly be less "fantastic."

The following approach assumes that the factual data and status of *Psi*-phenomena are no longer in question. This assumption, which science will not yet admit, is necessary in order to help break down the unwillingness even to consider the data because, it is alleged, the phenomena are utterly inconceivable.

Scientists have generally presented a solid front against the conclusions of those research workers who are investigating the phenomena of parapsychology. However, among the various scientific groups the physicists have been somewhat less hostile toward the positive results in this field. Physicists, more than other groups, recognize the possibility that future discoveries may provide a common basis of energy exchanges between what is obviously 'physical' and those exceptional phenomena termed 'Psi.' For example, nuclear physicists are aware that a great riddle exists in the nature of the forces that act between nucleons, forces quite unfamiliar in that, unlike gravitational and electromagnetic forces, they are very intense and of short range.

Knowing this qualitatively, the physicist may be less surprised at 'psychokinesis' and 'extra-sensory perceptions' because he is already conditioned to revolutionary discoveries which upset old ideas. For him *psi*-phenomena could be but one more upheaval in a century marked by upheavals.

II. Some Findings in the Field

In the volume, *Extra-Sensory Perception After Sixty Years*, Dr. J. B. Rhine and his collaborators summarize the findings in this field. Among the facts which are supposed to have been established are these: there is no positive physical relationship which regulates *ESP*; no known energy serves as the mediating causal link between the stimulus object and the recipient; *ESP* does not seem to be influenced by practice; it is independent of bodily orientation; it does not permit of introspective localization; and it is a most unstable ability, disappearing suddenly or gradually, often without recognizable cause. It must be noted, however, that although *ESP* is erratic, strong motivations (conditions arousing interest) seem to improve the functioning.

It is evident that the announced findings of parapsychology certainly pose baffling mysteries. It is precisely because of the unusual nature of *ESP* and *Pk* phenomena that orthodox psychologists veer away from the investigations. Among the many problems raised by the findings, several stand out as especially interesting.

III. Problems Raised by Psi-Phenomena

1) Why is the capacity to demonstrate *ESP* confined to relatively few persons who maintain a steady scoring level through months or even years of experimentation, while in the rest of us this ability is apparently non-existent, or at least difficult to demonstrate at all times?

2) What is the correlation between personality types and *ESP* scoring levels? Why are some kinds of persons more 'psychic' than others?

3) Why is the *ESP* scoring level apparently influenced by drugs, and modified by interest, emotion, and perhaps other subjective factors?

4) Why does the scoring level so often decline toward the end of the run of experiments?

5) How is it possible for *Psi*-phenomena to set aside the normal space and time relations of causal connections, especially the inverse square law, and proceed as if the ordinary limiting conditions of physical phenomena do not hold?

These are certainly difficult questions to answer. It is not surprising that relatively few theories have been put forth in this area.

IV. Tentative Advances Toward a Theory

My interest in the field of parapsychology is not new. In returning to a theory of extra-sensory perception[1] I presented in 1939 I find little to discard, although it is necessary to rework some ideas which were vague or incomplete. The development of the science of cybernetics since that writing certainly necessitates some expansion of my earlier views. Hence the following formulations may be required for a general theory of *Psi*-phenomena.

1. — *The cosmic background of Psi.* This was not a well developed component of the original theory.

2. — *A generalized notion of energy levels.* This culminates in the theory of isomorphic patterns (or homomorphic images), from atomic through biological to cortical levels of organization.

3. — *A theory of emergent evolution.*

4. — *The inheritance of archetypal forms in the collective unconscious of man.* This was not a part of the original theory, and it is not yet clear that it is essential in the present form of the theory.

5. — *A generalized theory of communication.* This phase of the new formulation, especially in relation to cybernetics, was not a part of the first effort at synthesis. It will appear that there are really two kinds of communication.

6. — *The theory of the electromagnetic society.* As corollaries of this concept, set forth in later publications, I shall have something to say about a 'mental foetus' which may preform the functional unity of an emerging planetary civilization.

7. — *The resonance between the homomorphic images in human mental patterns and the mind of the world sensorium.* This part constitutes a restatement of some earlier views.

8. — *The Psi-layer of the earth-organism.* This phase of the comprehensive theory is also new.

Let me preview what the present hypothesis involves, namely, a theory of a coming psycho-social unity involving a universal or all-world symbolism which provides the basis for a higher synthesis. That is, in the electromagnetic society of the future there will be gestalt patterns transposable across the social whole which make possible a psychic unity of mankind.

The development of such an hypothesis rests upon the use of a three-level analogy (homomorphism) between the functions of (1) the *electromagnetic brains* which are now constructed to 'think,' and (2) the *human nervous system*, with its high-level power of synthesis, and (3) a *coming electromagnetic society*, with its network of ganglia and electronic spiderwebs, — such as are employed in radio, television, and radar devices, — creating the matrix of a giant planetary brain within which the developing nerve cells (or neuroblasts) may proliferate.[2] The common denominator of the three levels of electrical communication is provided by the mechanisms which 'scan' the symbolism and transmit the form-patterns across the social whole.

In order to exfoliate this conception, it is necessary to investigate the homomorphic images which appear on the three levels of (1) the *electronic computers*, (2) the *human brain*, and (3) the *planetary cortex* of the world sensorium. This is our program in the remainder of this final chapter. Let us now consider in turn each of the eight formulations mentioned above.

V. The Cosmic Background

According to the present philosophy, the key to an understanding of *Psi*-phenomena is to be found in the rôle played by a transtemporal guiding field, a field of influence without the material properties of *mass* and *inertia* which controls the creation and the evolution of universes (galaxies). The supreme or most inclusive of these guiding fields is termed the *Cosmic Imagination*. My own views at this point were developed in harmony with the formulations of my collaborator, Mr. B. G. H. Vanderjagt, and the two sets of ideas are now harmonized into a world-view designated as the cyclic-creative cosmology.[3]

In the cyclic-creative cosmology there is a combination of two ideas: the notion of a steady-state universe (here we agree with Fred Hoyle's cosmology and disagree with the Lemaître-Gamow 'big bang' theory), plus the idea of a creative process of evolution within an all-encompassing Cosmic Field. Thus we posit a centroidal continuum (a field-plenum) with orderly cumulative energy forms emerging from the background reservoir across the threshold into the manifest universe of waves and particles. The complete circle of the passage of energy is from its undifferentiated source in the unmanifest world, through a Cosmic Lens as the impersonal formative agent, into the manifest world, and then on up the evolutionary ladder, from subatomic particles to mankind. At the end of the line there is a feedback of energy into the Cosmic Field, which completes one circle and begins the cycle anew. According to current physics, the energy of matter comes from an unknown source and proceeds outward toward an equally unknown destiny. If the *source* and the *sink* can be tied together in this manner (by way of an unmanifest universe supporting a manifest universe), we have an explanation of where matter gets its energy and why the universe has not run down long ago. This matter-energy cycle is reminiscent of the oriental image of eternity — a serpent swallowing its own tail, a cosmic *samsara.*

If this approach is correct, one prerequisite to an understanding of 'psychic' phenomena is the recognition of an intelligent (time-spanning) guiding field which stands outside all finite coördinate systems in space and time. The Supreme Imagination is the Cosmic Guiding Field. But *imagination*, whether divine or human, is defined as the *organizing field of influence which puts parts together in their right times and places to make products.* Everything in the universe, and the universe (galaxy) itself, is a *product,* and so it is possible to write the equation as follows:

$$Product = \int_{t_1}^{t_2} (Matter + Labor + Imagination)$$

According to this conception, the background material out of which universes (galaxies) are constructed is provided by atomic hydrogen, and hydrogen atoms are *products,* and therefore conform to the Vandergjagt formula:

$$P = \int_{t_1}^{t_2} (a\,dx + b\,dy + c\,dz),$$

where t_1 and t_2 are the time limits within which a product is made, x is the *matter* (electrons and nucleons), y is the *labor* (work), and z is the *imagination* (organizing field, without mass). Therefore, the Cosmic Imagination creates the hydrogen atoms, the 'mother stuff' of universes. But the hydrogen atoms are not created out of nothing, *ex nihilo,* as the Bondi-Hoyle cosmology maintains, but out of the field-plenum according to Einstein's equation, $E = mc^2$, and having once been created, the atomic hydrogen is transmuted into the heavier elements of the material world.[4]

If we can show that evolution is guided by the Cosmic Imagination, the emergence of a *world sensorium* becomes a plausible expectation, the foreshadowings of which can be discerned even now. In order to provide some of the building materials and lay the foundations for this philosophy of nature, I shall pause for a moment and discuss the general topic of 'linear programming.'

1. *Linear Programming and the Electronic Paradox*

As one considers recent developments in the field of cybernetics and atomic physics, it appears that modern science has maneuvered itself into a strange situation which may be referred to as the 'electronic paradox.' A newly developed branch of study, called "linear programming," has come into existence. Programming is a procedure used in the field of electronic computing machines in calculating the best possible solution to a problem stated in the form of linear equations which involve a number of variables. The problem is to find a maximum value for some course of action which is to be chosen. In the typical case, calling for the extension of statistical methods to the area of decision, this can be done by digital computer devices which solve the problems more economically than does the human brain.

In situations where one is faced by alternative courses of action (in a game of chess, for example), each choice admits of several possible consequences, thus introducing 'probability event chains' which make it difficult to anticipate the best possible solution. However, the use of electronic calculators reduces decision making to something like a science. To 'mechanize' decisions it is necessary to establish a value-system which is then integrated into a statistical procedure for predicting the outcomes of the possible choices. Thus all that is required is that one feed the machine the necessary data, set the machine in operation, and await the answer. This new development is related to 'operational research,' the 'theory of games,' and 'information theory.'

Other investigations have shown that guesses and hunches play an important rôle in even the most rigorously deductive reasoning. Among the studies dealing with the rôle of intuitions and guesses in mathematics is the earlier work of Henri Poincaré as reported in his book, *Science and Method*, and the more recent investigations of Professor George Polya as summarized in his two volume work, *Mathematics and Plausible Reasoning.* These studies indicate that in some instances the human mind does by 'hunches' what the electronic calculator does 'laboriously,' in the sense that reverberating feed-back circuits employing thousands of vacuum tubes are required. Up to this point there is no paradox, — only a possible ambiguity in the term 'laborious.'

Now we come to something more remarkable. In a very real sense the atom is also a 'programming' agent. Recently some scientists at the University of Illinois constructed a massive electronic brain, named *Illiac,* to solve problems of atomic physics which would take the lifetime of a mathematician to solve. Among such unsolved problems is that of the 'helium wave equation,' the problem of finding the equation for the movements of the particles in helium atoms. A similar problem has already been solved for the hydrogen atom; helium comes next, having two extra-nuclear electrons. However, it is interesting to note that *Illiac* gives only a law of probability for the distances of the electrons from the helium nuclei at any time.

Here we begin to see something puzzling: the electron is able to solve a problem which, when stated as a mathematical problem for the human thinker, cannot be solved by man. But a machine made by the mind of man can solve the problem! The machine is an electronic calculator, and it requires thousands of tubes, made of atoms, to solve an equation which the atoms themselves have already solved. But more remarkable still, the human thinker, also made of atoms, cannot solve the problems through step-by-step thinking, though by clever guessing he can sometimes hit upon the right answer (for example, de Broglie's wave equation for the electron or Planck's quantum constant).

If the reader doubts that the atom is a programming agent (perhaps a non-linear or wholistic rather than a linear agent) and does 'intuitively' what *Illiac* does laboriously by way of operations performed on information given as input, let him review the facts set forth by Pauli's 'exclusion principle,' according to which electrons in the atoms seem to 'know' about each other's presence even though they do not interact by known physical forces.[5] The interesting thing in this case is that in atomic processes we have something like *action at a distance.* Thus, Pauli's principle points to a phenomenon which is analogous to certain phenomena in parapsychology. If this is the case, is the wholeness of the atom analogous to *PK* (psychokinesis), in which the *organizing field* (*imagination*) of the atom-as-a-whole puts the parts together in their right times and places to make a product? Or is it that when an electron is put into its orbit, the other electron of the helium atom 'knows' by *ESP* (telepathy or clairvoyance) what the facts are and then makes its 'decision' in adjusting to the wholeness-situation?

All hydrogen atoms are alike according to the laws of quantum mechanics, which decree that in the wave-pattern of the atom the distance between two successive crests must be equal to the circumference of the circle divided by a whole number. When the hydrogen atoms are 'created', — as they must be, since the hydrogen of the universe, which is converted into helium, has not been used up, — how do the hydrogen atoms know how they should be constructed? At the present time physics has no answer to this question, though in the view here outlined there is a philosophical answer. In any case, the atom acts as if it had a knowledge of mathematics. For us the important point is that the wholistic properties of the atom are analogous to *ESP* or *Pk* effects in the sense that normal space and time relations are set aside within the atom. The implications of this for a theory of communication will appear later in the argument.

VI. The Generalized Notion of Energy Levels

The foregoing remarks deal with the cosmic background of natural phenomena. What is required next is a more detailed theory to explain the *why* and the *how* of the increasing complexity of the structure of matter, passing from *nuclear* → *atomic* → *molecular* → *cellular* → *multicellular organizations*, all in relation to corresponding energy levels, with specifications for the correlated energy spectra to which the various levels of reality respond. The energy relations within the atoms comprise billions of electron volts (of the same order of magnitude as cosmic rays); in extra-nuclear phenomena the energy is considerably less. On the level of biological synthesis, Professor Szent-Gyorgi's spiral model of enzymes indicates that the metabolism of enzymes of living molecules can be related to a quasi-continuous energy spectrum. On a still higher level, a similar idea is evidently intended by Warren McCulloch's statement that the memory storage units in the nervous system (enzymes of the brain resonant with protein molecules) involve energy exchanges in the first and second octaves of the infra-red spectrum. If the existence of frequencies in the energy continuum (which we shall later term the 'psychic ether') could be established, we might have a speculative basis for the explanation of *Psi*-phenomena.

VII. The Theory of Emergent Evolution

Our third concept, that of emergent evolution, is sometimes called the 'theory of levels' because the record of evolution up to the present is preserved in the ascending rungs or 'levels' of the ladder of emergence. Looking beyond what has been achieved to date, we anticipate as the next step the emergence of a true world organism with forces of unification appearing which are analogous to the binding forces of lower integrations. In that case we may set up the following analogy: *Individual Cells : Brain : : Human Brain : World Sensorium.*

We have postulated a three-level analogy between electronic calculating machines, the neural networks which are the basis of mental life, and a world sensorium which is in process of emerging. This phase of the theory of emergent evolution has not been developed by professional scientists and philosophers. Among the non-professional thinkers, my friend Dr. C. Hilton Rice advocated such a doctrine. Because of his untimely death, he did not publish his theory; but in my book, *The World Sensorium,* the combined view we were working on was set forth. The present ideas are a revision of these earlier views, modified in the light of additions due in part to another co-worker, Mr. Vanderjagt.

Dr. Rice regarded the entire earth as a living organism, and the evolution of life on earth as a part of the embryology of this giant organism. The metaphor, 'tree of life,' for a while provided a useful analogy, but it later proved inadequate as an explanation of the meaning of evolution. In line with the new viewpoint, Dr. Rice substituted 'gastrula' for 'tree,' concluding that plants and animals are in functional relation in a manner that reminds one of the two layers of the gastrula.

From this viewpoint the human race is the differentiating fore-brain of the organism in which our individual nervous systems are the neuroblasts, the embryonic nerve cells. Therefore, we surmise that these neuroblasts are by no means the perfect 'neurons' they will later prove to be. Moreover, if the world is an organism, it will have a mind with capacities for appropriate discriminations. Among these functions will be the ability to see, not in a literal sense and therefore not limited by the laws of physical optics, but an ability to perceive, — perhaps as though there were a psychic eye looking through a psychic ether, seeing everything, everywhere, in the space and time of our planet. This would be 'omniscience' on a limited scale.

Now how can this provide an essential part of a theory of *Psi*-phenomena? If human organisms are embryonic cells in a super-organism which is still on its way, individual human beings, as the neuroblasts of the emerging organism, are also not finished products. New functions may emerge as embryogenesis continues, and *Psi*-phenomena may provide the experimental basis for such developments. The *ESP* faculties in those persons who possess it may be due to mutational changes in a few cells first, then more and more cells in successive generations, until the whole organ, the world sensorium, has perfected a new function in all individuals.

To explain *ESP* (telepathy and clairvoyance) one may suppose that the perceptive centers can respond to sensory and non-sensory stimuli. Therefore, vision in man is splitting into sensory and extra-sensory components. The evolutionary changes that are bringing this about would not appear in the size or weight of the brain but in the morphology of the neuron; accordingly the external appearance may bear no obvious relation to the chemical mutational changes within the neurons. To see how this is possible one must explore the chemistry of proteins.

The new knowledge of chemical genetics starts from the fact that the gene is a complex protein molecule (a nucleo-protein) of specific chemical composition and spatial configuration. Given this as a starting point, many phenomena of biology are more easily understood, including the facts of memory, heredity, and ideation. All these manifestations of living systems call for protein synthesis in the neurons involved in these behavior-patterns. The analogy between memory and heredity, which is usually put aside by biologists because it seems to suggest a Lamarckian theory for its explanation, simply cannot be ignored any longer. Biologists must constantly return to the idea that the mechanisms for racial and individual memory have something in common, and in both sets of phenomena there is a common formation of ordered protein molecules from a template having the power of self-duplication through protein synthesis. Thus in the functioning of neurons, cells are synthesizing specific proteins (enzymes), and the inheritance of abilities is the inheritance of specific modes of protein synthesis in the neurons.

One great value of this line of thought is that it supplies a mechanism for mutations which occur when changes in the mode of synthesis in the genes takes place. Indeed, the investigations first initiated by M. Delbrück[6] even promise to bring biological mutations under the broader physical principles of quantum mechanical resonance. This broad synthesis was made possible through the pioneering work of Linus Pauling and others, who introduced the resonance theory of valence and brought a high degree of unity into chemistry. The confirmation on the biological side was supplied in a limited way by the geneticist H. J. Muller's theory that vibrational attractions are involved in the behavior of chromosomes. In any case, resonance plays a rôle, regardless of whether it is the genes or the chromosomes which will ultimately be regarded as the seat of genetic changes, as the current discussions of the enzymes and their substrates as resonating systems appear to indicate. Because of the importance of this for our thesis, let us consider heredity and memory in relation to the subject of 'information.'

VIII. Heredity, Memory, and Information

A complete philosophy must be concerned with the problem of the causes of biological evolution. We have previously dealt with this problem in the relevant chapters of *The Promise of Scientific Humanism*, but since then the new science of cybernetics has made its appearance and novel concepts of 'heredity' and 'variation' (especially in relation to 'communication') have become available, necessitating further discussion of this topic.

It is generally known that heredity, variation, struggle for existence, and survival of the fittest, are important factors that must be considered if we are to possess a satisfactory theory of biological evolution. *Heredity*, the transmission of traits from one generation to the next through units called *chromosomes*, in turn composed of *genes*, gives us a mechanism whereby animals can resemble their ancestors; *mutation*, on the other hand, designates the phenomenon of change between successive generations. For a moment, let us return to the role of heredity and observe how it may be dealt with as a form of 'communication.'

The general idea of heredity as a type of communication has been expounded by E. Taschdjian[7] and George Gamow[8], and a brief résumé of this line of thought is relevant. Instead of regarding the gene as a 'particle,' Dr. Taschdjian offers the concept of the *gene as a material symbol that is copied by heredity.* This concept suggests that gene multiplication is the same as the duplication of a set of symbols, while the phenomenon of mutation is said to be akin to 'noise disturbance' in the communication process.

For a more complete statement of this interesting theory the reader must consult the original papers. Without getting involved in technical details, I wish to record my doubts about the validity of the theory of mutation as analogous to noise. This presupposes a theory of 'chance' as a source of mutations (i.e., deviations from the norm of a significant *message*, which in inheritance corresponds to *repetition of pattern*). In our theory, however, mutation is the process whereby directed changes accumulate to the point where a new level of organization makes its appearance. And if, as Bergson argues, the vertebrate eye appears in order that the organism may see, the genes which produce the eye must contain the potentialities for precipitating the mutations which directed evolution (orthogenesis) even before the mutations become useful as survival factors. Thus 'chance' and 'noise' in gene mutations are not to be regarded as biological irrelevancies in the hereditary code transmission, i.e., as distortions of an intended message.

What must be realized is that information is relative to the level of emergence within which communication takes place. Rather than that mutation be regarded as merely distortion in the transmission of an old message, I suggest that it is the process whereby nature produces new transmission lines with the possibilities of higher level messages. If communication is 'entropic coupling' of entities on any given level, then mutations in the ladder of emergence represent the negentropy whereby 'life' creates higher levels of organization. Paraphrasing Bergson, we could say that whenever energy, descending the incline indicated by Carnot's law, meets with a cause of inverse direction, which retards the tendency toward the degradation of energy, there life appears. Thus life on any given level conforms to the second law of thermodynamics, but in the phylogenesis of new levels of emergence it transcends the degradation of energy, — it feeds on negative entropy as Schrödinger puts it. In this manner, the fabrication of chlorophyll in plants and hemoglobin in animals provides a way of rising above the leveling tendency of nature. This process also occurs in atoms and molecules as they exhibit higher levels of organization which are disentropic in the overall pattern of the cosmic cycle.

Putting these various ideas together, we come up with the following synthesis: *the use of symbolism is natural to man because symbols are the means whereby functional aggregates (proteins), which are maps, express themselves as genes, which are territories, in turn to become maps for the embryogenesis of mature organisms.* That is to say, symbolism exists on all levels of nature. The universe itself is the visible symbol of the invisible archetypal field; thus the hydrogen atom is the first stable physical expression of the morphogenetic patterns of the Cosmic Imagination, while the gene is the symbol produced by the architectonic of molecular patterns of integration. In turn, the genes produce human nervous systems which give rise to symbols because the brain is a proliferation of nucleo-proteins. Thus, we humans are the neuroblasts of an emerging world sensorium in which social symbols are the vehicles of messages whereby a new level of social synthesis is being achieved. The brain provides a map for mental visions (symbols) by the same kind of projective geometry whereby the invisible guiding field (the Cosmic Imagination) envisages and creates the physical universe of particles in space and time.

Neuroblasts as Homomorphic Images

The analogy between cells of the brain and human individuals as neuroblasts in a world sensorium is difficult to confirm. Some analogies (homomorphic images) carry over, and some probably do not. The individual cells of the brain (i.e., neurons) presumably do not know what the brain as a whole is doing. Therefore, if the human individual is a cell in a universal mind, how can the person know what is in the mind of the world sensorium? Or, to turn the problem around, if we humans can know what is in the universal consciousness, why is it that we don't know this all the time? If there is such a thing as clairvoyance, why aren't human minds more frequently in touch with events that are distant from them in time and space? How is it possible for most people most of the time to be 'out of touch' with an all-knowing consciousness?

The most general sort of answer would probably incorporate Bergson's theory that our knowledge is inhibited by our 'attention to life,' which obscures those experiences which are irrelevant to immediately practical problems. The mind is orientated for action on things in the external world. Indeed, a related view was proposed by Professor H. H. Price[9] in his hypothesis of a Psychic Ether as a Common Unconscious, where at their deeper levels all human personalities are in complete and continuous rapport. This theory suggests that telepathic impulses of great number are always reaching everyone, but normally they inhibit each other, or their effects obliterate each other, because the impulses are so numerous and diverse. This view would be quite in harmony with that proposed by René Warcollier in his book, *Experimental Telepathy*, where the world mind is termed a Collective Being, which provides the medium making possible telepathic communication between individuals.

The trouble with such theories is that they can neither be confirmed nor refuted. The situation is especially difficult in the case of Professor Price's hypothesis. The idea that we really know much more than we think we know is almost paradoxical. But respectable thinkers from Plato on have held such views. More recently we find the able psychologist Kurt Koffka making the following statement[10]: "It is . . . probable that the dreamer does know what his dream means, *but he does not know that he knows, and therefore he believes that he does not know*." It may be that we shall ultimately have to integrate the Price-Koffka approaches and produce a synthesis of ideas out of collateral speculations. However, let us first see what can be done independently before resorting to such hypotheses.

In order to explain the communication evident in *ESP*, where the human mind knows momentarily what the universal mind knows completely, I propose the idea that the human consciousness under special conditions may become aware of bits of a pattern on the screen on which the television-radio images of the universal consciousness are programmed. Our hypothesis postulates a blanket surrounding the earth in a manner resembling the ionosphere — a *Psi*-blanket which catches the sequence of images on the screen and reflects them back into human consciousness when it is possible to set up a kind of resonance or phase relation of the proper sort.

IX. The Generalized Theory of Communication

A society is like an organism and an organism is like a society. The parts of each are held together by a network of communications which integrates the system into the dynamic equilibrium such as we have in 'homeostasis' and feed-back systems. Both human society and an organism are bound into a form of unity by interlacing media for the acquisition, retention, transmission, and utilization of information coming from without and within the organism. Just as the organism is supplied with the accumulated information which is maintained by physiological structure and transmitted by biological heredity, so society must accumulate sufficient stored information, transmitted by social heredity, to respond to the cultural environment. In both cases there are complex energy exchanges which preserve the dynamic equilibrium, the integrity of the organism — whether it be a cell, a cell-colony, or society as a super-organism. This naturally leads to the supposition that if there is a super-organism, will not 'scanning' be a feature of the emerging world sensorium?

One consequence of the notion of a 'world sensorium' is the possibility that there are planetary electroencephalograms, with a record of the scanning as it appears on the screen of a giant cortex. When we watch the patterns on the face of a television set as the images are transmitted from the eye to the brain, there is a vast assemblage of moving electrons producing patterns of light and shade. The glow as consciously experienced by the organism is an emergent from the cortical alpha rhythm, an averaging effect which results from the inability of consciousness to discriminate impulses below a certain level of frequency. One reason for supposing that this cortical scanning is nothing other than the sweep of the alpha rhythm through the cortex is that this rhythm takes time, and it turns out that the frequency of the alpha rhythm is also the frequency at which one can consciously discriminate shapes or hear chords of music.

This analysis indicates that scanning on the cortical level involves treating something as unitary which, on its own level, is really discontinuous, and scanning is done in or by a dimension higher than, or at right angles to, the lower-dimensional series of discrete units. This seems to require either a pre-existent mind or an emergent orthogonal consciousness as a super-observer who can trade time for space. Evidently, in scanning, something like Wertheimer's *phi*-phenomenon of seen movement is involved, i.e., the percept must be grasped as a unity, not as a migrating series of impulses traversing a fiber or latticework. In the case of the atom, however, this 'scanning' by the organizing field does not take time, if Margenau's summary of Pauli's exclusion principle is correct. If every organic entity (atom, molecule, cell, etc.) has a guiding field, then a world organism also requires a world mind. Therefore, each human individual (as a neuroblast in the giant sensorium) has a function in a super-organic communication system comparable to the communication system within and across the human brain.

Accordingly, if the doctrine of emergent evolution is correct, there will be planetary encephalograms which are analogous to the alpha rhythms of the cerebral cortex, and this scanning mechanism for the world brain will require a symbolism appropriate to its level of transposable properties. In that case, the 'world sensorium' will know what is going on everywhere on the earth at the time at which it happens, and any *ESPer* who is 'tuned in' would know (at least in part) what happened at the time it was happening. But this leaves us with a great riddle: by what mechanism can any individual mind know in part what is the content of a more universal consciousness? I shall return to that problem in a moment.

The Role of Archetypal Forms

We are considering the possibility of archetypal forms in the collective unconscious. These archetypes, as posited by Carl Jung, are potentialities of ideas, deposits of racial experiences which well up in the individual from the realm of the unconscious of all humans. This concept *may* play a useful rôle in our schematism, especially if we have to face the problem of a conflict between any images or symbols as the content of the individual mind and what is going on in the more inclusive world sensorium. This may therefore throw light on the question of why the individual fails to receive possible knowledge through *ESP*.

My guess that the Jungian archetypes must constitute a part of the total picture is based upon some introspective evidences made available to me by Dr. C. Hilton Rice who reported on his *ESP* faculty in operation. When he tried to 'concentrate' on the cards there was a distinct effort of trying to 'see' the symbol, and when the image appeared, it was like the first crude telephoto. There was difficulty in getting the 'screen' cleared for reception of extra-sensory percepts, because they were easily blotted out by thought pictures. For example, he stated that if he thought a 'cross' was about due, he was able to force an image of a cross, but these projected thought pictures frequently deceived him. He wrote: "I score best by staring through closed eyelids and watching the fragments of images that appear; if a fairly clear image forms, I make the call. By this slow method, which fatigues me greatly, I have made some high runs on occasion."

The point here is that it is difficult for the human subject to be relaxed and free from the images that are usually popping into consciousness. But even in a 'relaxed' state, can we be sure that archetypal imagery is not thereby encouraged to filter into one's consciousness? Perhaps some of the success of the best subjects is due to their ability to free their minds of sensory percepts and memory images of all sorts, so that their screen can be cleared for extra-sensory percepts. The archetypal forms of Jung include the geometrical figures known as the 'Platonic solids,' and these overlap the geometrical figures of Rhine's deck of *ESP* cards, hence the possibility of confusing what comes from one's own inner consciousness and what comes from the 'outside' by way of extra-sensory perception. On the other hand, it is possible that the Jungian archetypes may in some manner facilitate extra-sensory perception. This is something that requires further study.

The concept of 'resonance' or 'tuning in' between the individual human mind and what is going on in the world sensorium poses an extraordinarily difficult problem. The answer seems to be that somehow, in extra-sensory perception, the individual human mind knows in part what the universal consciousness knows because it envisages a part of what the world mind sees on the screen on which the planetary images are programmed. Perhaps this will require the concept of a *Psi*-layer.

Our general philosophy of evolution makes such a dénouement rather plausible. On the level of psychic evolution the time-spanning property of wholism whereby *what is in the present* helps to determine *what will be in the future* is illustrated by the fact that mental evolution in man is not merely retracing the 'collective unconscious' of our racial heredity, as Jung supposes, but it points to the emergence in the future of an archetype-to-be which will become fixed in the mature creatures toward which present humanity is evolving.

In this view, the basic archetypes prefigure the emergent archetypes. That is, the activities on the microscopic levels somehow foreshadow the next level to come, — micropsychic rhythms prefigure macropsychic rhythms. It is for this reason that there are isomorphic patterns transposable from level to level. In the biological world, micro-evolution in the genes foreshadows macro-evolution on the phenomenological level of development. Ontogeny is able to 're-capitulate' phylogeny because phylogeny was the goal that was foreshadowed by what emerged. In any event, underlying all emergent archetypes are the basic and eternal patterns, — the Platonic solids and the forms of spherical harmonics, — which are resident in the Cosmic Field as potentialities for embodiment in the manifest world; these are the morphogenetic fields which help to organize the hierarchical levels of isomorphic patterns in the pyramid of evolution. That is why nature is orderly in its ladder of emergence.

X. The Electromagnetic Society

We come now to an even more speculative part of the present theory of social cybernetics. Our hypothesis may be stated in the form of a question: If there is an analogy (or homomorphic image) between electronic machines and brain machines, so that if you have a brain you can scan and when you can scan you have an essential feature of a brain, *does it not follow that as the world becomes more tightly knit into the interlacing network of radio, television, and telephonic systems, we human cells of the social organism are actually in the process of creating a world sensorium?*

Let us explore the possibilities. The hypothesis is based on the fundamental idea that as social evolution progresses and becomes ever more intimately interwoven with the proliferating spiderwebs of telephony, radio, television, radar, telegraphy, and other media of communication, we are in fact constructing what may be termed the electromagnetic society.

In order that the world may be integrated into an electromagnetic society, we shall require as a physical basis for world unity, a unified and world-wide symbolism such as C. K. Bliss has given us in his *Semantography*. We are all familiar with the integrative power of symbols (flags, dramas, parades, folkways, science notations, and the like), which secure this cohesive power from the potency of symbolism as a common denominator for ideational and emotional responses within and among humans. At the present time it looks as if the semantography of the coming world organism might start with the simple picture language of Bliss. If somehow it were possible to shrink all knowledge and all human history so that an all-world drama could be put on a universal symbolism basis for invariant transfer across the social whole, and if it were possible to use the full play of global techniques in a unified semantography for television sets, the epic space-time drama curving the planetary field and bending the arc of human evolution into the spiral of a time-binding synthesis would lift up the inner lives of peoples everywhere by sheer evocation of latent powers. Thus history would be salvaged from the dark domain of futility and despair.

Social Physics

Social physics is an empirical social science which is interested in relating a number of separate sciences: mathematics, physics, sociology, economics, linguistics, and others. Contributors to this field include George K. Zipf, John Q. Stewart, Stuart Carter Dodd, John von Neumann, W. F. Sutherland, and N. Rashevsky.

An important concept in social physics is the notion of *demographic energy*. As a working hypothesis, *demographic energy* refers to the *number of human relationships per unit of time* thought of not as static but as an impulse which happens like a wave along the string. The *accumulating total* of such happenings is the integral of the energy with respect to time, and seems to resemble *action* in physics.

Demographic energy defines the relation of N_1 people who are at a distance d from N_2 people. Hence the formula, $N_1 \cdot N_2/d$, worked out by Zipf, has for example been applied to the interchange of telephone calls between pairs of cities. The appearance in this formula of the factor of inverse distance (the d in the denominator) is theoretically reasonable, for the further apart people are the less interaction with each other, and has much empirical evidence in its favor. This demographic energy can be computed from a map showing *contours of potential* as these have been worked out at Princeton University.

To those who are versed in the science of electrical engineering, this has an element of familiarity because the formula, 'potential equals population divided by distance,' is analogous to Ohm's law, 'current equals voltage divided by resistance.' Some persons might think this isomorphism is accidental, — but not the social physicists! Two lines of supporting evidence may be introduced, one practical and one theoretical. Let us consider them.

Some indication of the fantastic developments in electrical integration, inspired largely by military needs, is the 'push button' system of defending the United States against possible air attacks. The system (called SAGE) involves the use of electronic brains at radar sites to count the approaching enemy planes, determine their altitudes, distances, flying speeds, etc., and flash this information to sub-sectors of the Direction Center. All the information from all centers is recorded on IBM-type cards which speed this information into a computer. On the basis of the total information, appropriate counter-measures are taken, — the decisions being made by 'thinking machines' which even specify what types of weapons are to be used in counter-measures. A similar development for commercial air transportation will soon be required by civil airports to control planes of the jet-age as they streak through the sky lanes at supersonic speeds. This spreading network of radar-controlled airports will require new kinds of computers with electronic memory devices to minimize the human element in the dawning air and ether age.

All this is but a hint of what is coming in all areas of communication, including television, radio, radar, and other media where we are moving into a situation in which sub-centers (ganglia) know everything about what is going on in their convolutions of the world brain, with higher-level integrations giving decisions at appropriate times based on information from the interwoven areas. One can be sure that if the 'West' is committed to such an electromagnetic pattern of integration, the 'East' will also follow suit with similar radar networks. One can only hope that global television programs will become the civilian peace-time substitutes for the military electromagnetic integrations.

On the theoretical side, a measure of support for the thesis that an electromagnetic society is emerging is provided by Mr. W. F. Sutherland's investigations. In a paper on 'The Dynamics of Economic Growth,' presented at the meeting of the AAAS in December, 1950, Mr. Sutherland (of the Toronto Hydro-Electrical System) showed in detail how laws regulating the human behaviorial economy resemble those of electrophysics. After noting the manner in which variations of current or voltage in an electric circuit follow patterns similar to those of the logistic curve, Mr. Sutherland indicated the way in which it is possible to define and measure 'economic force,' 'economic resistance,' and other parameters on the basis of the similarities between economic and electrical action patterns.

It is true that Mr. Sutherland's argument that the behavior of the economic system as a whole can be dealt with by the same equations which are used for the dynamo is based on reasoning by analogy, but the similarities between electrical machines and our electromagnetic society are certainly suggestive of reliable isomorphisms. Even the parallel between the non-linearity of brain physiology and social electrophysiology carries over, for as Mr. Sutherland points out, the growth potential (demographic energy) of a community is more than the sum of the individual potentials. This point is sufficiently important to justify a fuller statement.

The Non-Linearity of Field Physics

While the social physicists share in unity of viewpoint, there is one place where differences of opinion crop up. In the foregoing paragraph, I mentioned the analogy between the non-linearity of brain physiology and social electrophysiology. In our own theory of emergent evolution we have constantly emphasized that our field-theoretical approach, by way of levels of organization associated with new or emergent dimensionalities, specifically provides for gestalt properties which are transposable across the social (macroscopic) wholes. In such cases, where non-linear equations are appropriate, a function of the sum is not a sum of the functions.

We have also insisted that this type of situation appears in biology, psychology, and sociology, no less than in physics. A brief quotation will illustrate this idea in physics. In the Appendix to the 1953 edition of his book, *The Meaning of Relativity*, Albert Einstein announced that he had worked out equations which gave unity to gravitational and electromagnetic forces. These equations are 'non-linear partial differential equations', — much more complicated than those of the original relativity theory. This unified field theory cannot at present be tested because no one knows how to verify the equations.

In an article by Einstein and Infeld[11], the requirements of the situation in physics are clearly set forth as follows:

> "A linear law always means that the motion of singularities is arbitrary. If to a world-line of a singularity with mass m_1 there belongs a field F_1 and if to a world-line of a singularity with $mass_2$ there belongs a Field F_2, then the superposition of these two fields, that is $F_1 + F_2$, is also a solution of the linear equations. In such a solution the same two world-lines would appear together that appeared singly. Therefore the field with its linear laws cannot apply to any interaction between the singularities. Thus only non-linear field equations can provide us with equations of motion because only non-linearity can express the interaction between singularities."

If the reader will now substitute the term *neuron* for singularity, and *circuit* for *world-line* in this quotation, we have an analogue for the microscopic and macroscopic levels of the brain. And if, in relativity theory, the field constitutes a non-linear continuum wherein the familiar additive formula for the compounding of velocities and addition of vectors is set aside because of the non-linearity of the situation, how much more so do brain processes and social phenomena manifest non-linear, non-additive, or gestalt-wholistic properties?

This latter is my own extrapolation. It may be noted that this isomorphism in the non-linearity of physical fields, biological fields, cortico-mental fields, and psycho-social fields is neither accepted nor rejected by contemporary science, simply because the question is not even considered in current theorizing. However, a few investigators are beginning to realize the presence of the problem. Recently several social scientists have raised the question of whether the socio-cultural field is a non-linear field.[12] One author has used the term 'macro-economics' to refer to situations wherein the properties of the whole are not a sum of the properties of the parts.

The Limitations of Contemporary Social Science

Some of the difficulties encountered in current social science are certainly due to the inadequate conceptual foundations on which these 'sciences' rest. Economics, politics, and psychology are missing out because they deal with partial systems rather than wholes. Moreover, the newer quasi-sciences, mainly in the social domain, have not passed beyond the empirical stage because they have not yet derived their basic general laws. When these laws are formulated, they may approximate those of the physical sciences. The problem of 'analogies' among the sciences needs to be restudied in the light of *homomorphic images* analysis. To make this point more specifically, let us return to the subject of social physics.

The work in the area of social physics is in one sense a direct application of physical laws to physical things and events, and in another sense it is a study of isomorphic relations. Dr. John Q. Stewart, for example, considers 'mass' as being the sheer physical mass of the things mankind accumulates around itself, and also as being *analogous* to the idea of mass when society is treated as a gas subject to gas laws. Mr. Frank Sutherland also employs the concept of mass in this dual manner. He recognizes that physical space is important, but there is also the idea of economic organization as constituting a kind of economic (non-physical) space. The virtue of this is evident, since the consequence is a coherent set of dimensions which suffices to give homogeneity to the economic equational system, — a higher kind of isomorphism than the merely analogical. In a more general way, the new science of social cybernetics will furnish us with a bridge of isomorphism whereby certain archetypal forms may be given greater universality.

The right road is indicated by Sutherland when he points out that economic space is not physical space, nor is economic force the same as physical force. They are both isomorphic, though not identical. The electrical theory is used as a stepping stone to economic theory and, once established, this latter is able to stand on its own feet with its own set of dimensions and definitions. Both levels, however, are still 'organismic.'

The fact is that organismic action fields have not yet been recognized and dealt with adequately. Even feed-backs are essentially organismic since they occur only in action fields that are something more than linear. *Structure* is necessary in such cases. The living body contains a whole host of such action-fields, as do the economic and political domains. Most of these are of the negative variety, but positive feed-backs also occur. The cybernetics analysis should recognize this, especially when dealing with wholistic situations. But the forthright acceptance of an isomorphism between lower and higher dimensions carries us far beyond the old Aristotelian-Euclidian-Newtonian three-dimensional framework for the physical world, and this is clearly discernible in dimensional analysis as applied to higher function spaces. To the electrical engineer the foregoing ideas will come as old friends. In their own area the work they have done is considerable. To be sure, the application of such analysis to social systems has not gone very far, but when the coming electrical-social system attains its emergent being, electrodynamics will find its proper place in the new social science.

In these references to field-physics sociology we find support for our conception of gestalt properties of a macroscopic whole. Surely in time the social scientists will come to grips with this problem. Meantime, we must formulate our answer to the question: Is the psychic field which characterizes the world sensorium the product of the individual mental fields, or is it a wholistic, non-linear field which is *sui generis?* But in the latter case, how can it be an 'emergent'? Or is it possible that these alternatives are not mutually exclusive of each other?

Admittedly the hypothesis of a Psychic Field for the World Sensorium is highly speculative. But by long tradition philosophers are permitted to explore far beyond the already charted territories of knowledge. However, to confer upon our visions some measure of confirmation, let us for a moment return to the realm of established facts by quoting the following passage, which will then be used as a kind of springboard for another leap into a world of imagination. In his masterly work, *Man on his Nature*, Sir Charles Sherrington pictures the brain when it is asleep and awake. He asks us to imagine:

> "A scheme of lines and nodal points, gathered together at one end into a great ravelled knot, the brain, and at the other end trailing off to a sort of stalk, the spinal cord. Imagine activity in this shown by little points of light. Of these some flash rhythmically, faster or slower. Others are travelling points streaming in serial lines at various speeds. The rhythmic stationary lights lie at nodes. The nodes are both goals whither converge, and junctions whence diverge, the lines of travelling lights. Suppose we choose the hour of deep sleep. Then only at sparse and out-of-the-way places are nodes flashing and trains of light points running. The great knotted headpiece lies for the most part quite dark. Occasionally at places in it lighted points flash or move but soon subside.
>
> "Should we continue to watch the scheme we should observe after a time an impressive change which suddenly occurs. In the great head end which had been mostly darkness spring myriads of lights, as though activity from one of these local places suddenly spread far and wide. The great topmost sheet of the mass, where hardly a light twinkled or moved becomes now a sparkling field of rhythmic flashing points with trains of travelling sparks hurrying hither and thither. It is as if the milky way entered upon some cosmic dance. Swiftly the head mass becomes an enchanted loom where millions of flashing shuttles weave a dissolving pattern, always a meaningful pattern though never an abiding one. The brain is awake and with it the mind is returning."

In the foregoing comparison the distinguished physiologist depicts the brain asleep and awake. Our problem, somewhat different, — is to evolve a world brain which can then be 'awakened.' But since, for us, the cells are individual human beings, the 'awakening' will consist in linking the 'cell tubes' functionally through a communication system whereby messages that have an all-world meaning (that is, represent a gestalt picture like scanning in television) are transmitted. In other words, the awakening of a world sensorium corresponds to the fabrication of a social cortex because the interlacing networks of electrical proliferations are the transmission channels of the social nervous system. In order to provide the physical basis for world-level meanings, the world cortex spiderweb of action patterns must be synchronized by a central clocking device which arranges the 'program' in a temporal sequence. The immensely simple message to be written into the form of a universal picture language will be spelled out over a planetary network of interlacing lines uniting the peoples of the world into an electromagnetic society. This will be the incarnation of a planetary civilization with a unified symbolism providing the physical basis for a higher-level unity. In such a case, communication is not person-to-person, but person-to-world-mind-to-person. To develop this thought it is necessary to investigate the various types of fields available for the psychic unity of mankind.

XI. The Two Kinds of Fields

We have already noted that society is an organism and an organism is a society. In both cases the parts of the whole are held together by a network of intercommunications which integrates the whole into a behavioral unity. That is the manner in which living systems function. However, as we have seen, the advance from one rung in the ladder of emergence to the next calls for the supplementary process of mutation. Looking ahead, we pose the question: Is it possible that the next step in the forward advance of nature is at hand? If so, perhaps the intercommunication system which will synthesize the earth-organism will become functionally active when the giant embryo has proliferated the structure of a social brain which makes possible a scanning device as part of an information center capable of integrating and diffusing all-world messages. However, these messages may be able to function on several different levels.

In the philosophy of panpsychism it appears that there are two kinds or levels of communication. In the first instance, at the bottom level of nature where the 'ultimate constituents' of the manifest physical world emerge from the Cosmic Field to get synthesized into atoms, and, at a higher level of nature, where the human mind emerges from the brain, there is communication between the parts of the whole in the sense that information is available to the atom-as-a-whole and the brain-as-a-whole. This is possibly true for every emergent between the floor and the ceiling of reality. In such cases knowledge is not passed on by point-to-point transmission; that is, the organizing or guiding field controls the space-time coördinates of the particles of the aggregate by something like *action-at-a-distance*, and this "instantaneousness" approximates the infinite velocity that is possible in the sub-ether.

But on the levels of *inter*-particle communication between entities on the same level (e.g., between atoms, molecules, cells, — *not* communication *within* atoms, molecules, cells, etc.) this transmission of influence does take time. The building up of such macroscopic integrations from a synthesis of microscopic constituents also takes time — geological time. These high-level emergents perhaps represent the slow accumulation of angular momentum in the manifest world to create a macroscopic spin, the off-at-right-angles or orthogonal emergent dimension. In some instances this spin effect is a logarithmic spiral in the manifest world — a kind of mean between the point-source of energy whereby entry is made into the physical world of corpuscles, and the infinite-expanding angular velocity of the Cosmic Lens as it whirls out the energy-knots of matter which aggregate into systems.

Once a higher level has emerged, there will be transposable gestalt properties of the macroscopic whole which provide the exemplifications of isomorphisms (homomorphic images) such as polarity, entropy, dominance-subordination patterns, field-properties, patterns of symmetry, and the rest. (This is illustrated in Diagram IX (page 85).) Accordingly, the Cosmic Imagination not only knows the conditions of all "local" systems through a sub-ether communication system, but it creates atoms and their subsequent emergent integrations through its spiraling effect in nature. But the source of spin or angular momentum must be sought in the influence of field on matter.

In this cosmology, therefore, the Cosmic Imagination creates and guides the universe through spiral structures (galaxies, atoms, protoplasmic structures, and the spiral hierarchy of mental forms) because spirals are the manifestation of the endurance of angular momentum in time as this expresses the pressure of the field-plenum on matter. Thus the tempo of emergent evolution is a measure of the response of the manifest universe in space and time to the invisible world of archetypal forms, — Platonic solids, circles, spirals, and the higher patterns of spherical harmonics.

In this view the individuality and persistence of entities (or *behavior-stuffs*, as we have termed them) represent the central tendency of an ensemble of micro-rhythms, a statistical constant of very high stability. Also, *since every population of individuals is a synthesis of individual populations*, we conclude that there are two kinds of simplicity in nature: *simple simplicities* and *complex simplicities*. Above the level of ultimate particles, every entity is a simple simplicity when treated as a component of a higher aggregate and a complex simplicity when regarded as an emergent from its own antecedents in the history of physico-chemical evolution. However, the time-path of evolution is *not* relative, since the melody of emergence is unidirectional in that it is always striving to produce higher-order, or complex simplicities, out of relatively simple simplicities. Nature does this under the influence of guiding fields. Thus, molecular polarity arises out of an integration of atomic polarities, and so on, in a spiral hierarchy of isomorphic structures. For this reason patterns of symmetry, polarity, entropy, serial order, etc., are pervasive features of emergence at all levels. However, we have for the moment excluded so-called 'elementary' constituents, to which we now turn our attention.

In order to deal with the problem of the persistence of elementary particles in time, it is necessary to bring in the idea of 'constituent waves' of a sub-ether. These waves enter into the composition of 'group waves', wherein the nodes of overlapping give rise to the creation of particles. The wave-particle problem is resolved by making the field-aspect of the cosmos more fundamental than the particle-aspect. Discreteness or atomicity can be derived from the dynamics of the field-plenum, but continuity cannot be synthesized from unrelated discrete units. In that sense the Cosmic Field is supreme. For us, the 'material' world (as physical science studies it) is the *manifest world* which emerges from the *unmanifest world*, and this distinction brings us to the several kinds of 'fields' which are required if we are to understand the total situation.

Group Waves and Constituent Waves

The Cosmic Field, an ocean of electrical density, with its morphogenetic possibilities, is closer to the *sub-ether* of J. J. Thomson, as explained in his little book, *Beyond the Electron*, than to the electromagnetic field of Faraday, Maxwell, Einstein's 'unified field' or even Dirac's rehabilitated ether. Indeed, the Cosmic Field recedes from the manifest world so deep into the archetypal continuum of mathematical forms that the recent 'quantum fields' of H. A. Kramers, Julian Schwinger and F. J. Dyson represent a relatively far-removed and materialistic level of behavior. That so many fields (ethers) should be invoked may seem to constitute an objection in the eyes of some critics — space being overcrowded with ethers, as they may say. However, space cannot be overcrowded with fields, for above the level of ultimate entities, we conceive that each level of organization creates an emergent space, orthogonal to preexistent spaces, in a hierarchy of emergent dimensions which rise upon the foundations of the physical world.

At the lowest level of nature there are two kinds of waves: termed *group waves* and *constituent waves.* The distinction between these two kinds of waves and their velocities of transmission are discussed by Sir Joseph J. Thomson (in the book mentioned). He points out that in electromagnetic phenomena involving both types of waves, the product of the two velocities is always the same, the square of the velocity of light. That is, *the velocity of light is a mean between the velocity of the group waves and the guiding or constituent waves.*

Prior to the view set forth by Sir Joseph that group waves are a resultant of superposed constituent waves, Louis de Broglie had developed an undulatory theory of the electrons wherein particles appear as manifestations of group waves accompanied by guiding (or "ghost") waves which show the particles where to go. This theory has recently been revived and improved with the help of David Bohm. The guiding waves (as interpreted by Sir Joseph Thomson) do *not* travel with the speed of light; they travel faster, and the slower the electrons move the faster the constituent waves will move. In brief, if U is the velocity of the group waves and v the velocity of the constituent waves, then $Uv = c^2$, where c is the velocity of light.

Since the medium required for this is one in which waves travel at variable speeds, the older concept must be modified. Accordingly, a sub-ether having the required properties is postulated. In this conception, the proposition that energy waves may travel at any speed whatsoever does not contradict the relativity theorem concerning the constancy of the velocity of light *in vacuo.* That is to say, in an ether free of matter, radiation travels at a constant velocity, but the situation changes when electrical charges are introduced. In the case of an electrified space, the medium is said to be *super-dispersive.* Inside transparent matter, the effective velocity of radiation is decreased, but inside the electrified region of the Cosmic Field the wave velocity may travel at speeds according to wave lengths and thus approach an infinite velocity. The constituent waves of a super-dispersive medium like the sub-ether act as guiding waves which influence the behavior of matter *without injecting material energy* (i.e., energy having *mass* and *inertia) into the system.* Thus the guiding fields are like photons in that they have no "rest mass" and therefore do not upset the laws of physics, even when particles are created at regions where constituent waves give rise to matter at nodal points.

Up to this point things seem to hang together pretty well. We have the dual-communication scheme where there is: (a) the approaching-infinity velocity of communication in the unmanifest world, and (b) the finite-velocity communications systems between entities of the same level in the ladder of emergent evolution. We have also decided that negentropy designates the upward thrust of creativity against the dissipative tendency of energy toward an equilibrium; while entropy designates the tendency toward information-transfer whereby entities on the same level enter into wholeness situations.

Today, from our vantage-point as 'lords of creation,' we can look backward over the long road that nature has traveled. We discover that everything in the material universe is stamped with the trade mark of time. As Martin Johnson puts it, the discovery of the finite velocity of light in the seventeenth century marks the entry of time into physics as a factor essential to the communicability of knowledge. For us, however, the time-lag in the physical world, which is embedded structurally in logarithmic spirals in nature, is a manifestation of the reciprocal relation between the velocities of group waves and constituent waves. Therefore, light can function as the mean (medium) between a manifest and an unmanifest world, revealing the visible world to the eye-brain mechanism of man who looks upon the world which the Cosmic Imagination has envisioned. In a sense, time is the Cosmic Imagination's compassion for the Universe. Perhaps, too, the psychic field of *ESP* and *PK* is the superdispersive ether of the Cosmic Field of the Supreme Imagination, which knows all things by way of a universal consciousness and imparts bits of knowledge to human consciousness as we tap the reservoir and gain information about what is distant for us in space and time, but known to the Cosmic Imagination in the spaceless and timeless field of the unmanifest world.

XII. The *PSI*-Layer Again

We are told by the parapsychologists that space is not a limiting condition in *ESP*. Does this mean that intelligent beings (if any) on other planets, who might be endowed with *psi* capacities, could catch the thoughts of human beings as they leave the earth and 'wing' their ways through interplanetary space? Or are mental products of all sorts earth-bound, perhaps even cortex-bound, and in that sense limited by space? If so, what keeps the mental images and ideas from escaping our planet? Is there a layer which surrounds the earth, like the Kennelly-Heaviside layer, reflecting thoughts back to the earth as radio waves (but not radar) are reflected back by the ion blanket?

We have just seen that the hypothesis that humanity is the emerging social cortex of an embryonic world organism suggests the possibility that there is a psychic ether (a sub-ether) which provides the medium for the functioning of constituent waves as archetypal forms. If there is a 'psychic ether' for a universal morphogenetic consciousness, could it be that there is a *Psi*-layer surrounding the earth like the ion blanket, reflecting the images of mankind back to the earth creatures?

We have no knowledge here. It is known that a medium which is 'transparent' to one octave of frequencies may be 'opaque' to another set of waves. For example, a medium containing free electrons is characterized by the fact that electric waves below a critical frequency cannot travel through the medium. The explanation of such matters involves mathematical problems too technical for discussion here. But given the data about density of the medium, the phase and group velocity frequencies, and the like, one can tell whether the medium is or is not permeable to specified frequencies. It may be that the *psi* influences which have their origin on this planet are earth-bound for the reason given, — that there is a *Psi*-layer which prevents frequencies from penetrating an outer barrier. Is it possible that this hypothetical layer might also provide the medium for the functioning of psychic experiences for sensitives here on the earth?

If all this speculation has any basis in fact, the flickering and fitful phenomena studied by Dr. Rhine and his collaborators may be explained in due time. Whether one receives such extra-sensory perceptions thus reflected back to the earth would then depend not only on subjective factors, but also on where one is on the earth's surface at any given time relative to the source of the 'message' which is sent out (or in) the universal consciousness. The scanning mechanism of the world mind would exist outside or independent of the usual space-time manifold of the three dimensional world of physics. For that reason *Psi*-phenomena violate the ordinary inverse square laws of conventional energy relationships. In this sense the phenomena of parapsychology are super-physical, — but not supernatural.

If we may exploit our analogy still further, it would seem that *ESP* arises when a cone of influence from the universal consciousness, reaching downward as it were, makes contact with a cone of influence reaching upward from the individual. When the two cones of influence meet, something in the nature of information in the universal consciousness is communicated to the individualized consciousness, so that items that are distant in physical space and time are now apprehended as present (i.e., as an event happening in the percipient's 'now').

We have guessed that the intercommunication system, already partially functioning, which will unify the earth-organism into a well-integrated whole, will come into being when the neuroblasts of the emerging embryo have matured into a world sensorium with an all-world semantography. Our general thesis is that world history will acquire its meaning only when mankind is able to synthesize the action patterns of bio-social development into a drama which we all write and enact. But if one holds that the earth is to some extent magnetically self-contained, one may also conceive that these social images of the planetary iconography could be master-programmed and made visible on a universal television screen. Perhaps it may be possible to project archetypal culture-patterns into the heavens — a kind of sky-writing semantography, and these images could be reflected back for all to see. This kaleidoscopic sky-writing on the very dome of heaven would indeed be Bliss's *one writing for one world!*

As a technical problem, the job of programming this planetary cinerama would be difficult enough. The physical basis for the electromagnetic society is causally connected with the rotation of the earth on its axis, possibly even related to the solar-system-milky-way-galaxy-dynamics, and because of the earth's rotation. How shall we be able to project images on a moving screen and time the sequence, and where is the 'right-side-up' for our screen? The problems here leave one dizzy. As Grove Hambidge points out in his *1941 Yearbook to Agriculture*, "to visualize even the more elementary aspects of atmospheric circulation over the earth is not easy, since you have to imagine that you are a mile or two up in the air, on your stomach with your head toward the North Pole, a clock near by lying on its back so you can readily tell which is clockwise and which is counter-clockwise rotation — also a mirror so that you can see how everything would be reversed if you were in the Southern instead of the Northern Hemisphere, and you have to remember constantly that a south wind is a north wind, and an east wind a westward moving wind, and vice versa." Here we are only trying to visualize the circulation of the air around the earth's surface. But this is relatively simple as compared with the problem of how to project sky-images so that peoples around the spheroidal earth can watch a planetary television screen and perhaps help create a planetary semantography!

But perhaps the difficulties with a sky projection screen and program are exaggerated. In the human brain, for example, the conscious image is seen properly even if the retinal image is turned up-side-down on the cortex. It all comes out properly, provided there is an isomorphic relation between the external object and the phenomenal image in consciousness. In the same way, when we have learned to see properly the image on the sky-screen, the meaning will have the proper association with the symbolism. Since in this case we are creating the symbolism as we learn it, this gives us some operational control over our sky-writing semantography.

XIII. World Philosophy as A Morphogenetic Force

Our philosophy requires that we bring into play those form-producing forces which can create a world sensorium. This means imagining or envisioning a mental foetus which can embody the archetypal patterns for the embryogenesis of the neurons of the super-organism. When I search for help to implement this creative orthogenesis of humanity, I come upon the speculations of Dr. R. M. Bucke, author of the volume on *Cosmic Consciousness*, who believed that the secret of man's moral nature resides in his emotions. In another book, *Man's Moral Nature*, written quite some time before the newer knowledge of endocrinology, Maurice Bucke built upon the belief that there is an inner bond of causality between the sympathetic nervous system, the internal secretions (hormones), and the individual's character.

The interesting feature of Dr. Bucke's view is the intimation that man's moral nature, as it develops, modifies the functional pattern of the nervous system through the enhancement of the emotion of love, as opposed to fear and hate. Therefore, those who have developed this moral nature are likely to experience the mutation of illumination and carry forward the 'psychic revolution' of mankind. This becomes especially plausible if the proposal made by J. J. Cunningham in his study, *Hormones and Heredity*, turns out to be correct. Here it is suggested that these very potent chemical messengers, the hormones, may be the formative stimuli and bearers of racial memories — a theory which may help to solve the problem of the inheritance of acquired characteristics.

Thus we find a bit of encouragement for our biological theory that the moving force behind evolutionary advance is tied in with invisible fields of force that have biological connections. Starting with the most elementary configurations, those in which electrical units are organized into atoms, we find these guiding fields moving toward higher dynamic organizations which eventually culminate in human cortico-thalamic circuits with currents of thought emerging from neuro-muscular-glandular configurations of indescribable complexity.

This line of speculation poses an interesting problem: is it possible for an individual to refine his own physical organism to the point of gaining a new freedom? Is there a self-evolutionary development toward freedom which results from the individual 'taking thought,' thereby bringing new patterns of electrical action currents into existence? Can one deliberately coerce the evolution of his own nervous system toward the elaboration of more readily responsive cells? If so, man's mind, through fields of influence, is able to create types of brain cells with their own substance, thereby setting in motion approximations in the outer world of the self-generated pattern which begins the psychic revolution. Thus it may come about that the collective minds of human individuals will be able to create a new humanity to serve as the objective counterpart of the mental foetus. In that case, through the potency of an emergent sociality, we will set in motion the action currents whereby a world sensorium will come into being.

If this is indeed the case, we discern that the time-lag between human creativity on the subjective level and the objective world is merely the time-lapse between the archetypal world of thought (the guiding field) and the objectified material world. We conclude, therefore, that the brain evolves physically into more responsive cells in order to cut down the inertia between patterns of thought and material configurations. The ideal thinker, when he emerges, will be completely 'up-to-date' in the sense that, for him, there will be better synchronization between the subjective and the objective worlds. One can be sure that before this comes about, another 'decisive battle of the world' will have to be fought. Reactionary people in politics, business, and the authoritarian churches, will not easily surrender. However, if enough thoughtful and sensitive persons can focus on the idea of world federation, they may visualize a social lens and a body of symbols. If the minds of men can focus into a coherent image the form of a world unity, something in the nature of a collective thought-form, the bad 'scenes' on the screen of human consciousness may be dissipated. In that event we may achieve the mechanism for a social scanning of the universal symbols meaningfully transposable across the earth's whirling surface.

When all is said, however, it still remains true that the Cosmic Imagination knows the meaning of what is being done before the signals in the manifest world inform the outer universe of what is going on, and the meaning of what is going on (the sequence of images in the Supreme Imagination) *is* the history of the evolution of the physical world because the *outer signals* are only the *manifest symbols* of the 'inner' thoughts of a Thinker whose images are hydrogen atoms and galaxies, and everything in between.

XIV. Cosmic Humanism and Religion

The observant reader will have noticed that our concept of the Cosmic Imagination resembles the *Logos* of the Hellenistic-Christian theory, but it also has affinities with the *Brahman* of the Upanishads, where Brahman is a name for the cosmic principle that pervades and sustains all things. That is:

> "He from whom proceeds the creation, preservation, and the reconstruction of the universe, is Brahman."

When this search for unity is directed inward, we come upon *Atman*. The highest Hindu teaching is that God's dwelling place is in the heart of man. Therefore, Brahman and Atman are two names for the same reality. This unity of the soul with God is one of the common elements in several great ethical monotheisms of the world. For us, it is interesting to note that this 'perennial philosophy' is advocated by such literary figures as Aldous Huxley, but it is also defended on scientific grounds by a physicist of the stature of Erwin Schrödinger in his little masterpiece, *What Is Life?* Apparently the mystics of every time and place and faith have taught this doctrine, as did Buddha, and as did Jesus when he announced: *the kingdom of heaven is within you!*

In concluding this survey of the cyclic-creative cosmology in relation to parapsychology, let me remind the reader that in forming the image of Divinity as a Cosmic Lens, I am well aware that I am here translating a human construct into a cosmic reality and realize in doing so that the Lens itself and its use in human explanation are functions of man's imagination. We have proposed this thought-form as a substitute for the picture of God as a benevolent old man with a long white beard, which is the symbol of medieval religious painting. Thus we avoid thinking of God in human form. However, there is certainly no attempt here to limit the properties of Divinity to the features of a man-made tool. It would be premature to describe further the characteristics of the Cosmic Imagination. This could lead to idolatry, and would do little to explain the boundless mystery and pulsing beauty of a cosmos that awakens in us the sense of awe and sublimity. Man's highest mission is to increasingly understand and recreate the products of the Supreme Imagination as these are revealed in nature and in human nature. Such is the ecstasy, the mystery, and the agony of man's awesome journey through the vastness and the majesty of our eternal cosmos.

XV. Summary: The Psychic Revolution

The present theory of *psi*-phenomena rests upon a number of correlative formulations: as a working hypothesis it is tentatively assumed that there is a universal consciousness functioning through a cosmic field which surrounds and encloses the manifest or material world. This field, a hyper-dimensional medium in which the space-time-particle universe is suspended, is outside all spatial and temporal coördinate systems and therefore can 'know' what happens in all local systems. Perhaps the energy-continuum for the archetypal guidance of all systems and the memory-record for all events, — events which are either 'past,' 'present,' or 'future' as witnessed by observers in our 3-plus-1 dimensions of the physical world, — is like a super-dispersive ether to the extent that ordinary velocity-of-transmission-of-information relations and inverse-square laws of spatial relations are transcended in a higher manifold. In our physical world, 'scanning' is the lower space-time analogue for securing the information about what can be observed, and something like this on a higher level of 'observation' is required for the universal consciousness (All-knower).

Given this cosmic reservoir of knowledge, human beings with their cortico-psychic fields can achieve a condition favorable to receiving information from a more universal or inclusive field, — a field of knowledge at least planetary in scope and perhaps cosmic in sweep. This sensitivity of the 'psychic' personality seems to be related to inner talents and is perhaps also a function of the times and the places of the recipients, even though the Cosmic Field is not localized in any particular time and place. The inner talent may be related to chemical changes in the genes (mutations) whereby new traits come into being on the level of the resulting neuro-muscular-glandular types of personalities in whom the experience of illumination occurs. There is here a kind of 'tuning in' or 'resonance in phase relations' made possible by an isomorphism between evolutionary entities and the archetypal forms which control the embryogenesis of new forms.

The mutant personalities of the new humanity may then carry forward the progressing psychic revolution which will ultimately yield an electromagnetic society with gestalt patterns of symbolism transferable across the social whole. A global radio and television hook-up employing a planetary semantography is the earthly foundation for the coming psychic unity of mankind. In that event, the present variety of 'scientific humanism' would appear as the forerunner of a world religion, — a pantheism reminiscent of the best traditions of Oriental and Occidental civilizations. This would provide a higher plateau of understanding for the resolution of the otherwise endless and hopeless conflict of East and West.

FOOTNOTES CHAPTER XIII

[1]Cf. "A Theory of Extra-Sensory Perception," O. L. Reiser, *Journal of Parapsychology*, Vol. 3, 1939, 167-192.

[2]This theory of isomorphism was set forth in my article, "Symbolic Logic, Cybernetics, and Semantics," read at the Conference of the International Society for Significs, Amsterdam, 1953. This paper was printed in *Synthese*, Vol. IX, Nos. 5-8.

[3]This unified view was first set forth in my article, "A Resolution of the 'East-West Problem' by Way of a Scientific Humanism," *Philosophy of Science*, Vol. 16, 1949, 325-335.

[4]This cosmology was first explained in my article, "The Field Theory of Matter in a Pantheistic Cosmology," *Scientia*, Vol. XLVIII, 1954, July (pages 211-218) and August (251-259).

[5]On this matter see the article previously mentioned, "The Exclusion Principle and its Philosophical Importance," by Henry Margenau, *Philosophy of Science*, Vol. 11, 1944, 187-209.

[6]Cf. *Cold Springs Harbor Symposium on Quantitative Biology*, Vol. 9, 1941, pp. 122-126.

[7]See the article, "Heredity as a Communication," by E. Taschdjian, *Scientia*, February, 1955, 112ff.

[8]Cf. "Information Transfer in the Living Cell," by George Gamow, *Scientific American*, Vol. 193, 1955 (October).

[9]Cf. "Haunting and the 'Psychic Ether' Hypothesis," by H. H. Price, *Proceedings of the Society for Psychical Research*, Vol. XLV, 1939, 307-343.

[10]See Kurt Koffka's article "The Structure of the Unconscious," in the volume, *The Unconscious: A Symposium.*

[11]Cf. "On the Motion of Particles in General Relativity Theory," by A. Einstein and L. Infeld, *Canadian Journal of Mathematics*, Vol. 1, 1949, p. 210.

[12]On this matter see the following: "Utility Theories in Field Physics and Mathematical Economics," by A. G. Pikler, *British Journal of the Philosophy of Science*, May 1954, Vol. 5; "Mathematics and Economic Models," by David Gale, *American Scientist*, January, 1956; and "Diffusion Is Predictable," by Stuart Carter Dodd, *American Sociological Review*, Vol. 20, 1955, 392-401.

INDEX

A

B

D

I

N

O

Q

R

S

W

Y

Z